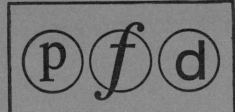

pfd

Drury House
34-43 Russell Street
London WC2B 5HA

Agent: R C	CV Database: ✓
Royalty Sheet No: 246380100	
Publication Date: 02/10/03	
Category: Children's Poetry	
Bay/Shelf:	

All the Best

Roger McGough is one of Britain's most popular
poets. He has been captivating children and
adults alike with his unique blend of compassion
and wit for more than three decades and with
more than thirty books. He is an international
ambassador for poetry and was awarded an OBE
for his work in 1997. In 2001 he was honoured
with the freedom of the City of Liverpool.

Other books by Roger McGough

BAD, BAD CATS
THE BEE'S KNEES
GOOD ENOUGH TO EAT
AN IMAGINARY MENAGERIE
LUCKY
NAILING THE SHADOW
PILLOW TALK
SKY IN THE PIE
YOU TELL ME (with Michael Rosen)

100 BEST POEMS FOR CHILDREN (Ed.)

Poetry for older readers

STRICTLY PRIVATE (Ed.)

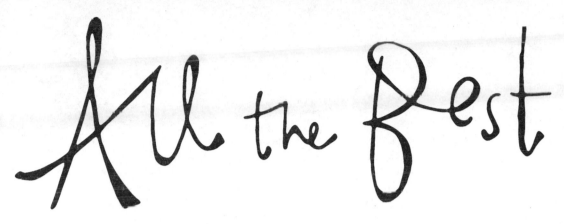

All the Best

The Selected Poems of Roger McGough

Illustrated by Lydia Monks

PUFFIN

PUFFIN BOOKS

Published by the Penguin Group
Penguin Books Ltd, 80 Strand, London WC2R 0RL, England
Penguin Putnam Inc., 375 Hudson Street, New York, New York 10014, USA
Penguin Books Australia Ltd, 250 Camberwell Road, Camberwell, Victoria 3124, Australia
Penguin Books Canada Ltd, 10 Alcorn Avenue, Toronto, Ontario, Canada M4V 3B2
Penguin Books India (P) Ltd, 11 Community Centre, Panchsheel Park, New Delhi – 110 017, India
Penguin Books (NZ) Ltd, Cnr Rosedale and Airborne Roads, Albany, Auckland, New Zealand
Penguin Books (South Africa) (Pty) Ltd, 24 Sturdee Avenue, Rosebank 2196, South Africa

Penguin Books Ltd, Registered Offices: 80 Strand, London WC2R 0RL, England

www.penguin.com

First published 2003
1 3 5 7 9 10 8 6 4 2

Text copyright © Roger McGough, 2003
Illustrations copyright © Lydia Monks, 2003

The moral right of the author and illustrator has been asserted

Set in Centaur MT

Printed in Great Britain by Mackays of Chatham

British Library Cataloguing in Publication Data
A CIP catalogue record for this book is available from the British Library

ISBN 0–670–91418–5

Contents

The Writer of This Poem

The writer of this poem
Is taller than a tree
As keen as the North wind
As handsome as can be

As bold as a boxing glove
As sharp as a nib
As strong as scaffolding
As tricky as a fib

As smooth as an ice cream
As quick as a lick
As clean as a chemist shop
As clever as a ✓

The writer of this poem
Never ceases to amaze
He's one in a million billion
(or so the poem says!)

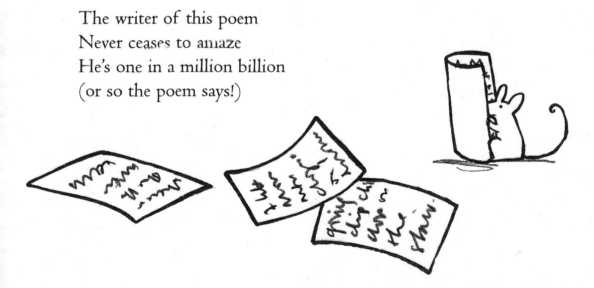

The Reader of This Poem

The reader of this poem
Is as cracked as a cup
As daft as treacle toffee
As mucky as a pup

As troublesome as bubblegum
As brash as a brush
As bouncy as a double-tum
As quiet as a sshhh . . .

As sneaky as a witch's spell
As tappy-toe as jazz
As empty as a wishing-well
As echoey as as as as as as . . . as . . . as . . .

As bossy as a whistle
As prickly as a pair
Of boots made out of thistles
And elephant hair

As vain as trainers
As boring as a draw
As smelly as a drain is
Outside the kitchen door

As hungry as a wave
That feeds upon the coast
As gaping as the grave
As GOTCHA! as a ghost

As fruitless as a cake of soap
As creeping-up as smoke
The reader of this poem, I hope,
Knows how to take a joke!

First Day at School

A millionbillionwillion miles from home
waiting for the bell to go. (To go where?)
Why are they all so big, other children?
So noisy? So much at home they
must have been born in uniform.
Lived all their lives in playgrounds.
Spent the years inventing games
that don't let me in. Games
that are rough, that swallow you up.

And the railings.
All around, the railings.
Are they to keep out wolves and monsters?
Things that carry off and eat children?
Things you don't take sweets from?
Perhaps they're to stop us getting out.
Running away from the lessins. Lessin.
What does a lessin look like?
Sounds small and slimy.
They keep them in glassrooms.
Whole rooms made out of glass. Imagine.

4

I wish I could remember my name.
Mummy said it would come in useful.
Like wellies. When there's puddles.
Yellowwellies. I wish she was here.
I think my name is sewn on somewhere.
Perhaps the teacher will read it for me.
Tea-cher. The one who makes the tea.

What I Love About School

What I love about school
    is the hurly-burly of the classroom,
    the sly humour of the teachers

What I hate about teachers
    is their reluctance to cartwheel
    down corridors

What I love about corridors
    is that the longer they are
    the louder the echo

What I hate about echo echo
    is its refusal to answer a straight
    question question

What I love about question
    is the proud admission
    of its own ignorance

What I hate about ignorance
    is the naive assumption
    that it is bliss

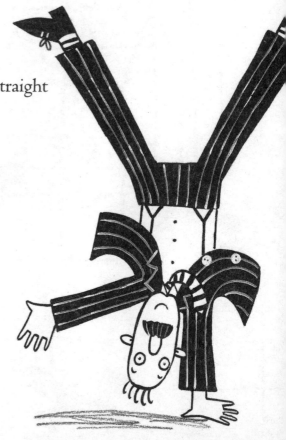

What I love about bliss
    is its willingness
    to rhyme with kiss

What I hate about kiss
    is the news of it going around
    like wildfire

What I love about wildfire
    is its dragon's breath
    and its hunger for life

What I hate about life
    is that as soon as you get the hang of it
    you run out of time

What I love about time
    is how it flies
    except when at school

What I hate about school
    is the hurly-burly of the playground,
    the sly humour of the teachers.

Head

The Head of our school
is called Mr Head.
Honestly, that's his name.

'My name is Head
and I'm the new Head,'
Is what he said when he came.

He's very, very nice
but it has to be said,
that our Head, Mr Head,
has a very large head.

It says 'Head' on his sports bag,
and 'Head' on the door,
but which of the heads
does the 'Head' stand for?

Class Warfare

I'm the most important
Person in the class

Twenty-four carat diamond
While all the rest are glass

Distinctions distinguish me
While others strive to pass

I'm en route for glory
While others are en masse

They're backdrops, they're bit parts
They're day-old candy floss

They provide the undercoat
For my enduring gloss

When I go down in history
I'll go down a storm

For I'm the most important
Person in the form

(If you don't believe me
Ask Daddy – he's the headmaster.)

Mums and Dads

My daddy's a lawyer
said Mort
He wears a wig when he goes to court

So does my mum
said Allister
And her wig's big cos she's a barrister

My dad drives a truck
said Gus
As wide as a playground as big as a bus

My mum's a chef
said Jocasta
She bakes her own bread and makes her own pasta

My daddy's a doctor
said Henrietta
He gives people pills to make them feel better

My mum's a model
said Rose
And she gets to keep all her beautiful clothes

My dad's a boxer
said Lee
So you'd better think twice before picking on me

My mum's a footballer
said Jane
And next week she's playing for England again

My dad's a runner
said Sid
Well that's what my mum said he did

My mum's a mum
said Sue
With three sons and five daughters what else
can she do?

My dad's a tattooist
said Liam
And Mum's got the crown jewels where no one can see 'em

My mum's a vicar
said Tessa
She works every day, even Sundays, God bless her

My dad's a detective
said Isabel
Though to look at him you couldn't tell

My mum's a dietitian
said Gaby
She shouts at ladies when they get flabby

My dad's unemployed
said Eliza
Though he used to be a careers adviser.

The Leader

I wanna be the leader
I wanna be the leader
Can I be the leader?
Can I? I can?
Promise? Promise?
Yippee, I'm the leader
I'm the leader

OK what shall we do?

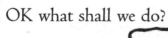

The Boy with a Similar Name

When Raymond Gough joined our class
He was almost a year behind.
'Sanatorium,' said Mrs McBride
'So I want you all to be kind.'

'Roger, your names are similar
So let Raymond sit next to you
He'll need a friend to teach him the ropes
And show him what to do.'

Then teacher went back to teaching
And we went back to being taught
And I tried to be kind to Raymond
But it was harder than I thought.

For he was the colour of candlewax
And smelled of Dettol and Vick.
He was as thin as a sharpened pencil
And his glasses were milk-bottle thick.

Not only that but unfriendly
All muffled up in his shell.
Hobbies? Interests? Ambitions?
It was impossible to tell.

I was afraid of catching his yellowness
And smelling of second-hand Vick
And the only time I could be myself
Were the days when he was off sick.

But what proved to be contagious
Was his oddness, and I knew
That he was a victim ripe for bullying
And so by proxy, I was too.

'How's your brother, Raymond?'
The class began to tease,
'Do you share his dirty handkerchief?
Do you catch each other's fleas?'

'He's not my brother,' I shouted,
My cheeks all burning hot,
'He's a drippy four-eyed monster,
And he comes from the planet Snot.'

They laughed and I saw an opening
(Wouldn't you have done the same?)
I pointed a finger at Raymond
And joined in the bullying game.

He stopped coming to school soon after,
'Sanatorium,' said Mrs McBride.
He never came back and nobody knew
If he moved elsewhere or died.

I don't think of him very often
For when I do I blush with shame
At the thought of the pain I helped inflict
On the boy with a similar name.

It Wasn't Me, Miss

It wasn't me, Miss, it was 'er, Miss
Every lesson it's the same
I never do nothin'
But I always get the blame

I didn't smash that window
Or throw water on the floor
It wasn't me who put the frog
In Mrs Kelly's drawer

I didn't make rude noises
When yer back was turned
I was nowhere near the library
When the books got burned

It wasn't me, Miss, it was 'er, Miss
Would I tell fibs to you?
An' I didn't paint the hamster
That lovely powder blue

I didn't scratch the piano
It wasn't me who broke the chair
And any road, if I did
It wasn't me, it was 'er

She acts all sweet and innocent
But the minute that you're gone
She's Frankenstein and Reservoir Dogs
All rolled into one.

It wasn't me, Miss, it was 'er, Miss
... What? ... Sit apart?
Don't be mean, Miss, we're a team, Miss
I'll be good, cross my heart!

Streemin

Im in the botom streme
Which meens Im not brigth
dont like reading
cant hardly rite

but all thesedivishns
arnt reely fair
look at the cemtery
no streemin there

Harum Scarum

I am harum
I disturb the peace
I go around
saying boo to geese

I am harum scarum
a one man gang
diddle dum darum
bang bang bang

Butterfingers

When I was a child
I caught measles. Then
I caught mumps. After that
I caught tonsillitis. A month later
I caught influenza. As soon as I was better
I caught pneumonia. So my mother took me to see
The old wives
Who advised dipping my fingers
In butter every morning.
So I did. And since then
I haven't caught a thing.

Easy Money

Guess how old I am?
I bet you can't.
I bet you.
Go on guess.
Have a guess.

Wrong!
Have another.

Wrong!
Have another.

Wrong again!
Do you give in?

Seven years four months two weeks
five days three hours fifteen
minutes forty-eight seconds!
That's 20p you owe me.

Reward and Punishment

If you are very good I will give you:

A pillow of blue strawberries
A swimming pool of Häagen-Dasz
A mirror of imagination
A pocketful of yes's
A hiss of sleigh rides
A lunch box of swirling planets
A doorway of happy endings
A hedgerow of diamonds
A surfboard of dolphins
A cat's paw of tickles
A carton of fresh rainbow-juice
A forest of chocolate wardrobes

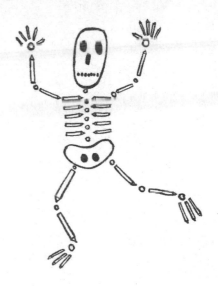

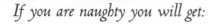

If you are naughty you will get:

A burst of balloon
A screech of wolf
A hoof of piggy bank
A twitch of sideways
A splinter of thirst
A precipice of banana skins
A tyrannosaurus of broccoli
A rucksack of bony elbows
A skeleton of lost pencils
A flag of inconvenience
A chill of false laughter
A blackboard of no way out

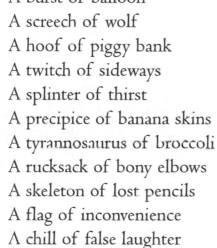

Plague Around

There's a plague around
There's a plague around
In every village
And every town

With big purple spots
And greenish ones too
There's a plague around
And it's waiting for you

There's a plague around
There's a plague around
Keep your eyes open
And don't make a sound

Or your ears will flap
And you'll start to cough
You'll sneeze and sneeze
Till your nose drops off

There's a plague around
There's a plague around
In every school
There's a playground

You'll burst out laughing
And run around
When you get into
The playground

There's a playground
There's a playground
In every school
There's a playground.

Riddle

I'm older than my eldest son
But younger than my mother
One hand has 'left' tattooed on
'Right' is on the other.
What am I?

Answer:
silly

The Magic Pebble

My favourite thing is a pebble
That I found on a beach in Wales
It looks like any other
But its magic never fails

It does my homework for me
Makes difficult sums seem clear
School dinners taste delicious
It makes teachers disappear

It turns water into lemonade
A bully into a frog
When I'm in need of company
It becomes a friendly dog

Close your eyes, make a wish
And you're in a foreign land
Space travel is so easy
Simply hold it in your hand

My favourite thing is a pebble
It means all the world to me
I couldn't bear to be without it
(... But it's yours for 20p)

My Brilliant Friend

He's brilliant at karate
He's brilliant at darts
He's brilliant at acting
He gets all the best parts

He's brilliant at swimming
He's brilliant at skates
He's brilliant at juggling
With real china plates

He's brilliant at poetry
He's brilliant at rhyme
He's brilliant at lessons
He comes top every time

He's Brilliant just Brilliant
With a capital B
(Although he's only average
In comparison with me).

A Good Poem

I like a good poem,
one with lots of fighting
in it. Blood, and the
clanging of armour. Poems

against Scotland are good,
and poems that defeat
the French with crossbows.
I don't like poems that

aren't about anything.
Sonnets are wet and
a waste of time.
Also poems that don't

know how to rhyme.
If I was a poem
I'd play football and
get picked for England.

A Great Poem

This poem is great.
Wondrous and fabulous
it can hardly wait

to get out there
among you all
and give it to you straight.

If it were a painting
they would hang it
in the Tate.

It's lyrical
It's musical
Intellectually first-rate.

Five-Six-Seven-Eight
What do we appreciate?
This poem.

(Who says it's great?)

Roger McGough

Apostrophe

'twould be nice to be
an apostrophe
floating
above an s
hovering
like a paper kite
in between the its
eavesdropping, tiptoeing
high above the thats
an inky comet
spiralling
the highest tossed
of hats

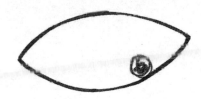

Watchwords

watch the words

watch words

the watchword

is watch

words are

sly as boots

takeyoureyesoffthemforaminute

and they're up and away all over the place

Smithereens

I spend my days
collecting smithereens.
I find them on buses
in department stores
and on busy pavements.

At restaurant tables
I pick up the leftovers
of polite conversation
At railway stations
the tearful debris
of parting lovers.

I pocket my eavesdroppings
and store them away.
I make things out of them.
Nice things, sometimes.
Sometimes odd, like this.

The Power of Poets

The man on the pavement
outside, giving change
to the old tramp and
feeling good isn't me.
I am the pavement.
I could have been
the tramp or even
the change. However
I choose to be the
pavement and it is
my poem. Such is
the power of poets.

A Poem Just For Me

Where am I now when I need me
Suddenly where have I gone
I'm so alone here without me
Tell me please what have I done?

Once I did most things together
I went for walks hand in hand
I shared my life so completely
I met my every demand.

Tell me I'll come back tomorrow
I'll keep my arms open wide
Tell me that I'll never leave me
My place is here at my side.

Maybe I've simply mislaid me
Like an umbrella or key
So until the day that I come my way
Here is a poem just for me.

The Super-Word Market

(A poem for forty-two words)

I want to write a new poem.
What words shall I choose?
I go in. The variety is endless.
Images stretch into infinity.

I dither. Can't make up my mind.
Inspiration becomes impatient.
Stamps its feet. Panicking
I grab the nearest forty-two

Choose the Rhyme

The sun's too hot and the moon's too cold
The clouds are too young and the stars too old
The Queen's too kind and the King's too grumpy
The pillow's too soft and the bed's too lumpy
The pig's too bare and the lamb's too fleecy
The stew's too thin and the soup's too greasy
The sea's too wet and the beach is too stony
The poem's too long and the poet's too ...

moany? groany? bony? macaroni? Al Capone?

Waxing Lyrical

I polish the dining room table
Bring a shine to the bentwood chairs
You can see your face in the wardrobe
Mind you don't slip on the stairs

I polish the eggs in the kitchen
The bread before I toast it
Cover the chicken with elbow grease
And rub before I roast it

I polish my grandfather's trousers
(At the knees, where he likes them to shine)
My grandmother's nose, how it sparkles!
And her dentures, aren't they divine?

I polish the flowers in the garden
The front of the house, brick by brick
If the clouds would stand still for a minute
I'd wipe the dust off right quick

I polish the car every Sunday
I polish the Sunday as well
I polish the years, and the yearnings
I polish the fears and the smell

I polish the reasons for living
I polish the truth and the lies
I polish your innermost secrets
I polish the earth and the skies.

I polish the language of angels
The horn of the unicorn too
If you think this poem is rubbish
Then I'll call round and polish off you!

I Wish I Were a Crochet

I wish I were a crochet
I'd sing and dance and play
among the dotted minims
all the livelong day

I'd swing from stave to stave
up and down I'd climb
Then crawl from bar to bar
singing all the time

I wish I were a crochet
or a semibreve
I'd find a lady quaver
and her I'd never leave

We'd run around the manuscript
a pair of little ravers
Get married pianissimo
and raise lots of semi-quavers

The All-Purpose Children's Poem

The first verse contains a princess
    Two witches (one evil, one good)
There is a castle in it somewhere
    And a dark and tangled wood.

The second has ghosts and vampires
    Monsters with foul-smelling breath
It sends shivers down the book spine
    And scares everybody to death.

The third is one of my favourites
    With rabbits in skirts and trousers
Who talk to each other like we do
    And live in neat little houses.

The fourth verse is bang up to date
    And in it anything goes.
Set in the city, it doesn't rhyme
    (Although, in a way it does.)

The fifth is set in the future
    (And as you can see, it's the last)
When the Word was made Computer
    And books are a thing of the past.

The Cackle

Cut the cackle
and get the gist

heat the kettle
and wet the wrist

raise the hackle
and cock the snook

shake the rattle
and sling the hook

trim the tackle
and nook the cranny

lick the pickle
and tickle your granny.

No Grannies in This Poem

There are no grannies in this poem
I wouldn't let one in if she tried
It's no way to treat old ladies, I know
But I've kept them waiting outside

It's not raining there at the moment
And we are in for a settled spell
They've got lots of things to chatter about
And they get on reasonably well

This poem, you see, is about witches
And subjects that grannies don't care for
Like vampires and aliens from outer space
Waging intergalactic warfare

So if you want a poem about grannies
I suggest you go look elsewhere
For there are no grannies in this poem.
Definitely not, definitely not.

Pillow Talk

Last night I heard my pillow talk
What amazing things it said
About the fun that pillows have
Before it's time for bed

The bedroom is their playground
A magical place to be
(Not a room for peace and quiet
Like it is for you and me)

They divebomb off the wardrobe
Do backflips off the chair
Use the mattress as a trampoline
Turn somersaults in the air

It's Leapfrog then Pass the Slipper
Handstands and cartwheels all round
Wrestling and swinging on curtains
And all with hardly a sound

But by and by the feathers fly
And they get out of puff
So with scarves and ties they bind their eyes
For a game of Blind Man's Buff

They tiptoe out on the landing
Although it's a dangerous place
(If granny met one on the stairs
Imagine the look on her face!)

It's pillows who open cupboard drawers
To mess and rummage about
(And you end up by getting blamed
For something they left out)

I'd quite fancy being a pillow
Playing games and lying in bed
If I didn't have to spend each night
Under your big snoring head!

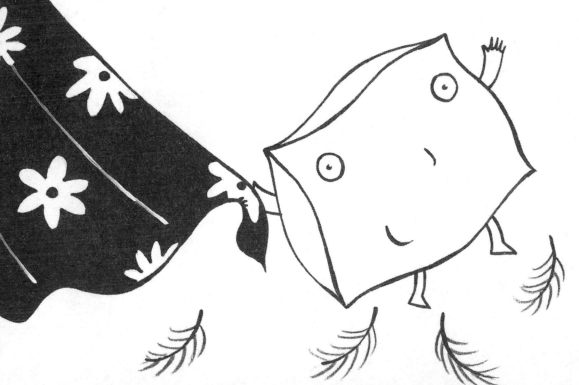

I've Taken to My Bed

I've taken to my bed
(And my bed has taken to me)
We're getting married in the spring
How happy we shall be

We'll raise lots of little bunks
A sleeping-bag or two
Take my advice, find a bed that's nice
Lie down and say: 'I love you.'

Wink

I took 40 winks
yesterday afternoon
and another 40 today.
In fact I get through
about 280 winks a week.
Which is about 14,560
winks a year.
(The way I'm going on
I'll end up looking like a wink.)

42

Top

Dad, risen and dizzy
from sleep, would say,
'I slept like a top.'

This puzzled me.
Top of what?
Top of the milk?
Top of the class?
Top of the wardrobe?
Top of the morning?

So I asked him.
'Spinning top,' he said.

Funny, I thought,
to spend all night
spinning round the bedroom.
No wonder he looked so tired every morning!

The Missing Sock

I found my sock
beneath the bed.
'Where have you been
all week?' I said.

'Hiding away,'
the sock replied.
'Another day on your foot
and I would have died!'

I've Got a Cold

I've got a cold
And it's not funny

My throat is numb
My nose is runny

My ears are burning
My fingers are itching

My teeth are wobbly
My eyebrows are twitching

My kneecaps have slipped
My bottom's like jelly

The button's come off
My silly old belly

My chin has doubled
My toes are twisted

My ankles have swollen
My elbows are blistered

My back is all spotty
My hair's turning white

I sneeze through the day
And cough through the night

I've got a cold
And I'm going insane

(Apart from all that
I'm as right as rain.)

Wouldn't It Be Funny If You Didn't Have a Nose?

You couldn't smell your dinner
If you didn't have a nose
You couldn't tell a dirty nappy
From a summer rose
You couldn't smell the ocean
Or the traffic, I suppose
Oh wouldn't it be funny
If you didn't have a nose?

You couldn't smell your mummy
If you didn't have a nose
You couldn't tell an orange
From a row of smelly toes
You couldn't smell the burning
(Think how quick a fire grows)
Wouldn't it be funny
If you didn't have a nose?

Where would we be without our hooters?
Nothing else would really suit us.
What would we sniff through?
How would we sneeze?
What would we wipe
Upon our sleeves?

You couldn't smell a rat
If you didn't have a nose
You couldn't tell a duchess
From a herd of buffaloes
And . . . mmmm that Gorgonzola
As it starts to decompose
Oh wouldn't it be funny
If you didn't have a nose?

Where would we be without our hooters?
Nothing else would really suit us.
And think of those who
Rub their noses
Life would be tough for
Eskimoses

You couldn't wear your glasses
If you didn't have a nose
And what would bullies aim for
When it came to blows?
Where would nostrils be without them?
When it's runny how it glows
Oh wouldn't it be funny
If you didn't have a . . .
        have a . . .
        have a . . .
           a . . .
           a . . . choo!

Hide and Seek

When I played as a kid
How I longed to be caught
But whenever I hid
Nobody sought.

Itch

My sister had an itch
  I asked if it was catching.
'Catch,' she said, and threw it.
    Now I'm the one who's scratching.

Tantrums

When my sister starts to frown
I'm always on my guard

Yesterday she threw a tantrum
But it missed me by a yard.

Bottom

Who'd be a bottom? Not me.

Always facing the wrong way.
To go for a walk
And not be able to see
Where you are going.

To be sat upon all day.
Smacked. Called rude names.
Whistled at. Laughed at.
The butt of a hundred jokes.

Faithful to the end.
An undercover agent
Working all hours
And getting no thanks for it.

Alas, poor bottom.

Sky in the Pie!

Waiter, there's a sky in my pie
Remove it at once if you please
You can keep your incredible sunsets
I ordered mincemeat and cheese

I can't stand nightingales singing
Or clouds all burnished with gold
The whispering breeze is disturbing the peas
And making my chips go all cold

I don't care if the chef is an artist
Whose canvases hang in the Tate
I want two veg. and puff pastry
Not the Universe heaped on my plate

OK I'll try just a spoonful
I suppose I've got nothing to lose
Mm … the colours quite tickle the palette
With a blend of delicate hues

The sun has a custardy flavour
And the clouds are as light as air
And the wind a chewier texture
(With a hint of cinammon there?)

This sky is simply delicious
Why haven't I tried it before?
I can chew my way through to Eternity
And still have room left for more

Having acquired a taste for the Cosmos
I'll polish this sunset off soon
I can't wait to tuck into the night sky
Waiter! Please bring me the Moon!

The Burp

One evening at supper
A little girl burped.
'Tut, tut,' said mother.
'What do you say?' said father.

Her brother giggled.
'It's not funny,' said father.
'Pardon,' said the little girl.
'That's better,' said mother.

And all was quickly forgotten.
Except, that is, by the burp.
It had only just been born
And already everybody was apologizing.

What sort of person gives birth
And then says 'pardon'?
What sort of relative giggles
Then looks away, embarrassed?

Hurt, the baby burp hovered near the ceiling
Looked down at the one who had brought it up
Then escaped through an open window,
Never to return.

Lollidollops

I like a nice
dollop of ice cream
on my porridge

I like a nice
dollop of ice cream
in my tea

But the dollop
I like the most
is the one
I have on toast

With my eggs, bacon,
mushrooms, beans, sausages,
spaghetti, black puddings, pancakes,
apple pie, mushy peas, tomatoes, kidneys and custard.

Bun Fight

The buns are having a fight
There are currants on the floor
The custards egg them on
'More,' they chorus, 'more.'

The doughnuts form a ring
'Ding, ding!' and the seconds are out
An eccles cake is taking bets
As to who will win the bout.

The referee is a muffin
The timekeeper is a scone
There are five rounds still to go
And the custards egg them on.

The chelsea bun is tiring
And hoping for a draw
When the bath bun throws an upper-cut
That brings him to the floor.

The muffin slowly counts him out
And the bath bun's arm is raised
While through the window, passers-by
Look into the cake-shop, amazed.

No Peas For the Wicked

No peas for the wicked
No carrots for the damned
No parsnips for the naughty
  O Lord we pray

No sprouts for the shameless
No cabbage for the shady
No lettuce for the lecherous
  No way, no way

No potatoes for the deviants
No radish for the riff-raff
No spinach for the spineless
  Lock them away

No beetroot for the boasters
No mange tout for the mobsters
No corn-on-the-cob et cetera
  (Shall we call it a day?)

Keep Your Eyes Peeled

In my field of vision
In that watery field
Grow potatoes with eyes in
Which is why I keep them peeled.

Cabbage

The cabbage is a funny veg.
All crisp, and green, and brainy.
I sometimes wear one on my head
When it's cold and rainy.

Vegetarians

Vegetarians are cruel, unthinking people.
Everybody knows that a carrot screams when grated.
That a peach bleeds when torn apart.
Do you believe an orange insensitive
to thumbs gouging out its flesh?
That tomatoes spill their brains painlessly?
Potatoes, skinned alive and boiled,
the soil's little lobsters.
Don't tell me it doesn't hurt
when peas are squeezed from the pod,
the hide flayed off sprouts,
cabbage shredded, onions beheaded.

Throw in the trowel
and lay down the hoe.
Mow no more
Let my people go!

'US Flies in Hamburgers'

*Newspaper headline referring to hamburgers being
airlifted to feed homesick US marines.*

If you go down the High Street today
You'll be sure of a big surprise
When you order your favourite burger
With a milkshake and regular fries.

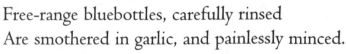

For the secret is out I tell you no lies
They've stopped using beef in favour of flies.

Flies, flies, big juicy flies,
Flies as American as apple pies.

Horseflies, from Texas, as big as your thumb
Are sautéed with onions and served in a bun.

Free-range bluebottles, carefully rinsed
Are smothered in garlic, and painlessly minced.

Black-eyed bees with stings intact
Add a zesty zing, and that's a fact.

Colorado beetles, ants from Kentucky,
Rhode Island roaches, and if you're unlucky

Baltimore bedbugs (and even horrider)
Leeches as squashy as peaches from Florida.

Flies, flies, big juicy flies,
Flies as American as Mom's apple pies.

It's lovely down in MacDingles today
But if you don't fancy flies
Better I'd say to keep well away
Stay home and eat Birds' Eyes.

A Weak Poem

(To be read lying down)

Oh dear, this poem is very weak
It can hardly stand up straight
Which comes from eating junk food
And going to bed too late.

The Fight of the Year

'And there goes the bell for the third month
and Winter comes out of its corner looking groggy
Spring leads with a left to the head
followed by a sharp right to the body
  daffodils
  primroses
  crocuses
  snowdrops
  lilacs
  violets
  pussy willow
Winter can't take much more punishment
and Spring shows no signs of tiring
  tadpoles
  squirrels
  baa-lambs
  badgers
  bunny rabbits
  mad march hares
  horses and hounds
Spring is merciless
Winter won't go the full twelve rounds

bobtail clouds
scallywaggy winds
the sun
a pavement artist
in every town
A left to the chin
and Winter's down!
tomatoes
radish
cucumber
onions
beetroot
celery
and any
amount
of lettuce
for dinner
Winter's out for the count
Spring is the winner!'

Autumn Poem

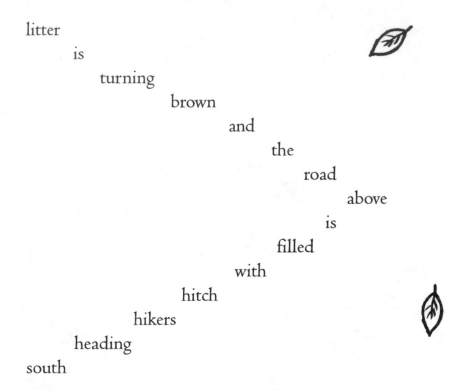

litter
    is
       turning
          brown
             and
               the
                 road
                   above
                 is
              filled
            with
        hitch
      hikers
    heading
south

First Haiku of Spring

cuck oo cuck oo cuck
oo cuck oo cuck oo cuck oo
cuck oo cuck oo cuck

Trees Are Great

Trees are great, they just stand and wait
They don't cry when they're teased
They don't eat much and they seldom shout
Trees are easily pleased

Trees are great, they like to congregate
For meetings in the park
They dance and sway, they stay all day
And talk till well after dark

Trees are great, they accept their fate
When it's pouring down with rain
They don't wear macs, it runs off their backs
But you never hear them complain

So answer me, please, if there weren't any trees
Where would naughty boys climb?
Where would lovers carve their names?
Where would little birds nest?
Where would we hang the leaves?

Why Trees Have Got It All Wrong

Trees have got it all wrong
because they shed their leaves
as soon as it gets cold.

If they had any sense
they'd take them off in June
and let the scented breezes

whiffle through the branches
cooling the bare torso.
In high summer, more so.

*   *   *

Come autumn (not the fall)
they'd put on a new coat:
thick leaves, waxed and fur-lined

to keep them warm as toast,
whatever the weather.
Trees, get it together!

* Storm

They're at it again
the wind and the rain
It all started
when the wind
took the window
by the collar
and shook it
with all its might
Then the rain
butted in
What a din
they'll be at it all night
Serves them right
if they go home in the morning
and the sky won't let them in

The Snowman

Mother, while you were at the shops
and I was snoozing in my chair
I heard a tap at the window
saw a snowman standing there

He looked so cold and miserable
I almost could have cried
so I put the kettle on
and invited him inside

I made him a cup of cocoa
to warm the cockles of his nose
then he snuggled in front of the fire
for a cosy little doze

He lay there warm and smiling
softly counting sheep
I eavesdropped for a little while
then I too fell asleep

Seems he woke and tiptoed out
exactly when I'm not too sure
it's a wonder you didn't see him
as you came in through the door

(oh, and by the way,
the kitten's made a puddle on the floor)

Haiku

Snowman in a field
listening to the raindrops
wishing him farewell

Snow and Ice Poems

(i)   Our street is dead lazy
especially in winter.
Some mornings you wake up
and it's still lying there
saying nothing. Huddled
under its white counterpane.

But soon the lorries arrive
like angry mums,
pull back the blankets
and send it shivering
off to work.

(ii)   To
boggan?
or not
to boggan?
That is the question.

(iii)   Winter
morning.
Snowflakes
for breakfast.
The street
outside
quiet
as a
long
white
bandage.

(iv)   The time I like best
is 6 a.m.
and the snow is six inches deep

Which I'm yet to discover
cos I'm under the cover
and fast, fast asleep.

The Midnight Skaters

It is midnight in the ice rink
   And all is cool and still.
Darkness seems to hold its breath
   Nothing moves, until

Out of the kitchen, one by one,
   The cutlery comes creeping,
Quiet as mice to the brink of the ice
   While all the world is sleeping.

Then suddenly, a serving-spoon
   Switches on the light,
And the silver swoops upon the ice
   Screaming with delight.

The knives are high-speed skaters
   Round and round they race,
Blades hissing, sissing,
   Whizzing at a dizzy pace.

Forks twirl like dancers
   Pirouetting on the spot.
Teaspoons (who take no chances)
   Hold hands and giggle a lot.

All night long the fun goes on
   Until the sun, their friend,
Gives the warning signal
   That all good things must end.

So they slink back to the darkness
   Of the kitchen cutlery-drawer
And steel themselves to wait
   Until it's time to skate once more.

At eight the canteen ladies
   Breeze in as good as gold
To lay the tables and wonder
   Why the cutlery is so cold.

In Good Hands

Wherever night falls

The earth is always

There to catch it.

Downhill Racer

Down
     the
        snow
           white
      page
  we
slide.
     From
        side
          to
             side
         we
      glide.
        Pass
          obstacles
             with
               ease.
            Words
         on
       skis.
    Look out.
       Here
        comes
       a
      poem
       in
       a
            hurry!

Uphill Climb

Wheeeeee

Three
Two
One
go.
another
have
to
top
the
to
back
way
the
all
climb
the
is
part
boring
only
The

Pinning up a Notice

the sun
hasn't got me fooled
not for a minute
just when
you're beginning to believe
that   grass is green
and   skies are blue
and   colour is king
hey   ding a ding ding
and
a
  host
        of
            other
                golden
                    et ceteras
before you know where you are
he's slunk off somewhere
and pinned up a notice saying:

MOON

Mrs Moon

Mrs Moon
sitting up in the sky
little old lady
rock-a-bye
with a ball of fading light
and silvery needles
knitting the night

Icy Fingers

Despite the cold
A line of old trees
Playing with the moon

Tossing it
From one to the other
Never missing a catch.

The Sad Astronomer

His telescope is beyond repair.
Tonight he opens the sky
but cannot read it.
The stars, a jumble,
dance before his eyes.

Mad Ad

An advertising whizz-kid
thought it a disgrace
That no one had exploited
the possibilities in space
Discussed it with a client
who agreed and very soon
A thousand miles of neon tubing
were transported to the moon.

Now no one can ignore it
the product's selling fine
The night they turned the moon
into a Coca-Cola sign.

One More Battle

Who's that sailor
stern and solemn?
'Tis Lord Nelson
down from his column.

Why goes he limping
up the street?
In search of a long-lost
English Fleet.

Why driven now
to such despair?
The need to breathe
some clean fresh air.

Give and Take

I give you clean air
You give me poisonous gas.
I give you mountains
You give me quarries.

I give you pure snow
You give me acid rain.
I give you spring fountains
You give me toxic canals.

I give you a butterfly
You gave me a plastic bottle.
I give you a blackbird
You gave me a stealth bomber.

I give you abundance
You give me waste.
I give you one last chance
You give me excuse after excuse.

Five-Car Family

We're a five-car family
We got what it takes
Eight thousand cc
Three different makes

One each for the kids
I run two
One for the missus
When there's shopping to do

Cars are Japanese of course
Subaru and Mazda
And the Nissan that the missus takes
Nippin' down to Asda

We're a load of noisy parkers
We never do it neat
Drive the neighbours crazy
When we take up half the street

Unleaded petrol?
That's gotta be a joke
Stepping on the gas we like
The smoke to make you choke

Carbon monoxide
Take a deep breath
Benzine dioxide
Automanic death

Cos it's all about noise
And it's all about speed
And it's all about power
And it's all about greed

And it's all about fantasy
And it's all about dash
And it's all about machismo
And it's all about cash

And it's all about blood
And it's all about gore
And it's all about oil
And it's all about war

And it's all about money
And it's all about spend
And it's all about time
That it came to an end.

Everything Touches

Everything touches, life interweaves
Starlight and wood smoke, ashes and leaves
Birdsong and thunder, acid and rain
Everything touches, unbroken chain

Rainstorm and rainbow, warrior and priest
Stingray and dolphin, beauty and beast
Heartbeat and high tide, ebb tide and flow
The universe in a crystal of snow

Snowdrop and deathcap, hangman and clown
Walls that divide come tumbling down
Seen through the night, the glimmer of day
Light is but darkness worn away

Blackness and whiteness, sunset and dawn
Those gone before, those yet to be born
Past and future, distance and time
Atom to atom, water to wine

Look all around and what do you see?
Everything touches, you're touching me
Look all around and what do you see?
Everything touches, you're touching me.

Borrowed Time

Apparently we are all living
On Borrowed Time.
What I want to know is
Who borrowed it, and from whom?

And another thing . . .
If we give it back
Can we borrow another?

Eye Sore

I saw
a building
soar
into the sky

making
the sky's
eye
sore.

Estate

Mother!
They're building a town centre in the bedroom
A car park in the lounge, it's a sin.

There's a block of flats going up in the toilet
What a shocking estate we are in.

Neighbourhood Watch

It's a sin
It's a crime
Now we can't tell the time
Our neighbourhood watch
Has been stolen!

Fire Guard

My wife bought a fire guard for the living room
Seems a nice sort of chap.

Zebra Crossing

There is a Lollipopman
At the zebra crossing
With lollipops
He is trying
To lure zebras across
He makes me cross.
I cross.

I Say I Say I Say

I say I say I say
A funny thing happened on my way here today
The buildings had hiccups, the road ran away
Buses grew hair in the silliest places
Traffic lights chuckled and pulled funny faces
Three-legged lamp posts chased little dogs
The moon was mugged by stars wearing clogs
Policemen and policewomen danced on the beat
A zebra crossing galloped off down the street
Beggars gave money to passers-by
There was an old lady who swallowed a ...?
The town's in a tizzy, it's gone off its head
It's making me dizzy, I'm going back to bed.

A Cat, a Horse and the Sun

a cat mistrusts the sun
keeps out of its way
only where sun and shadow meet
it moves

a horse loves the sun
it basks all day
snorts
and beats its hooves

the sun likes horses
but hates cats
that is why it makes hay
and heats tin roofs

Pussy Pussy Puddle Cat

Pussy pussy puddle cat
what do you think
you're playing at
making puddles
on the mat
chairs and tables
don't do that!

Marmalade

A ginger tom
name of Marmalade
shaved his whiskers
with a razor blade

Last mistake
he ever made.

The Cats' Protection League

Midnight. A knock at the door.
Open it? Better had.
Three heavy cats, mean and bad.

They offer protection. I ask, 'What for?'
The Boss-cat snarls, 'You know the score.
Listen man and listen good

If you wanna stay in the neighbourhood,
Pay your dues or the toms will call
And wail each night on the backyard wall.

Mangle the flowers, and as for the lawn
A smelly minefield awaits you at dawn.'
These guys meant business without a doubt

Three cans of tuna, I handed them out.
They then disappeared like bats into hell
Those bad, bad cats from the CPL.

Mafia Cats

We're the Mafia cats
    Bugsy, Franco and Toni
We're crazy for pizza
    With hot pepperoni

We run all the rackets
    From gambling to vice
On St Valentine's Day
    We massacre mice

We always wear shades
    To show that we're meanies
Big hats and sharp suits
    And drive Lamborghinis

We're the Mafia cats
    Bugsy, Franco and Toni
Love Sicilian wine
    And cheese macaroni

But we have a secret
    (And if you dare tell
You'll end up with the kitten
    At the bottom of the well

Or covered in concrete
    And thrown into the deep
For this is one secret
    You really must keep.)

We're the Cosa Nostra
    Run the scams and the fiddles
But at home we are
    Mopsy, Ginger and Tiddles.

Cousin Reggie

Cousin Reggie
who adores the sea
lives in the Midlands
unfortunately.

He surfs down escalators
in department stores
and swims in the High Street
on all of his fours.

Sunbathes on the pavement
paddles in the gutter
(I think our Reggie's
a bit of a nutter).

Cousin Nell

Cousin Nell
married a frogman
in the hope
that one day
he would turn into a
handsome prince.

Instead he turned into
a sewage pipe
near Gravesend
and was never seen again.

Uncle Terry

Uncle Terry was a skydiver.
He liked best
the earth spread out beneath him
like a spring-cleaned counterpane.
The wind his safety net.

He free fell every day
and liked it so much
he decided to stay.
And they say he's still there
sunbathing in the air.

He sleeps each night
tucked up in moonlight
wakes at dawn
and chases clouds.

Living off the food birds bring
Uncle Terry on the wing
Away from it all
Dizzy with joy.

Eno

To be a sumo wrestler
  It pays to be fat.
'Nonsense,' said Eno,
  'I don't believe that.'

So he took his skinny
  little frame
to Tokyo
  in search of fame.

But even with God on
  his side
Eno got trod on
  and died.

All's Well That Ends

Peter was awake as soon as daylight sidled into his
bedroom. Saturday at last. He jumped out of bed and
flung open the curtains. Thank goodness, he thought,
not a cloud in the sky. As he gazed out of the window, he
wondered about the day ahead. Would his school team
win the county cricket trophy? (*No.*) Would he score his
first century? (*No, lbw second ball.*) Would
Helen be at the party in the evening? (*Yes.*) Would she
let him dance with her, walk her home and kiss her? (*No,
she'd spend all night smooching and snogging with O'Leary.*)
Would the police discover Grandma's body
behind the woodshed? (*Yes, on Monday.*) And if so,
would they think it was an accident? (*No, sorry.*) Or
suicide? (*Hardly.*) Would he be incarcerated? (*What's
that?*) Put in prison (*Yes.*)

But during his time inside, wouldn't he determine to
make amends, study hard and gain early parole?
Wouldn't he find a steady job and settle down? One day
meet a decent girl and raise a family? Eventually,
wouldn't he own a national chain of DIY supermarkets,
give money to charity, become a model citizen respected
and loved by the whole community?
Say yes (*No.*)
But surely all's well that ends? (*Well . . . . . .*

Cautionary Tale

A little girl called Josephine
Was fair of face and reasonably clean
But at school she wore a dunce's cap
And her father, taking out a map

Said: 'She'll learn more if she comes with me
About the world and life at sea.
What she needs is a trip on my schooner
I'm surprised I didn't think of it sooner.

For I'm captain of the *Hesperus*
And I think I know what's best for us.'
And thereupon a most dreadful fate
Befell her, which I'll now relate.

It was winter when they left the port
(in retrospect they shouldn't ought)
Setting sail for the Spanish Main
Despite warnings of a hurricane.

Three days out there came the gale
Even the skipper he turned pale
And as for little Josephine
She turned seven shades of green

As the schooner rocked from port to starboard
Across the decks poor Josie scarpered
She ran from the fo'c'sle to the stern
(Some folks'll never learn)

Crying: 'Stop the boat, I want to go home.'
But unheeding, the angry foam
Swamped the decks. Her dad did curse
Knowing things would go from bad to worse

He called his daughter to his side
'Put on my seaman's coat,' he cried
'You'll be safe 'til the storm has passed.'
Then bound her tightly to the mast.

And pass it did, but sad to say
Not for a fortnight and a day.
By then the ship had foundered
And all the crew had drownded.

And reported later in the press
Was a story that caused much distress
Of a couple walking on the shore
And of the dreadful sight they saw

Tied to a mast, a few bones picked clean
All that remained of poor Josephine.

MORAL
Stay on at school, get your GCSEs
Let others sail the seven seas.

Moany Margaret

Moany Margaret
Day and night
One's too dark
One's too bright

Moany Margaret
Bread and honey
One's too chewy
One's too runny

Moany Margaret
Cello and flute
One's too stringy
One's too cute

Moany Margaret
Sea and sand
One's too wet
One's too bland

Moany Margaret
Cat and pony
One's too furry
One's too bony

grumble

groan

lament

wail

complain

Moany Margaret
Nat and Matty
One's too fat
One's too chatty

Moany Margaret
Mum and dad
One is gone
One is sad

Moany Margaret
So they name her
Margaret moans
Who can blame her?

sigh

carp whine

gripe

grouse

moan

whinge

fuss

Bucket

every evening after tea
grandad would take his bucket for a walk

An empty bucket

When i asked him why
he said because it was easier to carry
than a full one

grandad had
an answer
for everything

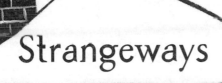

Strangeways

Granny's canary
Escaped from its cage
It's up on the roof
In a terrible rage

Hurling abuse
And making demands
That granny fails
To understand

'Lack of privacy'
'Boring old food'
It holds up placards
Painted and rude

It's not coming down
The canary warns
Till gran carries out
Major reforms

The message has spread
And now for days
Cage-birds have been acting
In very strange ways.

Blue Macaw

I used to keep
   a blue macaw
in my bedside
   bottom drawer

But he was never
   happy there
among my socks
   and underwear

He pined for sunshine
   trees galore
as in Brazil
   and Ecuador

Knowing then
   what I must do
I journeyed south
   as far as Kew

In the Gardens
   set him free
(wasn't that macaw-
   ful of me?)

Wiwis

To amuse
    emus
on warm summer nights

    Kiwis
do wiwis
from spectacular heights.

Ostrich

One morning
an ostrich
buried his head
in the sand
and fell asleep

On waking
he couldn't remember
where he'd buried it.

Crow

A crow is a crow is a crow
In the bird popularity poll
We are the lowest of the low
But do we care? No.

While others twitter on and on, or worse
Bang out the same three notes
Of musical Morse, we refrain.
If there's 'owt to caw, we caw.

Long since banned from the dawn chorus
We lie in bed until lunchtime
Then leisurely flap down
And bag a few smug worms.

Potter about in the afternoon
Call on friends, or simply bide.
For the night that others hide from
Is the time that we like best.

Nestled in treetops gently swaying
We stretch out to the sky
And hold court with the moon.
Stargazers we. The thinkers.

Looking deep into the heavens
We drift and drift and drift
Up and up into the blue black
Into the very crowness of the universe.

A crow is a crow is a crow
In the bird popularity poll
We are the lowest of the low
But do we care? No.

Seagulls

Seagulls are eagles
with no head for heights

For soggy old crusts
they get into fights

Out-of-tune buskers
beggars and screechers

Seagulls are not
my favourite creatures.

Love a Duck

I love a duck called Jack
He's my very favourite pet
But last week he took poorly
So I took him to the vet.

The vet said: 'Lad, the news is bad,
Your duck has lost its quack
And there's nowt veterinary science
Can do to bring it back.'

A quackless duck? What thankless luck!
Struck dumb without a word
Rendered mute like a bunged-up flute
My splendid, tongue-tied bird.

All day now on the duvet
He sits and occasionally sighs
Dreaming up a miracle
A faraway look in his eyes.

Like an orphan for his mother
Like a maiden for her lover
Waiting silently is Jack
For the gab to come back

For the gift of tongues that goes . . .

Why Do Sheep

Why do sheep
have curly coats?

To keep the wind
out of their froats

A Domesticated Donkey

A domesticated donkey from Slough
Wished to knit a new jumper but how?
  Attempts with her ears
  Resulted in tears
So instead, she knitted her brow.

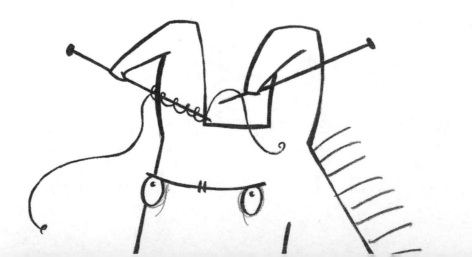

Poor Old Dead Horses

Don't give your rocking horse
To the old rag and bony

He'll go straight to the knacker
And haggle for money

The stirrups are torn off
The bridle and harness

Chopped up for firewood
It is thrown on the furnace

And the water that boils
Is chucked down the sluices

To wash away what remains
Of poor old dead horses.

Hundreds and Thousands

The sound of hounds
on red sand thundering

Hundreds and thousands
of mouths glistening

The blood quickening
Thunder and lightning

The hunted in dread
of the hundreds running

The sound of thunder
A white moon reddening

Thousands of mad hounds
on red sand marauding

Thundering onwards
in hundreds and thundreds

Thundreds and thundreds
Thundering   Thundering

Said the Water Boatman

Said the Water Boatman
   To the Water Boatmaid
'Won't you marry me?
   We'll leave this boring pond behind
And sail across the sea.'

   Said the Water Boatmaid
To the Water Boatman
   'Thanks, but I've no wish
To leave my natural habitat
   And feed the deep-sea fish.'

So the Water Boatman
   Set off the next day
To cross the ocean wide
   Some say he lives on a tropical isle
Others say he died.

   Said the Water Boatmaid
'How good to be free
   And frail and pretty and young.'
And she sang a wee song
   As she drifted along.

And she didn't hear the snap
Of the dragonfly's tongue.

And she didn't hear the snap
Of the dragonfly's tongue.

A Porcupine

A porcupine
   that lost its quills
ran away from home
   and took to the hills

All day long
   it cried as it crawled
'No one can love
   a creature so bald.'

But it was wrong.

A handsome kestrel
   dropped by to say
'I Love You! I Love You!'
   Then snatched it away.

Pull the Other One

A crab, I am told,
  will not bite
or poison you
  just for spite.

Won't lie in wait
  beneath a stone
until one morning,
  out alone

You poke a finger
  like a fool
into an innocent-
  looking pool.

Won't leap out
  and grab your hand
drag you sideways
  o'er the sand

To the bottom
  of the sea
And eat you, dressed,
  for Sunday tea.

A crab, I am told,
    is a bundle of fun
(With claws like that
    Pull the other one.)

Goldfish

Goldfish
are not
boldfish

They cry
when they
fall over

They tittletat
and chew
the fat

And are glad
when it's
all over.

Didgeridoo

Catfish
take catnaps on seabeds
Sticklebacks
stick like glue
Terrapins
are terrific with needles
But what does a didgery do?

Bloodhounds
play good rounds of poker
Chihuahuas
do nothing but chew
Poodles
make puddles to paddle in
But what does a didgery do?

A puffin
will stuff in a muffin
A canary
can nearly canoe
Hummingbirds
hum something rotten
But what does a didgery do?

Tapeworms
play tapes while out jogging
Flies
feed for free at the zoo
Headlice
use headlights at night-time
But what does a didgery do?

What does a didgery
What does a didgery
What does a didegeridoo?

Ticklish

When is a
stickleback
ticklish?

When it's
tickled
with a
little stick
of liquorice.

Handfish

Handfish
are grand fish

they swim
about in pairs

hold each other
when they fall in love

and when
they say their prayers.

*   *   *

They tickle
the sea's bare bottom

playful
as little kittens

and when
there's a nip in the ocean

wear brightly
coloured mittens.

118

Whales

whales
are floating cathedrals
let us rejoice

cavorting mansions
of joy
let us give thanks

divine temples
of the deep
we praise thee

whaleluja!

Cross Porpoises

The porpoises
were looking really cross
so I went over
and talked at them

Soon they cheered up
and swam away
leaving laughter-bubbles
in their wake

It never fails,
talking at cross porpoises.

A Conger Eel

Is there
a longer meal
than a
conger eel?

Old Hippos

Old hippos
   one supposes
have terrible
   colds in the noses

Attracted to these
   nasal saunas
germs build their nests
   in darkest corners

Then hang a sign
   that says politely
(streaming, streaming,
   day and nightly)

'Thank you for havin' us
in your nostrils so cavernous.'

Poor Old Moose

Short-sighted hunters
choose moose

A target as large
as an orphanage wall

The quicker the trigger
the harder they fall

Short-sighted hunters
go home to their wives

Hang hats on the antlers
live short-sighted lives.

Shark in the Park

Ever see
a shark
picnic
in the park?

If he offers
you a bun

run.

Crocodile Farm

Come wi' me
Down to Crocodile Farm
If you keep your eyes open
You'll come to no harm

There's the old milking shed
Where it's all done by hand
Though we've lost quite a few
As you'll well understand

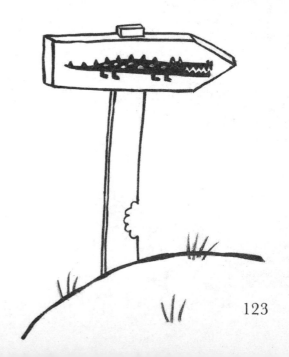

We make crocodile butter
Yoghurt and cream
Though nobody buys it
It's all lumpy and green

High up on the pastures
They're put out to graze
Where they round up the shepherds
And worry them for days

Then we fatten them up
And kill them humanely
The ones we can catch –
They kill us, mainly

But crocodile meat
is an acquired taste
A cross between sewage
And stale salmon paste

So I'm giving up crocodiles
Cos my account's in the red
And starting a farm
For alligators instead.

The Allivator

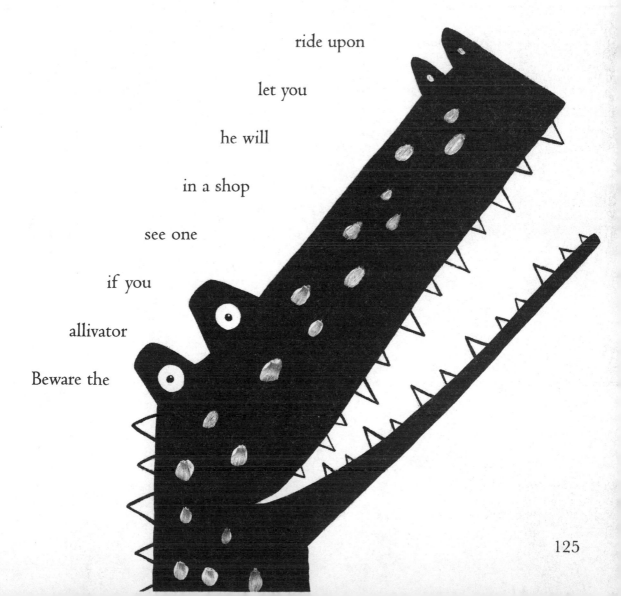

at the top.

then eat you

his back

ride upon

let you

he will

in a shop

see one

if you

allivator

Beware the

An Anaconda

Ever see
an anaconda
drive through town
on a brand-new Honda?

Don't ask him
for a ride

You might end up
inside.

A Water Bison

A
water bison
is what
yer wash
yer face in.

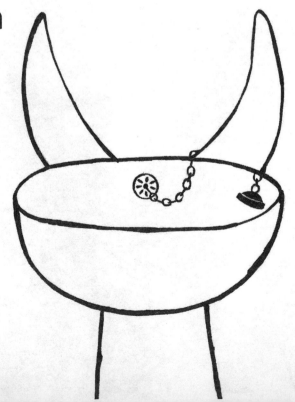

A Teapet

A teapet
I can recommend
to those who need
a loyal friend

Quiet, reliable
he'll never stray
content to sit
on his kitchen tray

Give him water
stroke his spout
say 'thank you'
when the tea comes out.

A Catapillow

A catapillow
is a useful pet

To keep
upon your bed

Each night you simply
fluff him up

Then rest
your weary head.

A 13-Amp Slug

A 13-amp slug
you are likely to find
in the garden under a rock

Be careful
how you pick it up

You might get
a nasty shock.

The Brushbaby

The Brushbaby
lives under the stairs
on a diet of dust
and old dog hairs

In darkness, dreading
the daily chores
of scrubbing steps
and kitchen floors

Dreaming of beauty
parlours and stardom
doomed to a life
of petty chardom.

Bookworms

Bookworms
   are the cleverest
of all the worms I know

While others
   meet their fate
on a fisherman's hook as bait

Or churn out silk
   or chew up earth
or simply burn and glow

They loll
   about in libraries
eating words to make them grow

(Vegetarians mainly,
   they are careful
what they eat

Avoiding names
   of animals
or references to meat)

They live
to ripe old ages
and when it's time to wend

They slip
between the pages
curl up, and eat 'The End'.

A War Thog

A war thog
is a mercenary beast

Who will show you
no mercy
until you're deceased

Armed to the teeth
with tusks
like scimitars

If you see one
give it
the widest perimeters.

Born to Bugle

He was born to bugle
To be a bugler-boy
Not a teddy bear or a bouncy ball
But a bugle his first toy

He bugled before breakfast
In the bath-tub and in bed
And in between he practised
Bugling on his head

He bugled on his bicycle
He bugled on the bus
At the zoo played boogie-woogie
With a hip hippopotamus

He bugled in Bulgaria
Botswana and Bahrein
Stowed below in cargo
Blowing bugle on a plane

He was born to bugle
Be bugling still today
But a burglar burgled his bugle
and took his breath away

And though we mourn the bugle
We mourn the bugler most
As laid to rest we do our best
To whistle 'The Last Post'.

Bubble Trouble

The trouble with Bobby is bubbles
Been his hobby since he was a boy
When Santa brought him a bubble
One Christmas instead of a toy

Since then he has tried to recapture
The magic of that shimmering sphere
And decided the blowing of bubbles
Would be his chosen career

Fairy Liquid he pours on his cornflakes
Scented soap he spreads on his toast
To be undisputed world champion
'A billion I'll blow!' his proud boast

Golden globes, silver orbs and Belishas
All manner of ball he creates
And with a fair wind behind him
A small Zeppelin our hero inflates

But the trouble with all of his bubbles
Though perfect in every way
Though fashioned with love and attention
(And we're talking a thousand a day)

These incandescent flotillas
These gravitational blips
These would-be orbiting planets
Within seconds of leaving his lips

Go POP! Just like that

Good Mates

There's good mates and bad mates
   'Sorry to keep you waiting' mates
Cheap skates and wet mates
   The ones you end up hating mates
Hard mates and fighting mates
   Witty and exciting mates
Mates you want to hug
   And mates you want to clout
Ones that get you into trouble
   And ones that get you out.

Me and My Shadow

Me and my shadow
Went out to a club last night.
Me and my shadow
Came home just a little tight

At twelve o'clock
We reached the flat
Unlocked the door
Tripped over the mat

Then suddenly noticed
Lying in the spinning hall
The shadow I lay with
Clearly wasn't mine at all

So who's got my shadow
Will the one who's taken it
Please send my shadow
Back because this one is several sizes too big and doesn't fit!

A Gottle of Geer

('To be read aloud without moving the lips)

I an a little wooden dunny
With a hand inside ny gack
How I niss ny daddy and nunny
Now the future's looking glack

Locked all day in a suitcase
I seldon see the sun
I've never tasted lenonade
Or a guttered hot cross gun

The owner takes ne out at night
To sit on his gony knee
He talks a load of ruggish
I think you will agree

Gut the audience go gananas
'Gravo!' 'Gravo!' they cheer
As he drinks a glass of water
And I say: 'A bottle of beer.'

Potato Clock

A potato clock, a potato clock
  Has anybody got a potato clock?
A potato clock, a potato clock
  Oh where can I find a potato clock?

I went down to London the other day
Found myself a job with a lot of pay
Carrying bricks on a building site
From early in the morning till late at night

No one here works as hard as me
I never even break for a cup of tea
My only weakness, my only crime
Is that I can never get to work on time

A potato clock, a potato clock
  Has anybody got a potato clock?
A potato clock, a potato clock
  Oh where can I find a potato clock?

I arrived this morning half an hour late
The foreman came up in a terrible state
'You've got a good job, but you're in for a shock,
If you don't get up at eight o'clock.'

Up at eight o'clock, up at eight o'clock
  Has anybody got up at eight o'clock?
Up at eight o'clock, up at eight o'clock
  Oh where can I find up at eight o'clock?

Simple Questions

Is a well-wisher
  someone
who wishes at a well?

Is a bad speller
  one
who casts a wicked spell?

Is a shop-lifter
  a giant
who goes around lifting shops?

Is a popsinger
  someone
who sings and then pops?

Is a fly fisherman
    an angler
who fishes for flies?

Is an eye-opener
    a gadget
for opening eyes?

Is a night nurse
    a nurse
who looks after the night?

Who puts it to bed
    and then
turns out the light?

Is a big spender
    a spendthrift
who is exceedingly big?

Is a pig farmer
    really
a land-owning pig?

Is a potholer
    a gunman
who shoots holes in pots?

Does a babysitter
    really
sit on tiny tots?

Is a tree surgeon
   a doctor
made out of wood?

Is a blood donor
   pitta bread
stuffed with blood?

Is a cardsharp
   a craftsman
who sharpens cards?

Who guards women
       when
a guardsman guards?

Is a batsman
   a man
who is completely bats?

Is a cat burglar
   a thief
who likes stealing cats?

Is a flat tyre
   a tyre
that you keep in a flat?

Is a hat-trick
   a method
of stealing a hat?

Will a pain-killer
   kill you
in terrible pain?

Is a rain hood
   a gangster
who sings in the rain?

Is a tail gunner
   a gunner
with a big long tail?

Do shoppers buy
   giants
in a giant sale?

Does a lightning conductor
   conduct
orchestras fast?

Is a past master
    a master
who has mastered the past?

Is a light bulb
    a bulb
that is as light as a feather?

Does an opera buff
    sing
in the altogether?

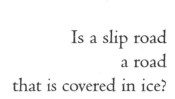

Is a slip road
        a road
that is covered in ice?

Are price cuts
        wounds
you get at a price?

Is a waiting room
    a room
that patiently waits?

Is a gatekeeper's
    hobby
collecting gates?

Is a prayer mat
     a carpet
that sings hymns and prays?

Is a horsefly
     a fly
that gallops and neighs?

Does a pony trap
          trap ponies
going to the fair?

Is fire-hose
     stockings
that firemen wear?

Is witchcraft
     jewellery
made by a witch?

Does a battery hen
     cry
when you turn the switch?

Is a scratch team
          so itchy
          it scratches?

When a bricklayer
     lays a brick
what hatches?

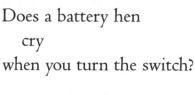

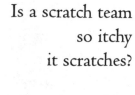

Is sandpaper
   used
for wrapping up sand?

If you lay down
   your arms
can you still lend a hand?

Is a sick bed
      a bed
that is feeling unwell?

Is a crime wave
   a criminal's
wave of farewell?

Is a cop shop
   a shop
where you can purchase a cop?

Is the last laugh
   the long one
before the big drop?

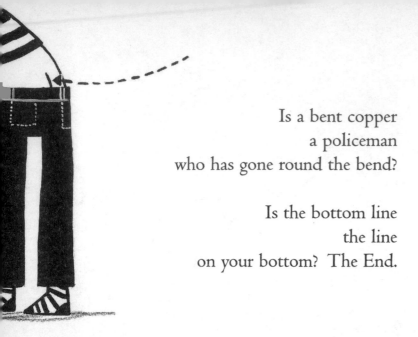

Is a bent copper
a policeman
who has gone round the bend?

Is the bottom line
the line
on your bottom? The End.

Zombie

I'm a fish out of water
I'm two left feet
On my own and lonely
I'm incomplete

I'm boots without laces
I'm jeans without the zip
I'm lost, I'm a zombie
I'm a dislocated hip.

The Going Pains

Before I could even understand
The meaning of the word 'command'
I've had them. The going pains.

Go to your room
Go to bed
Go to sleep

Twinges that warned of trouble in store
And once in the classroom, the more
I felt them. The going pains.

Go to the back
Go and start again
Go to the Headmaster

From year to year I hear it grow
That unrelenting list of GO.
That bossy word that rhymes with NO
Still can hurt. The going pains.

Go
Go now
Why don't you just go.

A Ring

'Give me a ring,' said Amanda
To the boy she met on a train
'Sure thing,' said Harry, excited
At the thought of seeing her again

So he telephoned next morning
And they chatted till late afternoon
Then she rang back in the evening
And they talked the light off the moon

They talked the hind legs off donkeys
They talked the leaves off the trees
They talked the sheep off the hillsides
They talked the wind off the seas

They talked the colours off rainbows
They talked the carpets off floors
They talked the chimneys off rooftops
They talked the numbers off doors

They talked the laces off trainers
They talked the diamonds off crowns
They talked the skins off bananas
They talked the noses off clowns

They talked the witches off broomsticks
They talked the whiskers off cats
They'd have talked till the Last Trumpet sounded
Had phone bills not dropped on their mats

'Give me a ring,' said Amanda
'Hip hip,' said Harry, 'hooray!'
And with the cash they'd have squandered
Got married the following day.

What She Did

What she did
was really awful
It made me feel quite ill
It was wrong and quite unlawful
I feel queasy still.

What she did
was quite uncalled for
How could she be so cruel?
My friends were all appalled, for
she made me look a fool.

What she did
was out of order
It made me blush and wince
From that instant I ignored her
And haven't spoken since.

What she did
was really rotten.
But what it was
I've quite forgotten.

Joy at the Sound

Joy at the silver birch in the morning sunshine
Joy at the spring-green of its fingertips

Joy at the swirl of cold milk in the blue bowl
Joy at the blink of its bubbles

Joy at the cat revving up on the lawn
Joy at the frogs that leapfrog to freedom

Joy at the screen as it fizzes to life
Joy at The Simpsons, Lisa and Bart

Joy at the dentist: 'Fine, see you next year'
Joy at the school gates: 'Closed'

Joy at the silver withholding the chocolate
Joy at the poem, two verses to go

Joy at the zing of the strings of the racquet
Joy at the bounce of the bright yellow ball

Joy at the key unlocking the door
Joy at the sound of her voice in the hall.

Fame

The best thing
about being famous

is when you walk
down the street

and people turn round
to look at you

and bump into things.

Superman's Little Brother

Being Superman's short-sighted, weedy,
scrawny kid brother isn't easy.
Sticky-fingered toddlers pick fights
with me in misadventure playgrounds.

On beaches, 7-stone weaklings
kick sand in my eyes
vandalize my pies
and thrash me with candyfloss.

They all tell their friends
how they licked Superman ...
(well, not Superman exactly
but his titchy, snotty-nosed, four-eyed little brother.)

Bullied by Brownies
Mugged by nuns
without a doubt, the fun's gone out
of being related to a comic-book hero.

When I grow up I want to marry
Wonderwoman's freckly, podgy little sister.
She's certainly not pretty
She may not be bright
In fact, she's so ordinary
I think we'd get on just right.

Goodbat Nightman

God bless all policemen
and fighters of crime,
May thieves go to jail
for a very long time.

They've had a hard day
helping clean up the town,
Now they hang from the mantelpiece
both upside-down.

A glass of warm blood
and then straight up the stairs,
Batman and Robin
are saying their prayers.

*   *   *

They've locked all the doors
and they've put out the bat,
Put on their batjamas
(They like doing that)

They've filled their batwater-bottles
made their batbeds,
With two springy battresses
for sleepy batheads.

They're closing red eyes
and they're counting black sheep,
Batman and Robin
are falling asleep.

The Figment Tree

I believe in fairies
And each Sunday after tea
At the bottom of the garden
Beneath the figment tree
Alone, I sit and wonder
If they believe in me.

When to Cut Your Fingernails

Cut them on Monday
There's a good week ahead

Cut them on Tuesday
Better go straight to bed

Cut them on Wednesday
You're going to be rich

Cut them on Thursday
You might meet a witch

Cut them on Friday
You'll be walked off your feet

Cut them on Saturday
You're in for a treat

But cut them on Sunday
Without saying a prayer
And your nails will grow
As long as your hair!

Tears For the Tooth Fairy

The Tooth Fairy is crying.
Not tears of pain, but of disappointment.
Yesterday morning,
Not looking where she was flying
She flew straight into a toadstool
And knocked out her front tooth.

So, sleepy at bedtime
She put it under her pillow
Before turning off the light,
Made a wish and fell asleep.
And guess what? You're right.
This morning the tooth was still there!

Gruesome

I was sitting in the sitting room
toying with some toys
When from a door marked: 'GRUESOME'
there came a GRUESOME noise.

Cautiously I opened it
and there to my surprise
A little GRUE lay sitting
with tears in its eyes

'Oh little GRUE please tell me
what is it ails thee so?'
'Well I'm so small,' he sobbed,
'GRUESSES don't want to know'

'Exercises are the answer,
Each morning you must do some'
He thanked me, smiled,
and do you know what?
The very next day he . . . grew some.

Film

Went to the cinema
Friday.
Tried to leave before
the end.

Couldn't get out.
It was a cling film.

Cling-Film

I'm clingy
I cling
to any old thing
a sandwich, a shoe, whatever you bring

I'm clingy
I cling
you can see right through
and when I cling, I cling like glue

I'm clingy
I cling
and I'm coming for you
cling cling cling

Gotcha!

The Scarecrow

The scarecrow is a scary crow
Who guards a private patch
Waiting for a trespassing
Little girl to snatch

Spitting soil into her mouth
His twiggy fingers scratch
Pulls her down on to the ground
As circling birdies watch

Drags her to his hidey-hole
And opens up the hatch
Throws her to the crawlies
Then double locks the latch

The scarecrow is a scary crow
Always out to catch
Juicy bits of compost
To feed his cabbage patch

So don't go where the scarecrows are
Don't go there, Don't go there
Don't go where the scarecrows are
Don't go, Don't go . . .

Don't go where the scarecrows are
Don't go there, Don't go there
Don't go where the scarecrows are
Don't go, Don't go . . .

Don't go where the scarecrows are
Don't go there, Don't go there

161

Only a Dream?

I woke up, and it was only a dream.
With a huge sigh of relief, I got out of bed
and then I saw it, hovering in the corner ...

A skull dripping blood and green slime.
Its eye sockets staring, not at me,
but at some unspeakable horror beyond.

I turned and ran towards the door.
But too late. It slammed shut
locking me in from the outside.

As I tugged at the handle, it broke off
and became white-hot. I dropped it
on the carpet which burst into flames.

The smoke was acrid, burning. I staggered
across the room, hands over my eyes
and collapsed unconscious on the bed.

I woke up and it was only a dream.
With a huge sense of relief I got out of bed
and then I saw it, hovering in the corner ...

Pantomime Poem

'HE'S BEHIND YER!'
chorused the children
but the warning came too late.

The monster leaped forward
and fastening its teeth into his neck,
tore off the head.

The body fell to the floor
'MORE,' cried the children

'MORE, MORE, MORE

MORE

MORE.'

Customer Service

Last Thursday, the telephone
never stopped ringing.
All day. Never stopped.
Even when I answered it.

So I rang British Telecom
and complained. Told them
it was making my head ache
and would they cut it off.

Sure enough, they sent a man
with an axe, the very next day.
(It's dark down here in the cellar
I wish he'd go away.)

I'm a Grown Man Now

I'm a grown man now
Don't easily scare
(if you don't believe me
ask my teddy bear).

Limps

Limps lie around
occasionally in pairs
in wait for someone walking
completely unawares

At the sound of a footstep
they prick up their ears
licking their lips
as the victim appears

They whiplash the foot
as it passes by
then sink in their teeth
as you let out a cry

Holding fast to your ankle
they feed off the pain
as you stumble like someone
dragging a chain

And when at last the doctor
says, 'It's only a sprain'
they've scuttled off cackling
to lie in wait again

The Kleptomaniac

Beware the Kleptomaniac
Who knows not wrong from right
He'll wait until you turn your back
Then steal everything in sight:

The nose from a snowman
(Be it carrot or coal)

The stick from a blindman
From the beggar his bowl

The smoke from a chimney
The leaves from a tree

A kitten's miaow
(Pretty mean you'll agree)

He'll pinch a used teabag
From out of the pot

A field of potatoes
And scoff the whole lot

(Is baby still there,
Asleep in its cot?)

He'll rob the baton
From a conductor on stage

All the books from the library
Page by page

He'll snaffle your shadow
As you bask in the sun

Pilfer the currants
From out of your bun

He'll lift the wind
Right out of your sails

Hold your hand
And make off with your nails

When he's around
Things just disappear

F nnily eno gh I th nk
Th re's one ar und h re!

The Man Who Steals Dreams

Santa Claus has a brother
A fact few people know
He does not have a friendly face
Or a beard as white as snow

He does not climb down chimneys
Or ride in an open sleigh
He is not kind and giving
But cruelly takes away

He is not fond of children
Or grown-ups who are kind
And emptiness the only gift
That he will leave behind

He is wraith, he is silent
He is greyness of steam
And if you're sleeping well tonight
Then hang on to your dream

He is sour, he is stooping
His cynic's cloak is black
And if he takes your dream away
You never get it back

Dreams with happy endings
With ambition and joy
Are the ones that he seeks
To capture and destroy

So, if you don't believe in Santa
Or in anything at all
The chances are his brother
Has already paid a call.

The Tongue-twister

Watch out for the dreaded Tongue-twister
When he pulls on his surgical gloves.
Keep your eyes open, your mouth tightly shut,
Twisting tongues is the thing that he loves.

It's the slippery, squirmy feel of them
As they wriggle like landed fish.
When he pulls and tugs and grapples
You'll gasp and gurgle and wish

That you'd never pulled tongues at teacher
Or a stranger behind their back,
As he twists out your tongue and pops it
Into his bobbling, twisted-tongue sack.

The Sound Collector

A stranger called this morning
Dressed all in black and grey
Put every sound into a bag
And carried them away

The whistling of the kettle
The turning of the lock
The purring of the kitten
The ticking of the clock

The popping of the toaster
The crunching of the flakes
When you spread the marmalade
The scraping noise it makes

The hissing of the frying pan
The ticking of the grill
The bubbling of the bathtub
As it starts to fill

The drumming of the raindrops
On the windowpane
When you do the washing-up
The gurgle of the drain

The crying of the baby
The squeaking of the chair
The swishing of the curtain
The creaking of the stair

A stranger called this morning
He didn't leave his name
Left us only silence
Life will never be the same.

Lullaby

No monsters are hiding under the bed
  I give you my word
The idea of vampires thirsting for blood
  Is plainly absurd

There are no such things as ghosts I promise
  They're all in the mind
Headless horsemen, hobgoblins and aliens
  All nonsense you'll find

You will not fall under a witch's spell
  You are not Snow White
Nor am I a handsome prince, but still
  A kiss, God bless, good night.

Index of First Lines

Position of Trust

A football dream betrayed

ANDY WOODWARD

With Tom Watt

CORONET

First published in Great Britain in 2019 by Coronet
An Imprint of Hodder & Stoughton
An Hachette UK company

1

A CIP catalogue record for this title is available from the British Library

Hardback ISBN 9781473699670
eBook ISBN 9781473699700

Typeset in Minion by Palimpsest Book Production Ltd, Falkirk, Stirlingshire

Printed and bound in Great Britain by Clays Ltd, Elcograf S.p.A.

Hodder & Stoughton policy is to use papers that are natural, renewable
and recyclable products and made from wood grown in sustainable forests.
The logging and manufacturing processes are expected to conform to the
environmental regulations of the country of origin.

Hodder & Stoughton Ltd
Carmelite House
50 Victoria Embankment
London EC4Y 0DZ

www.hodder.co.uk

Christmas 2009

This book is dedicated to
Jacob, Joseph, William, Luke and Izaak
The one uncomplicated thing
in my life is my love for my sons.

And to Mum, Dad and my sisters.
This has been their journey too.

Part 1

1.

How old is my dad, Terry, in that picture? Nineteen? Twenty? He was born in 1950, and married Mum in 1971. He looks the part: not a hippie, exactly, but the moustache and the shaggy haircut and the flares; pretty cool-looking. A young Burt Reynolds, maybe. I know for sure the picture was taken in the Cotswolds and maybe it was my mum, Jean, who took it. Dad grew up in Stockport, but he had family – a might-have-been family – down in Gloucestershire where he was born. Maybe he'd taken Mum there for the weekend to meet them. I remember us going down to visit Dad's aunts and uncles in Bibury loads of times when I was a boy.

Dad's natural father came from Calcot, a tiny village in the Cotswolds. His name was Anthony Richard Smith. He died before Dad was born and when Dad's sister, my Auntie Mary, was just four months old. I'm not sure my gran, Beryl, even knew she was pregnant at the time. In the local paper, it said she was at the Smith family home when the telegram from the Admiralty arrived. A submarine, HMS *Truculent*, had been sunk after a collision in the Thames Estuary. Anthony, the telegram said, was still missing, and presumed drowned.

Anthony had been at home in Calcot on leave, seeing in the New Year, just a fortnight before the disaster. He was a stoker-mechanic on board the *Truculent*, which was making its way back to base after refitting at Chatham Docks. At seven o'clock on the evening of 12 January 1950 the submarine hit a Swedish oil tanker, the *Davina*, and sank in just a few minutes. It was two months before they were able to pull the wreck off the bottom of the North Sea.

It's only recently I've seen old Pathé newsreels of the disaster. There were ten survivors; you can see the fear and the confusion while they're being interviewed back on dry land. They're wrapped up in other people's greatcoats, hair all over the place: pale, shivering. Still terrified. Sixty men, including Anthony Smith, lost their lives, trapped in the hulk of the sub or drowned in the freezing water. Thinking about it now, Anthony would have been right around the same age in 1950 as his son was when Dad's picture was taken down in the Cotswolds, twenty years later.

Beryl, my dad's mum, was also from the Cotswolds but she moved to Manchester, with a daughter and young son to bring up, a while after Anthony died on the *Truculent*. Although they met down in Gloucestershire, Beryl's second husband, George, was from Burnage. George adopted Beryl's children after they got married. Strange, though: my dad didn't find out that he was adopted – that George wasn't his real dad – until he was thirteen or fourteen. I don't know why that was and I don't think he ever did either. Anyway, my dad, Terence Smith, became Terry Woodward. Anthony, though, was always his middle name.

It's a Chinese takeaway now but, forty years ago, my grandparents – George and Beryl – owned the Regal Fish Bar on Hempshaw Lane in Offerton, just outside Stockport. My mum used to work there and my older sister, Lynda, and I would spend hours sat in the shop's back kitchen, drawing pictures, left to amuse ourselves. My mum would poke her head round the door when there weren't too many customers, checking we were okay or whether we wanted some chips. Those are some of my earliest memories: Lynda and me content in each other's company, Mum next door and the smell of fried fish hanging in the air. I was probably three or four years old.

Grandad worked at the Regal. Gran, too. But they needed the extra help when the shop got busy. And my mum and dad definitely needed the money. The Regal's counter was out front and my grandparents lived upstairs over the shop in what always felt to me like a dark, miserable flat. Outside the back door, though, where the garden would usually be in a suburban semi, was another world: George kept koi carp. He'd built this tank out there that was like a swimming pool, covered over and full of his fish. Huge, some of them were.

People used to make jokes about George frying them up if he ran short on cod. But everybody knew that those koi were his pride and joy. He used to take them to shows, win prizes and everything. Every now and again, we'd be invited round for the evening. It seemed like every friend Grandad had was as mad about koi as he was; people used to turn up – koi people – from all over the country. From other countries as well. We'd go along out of politeness but we'd never be there very long.

The story was that George used to go off to Japan on a plane and pick out the very best specimens to have shipped home. I'm not sure about that, but those koi fascinated me – haunted me – as a little boy: dead eyes, mouths flexing and their bodies twisting and turning in the water as they slithered over each other. They were spooky, especially a huge one he'd had stuffed and mounted in a frame at the top of the stairs. To me, that thing hung there looked like it might still be alive, ready to jump out from behind the glass.

Although it was my gran and George who kept the Regal, I can only ever remember being there when Mum was around. There was always something cold about how my dad and grandad were with each other. Grandma Beryl was as sweet as anything with us kids but Grandad hardly ever spoke to us when we were young. Not until we were teenagers, anyway. But he seemed to communicate with my dad, his stepson, even less.

As a boy, I didn't think it was any of my business: it wasn't up to me to spend time trying to work out why people were the way they were with each other. It was only much later – early 2017 – that I found out the truth of it. Maybe we've always had secrets to hide in my family. And Dad had his. Was it because I was speaking publicly about my own experiences? Or was it because he was already ill with the motor neurone disease that eventually killed him? I don't know, but I remember Dad opening up: *Andy, you know your grandad isn't the bloke you imagine him to be.*

It turned out that all the time Dad was growing up he was on the end of physical abuse from his stepdad, George. He could remember being hit with a chair leg, beaten up and all sorts. He had a stepbrother and a stepsister, who were definitely treated differently. They were George's own children, of course. Dad got nothing but grief as a boy; lived in fear, really. Which maybe explains why he was off work with 'bad nerves' so often while I was growing up; why Mum used to do all those hours to earn cash at the Regal.

My gran was probably scared of her husband, too. So she did what people do. Just boxed it off, I think. Maybe she convinced herself she didn't even see what was going on with Dad. She had a great relationship with him down the years, or so it seemed, anyway; used to ring him every day. He was her son, after all, even though my dad always felt isolated, like an outsider, when it came to the rest of that family.

When he got older my grandad mellowed a bit. Started talking to us. Started maybe having some kind of relationship with my dad. But I'm sure Dad couldn't just let it go. He couldn't forget it or wish it away. All the time we were growing up, if we ever had to go round there for any reason, he'd say: *Well, we've got to go. But we're not staying long.* From almost as soon as he met my mum, I think Dad used to spend as much time as he could at her house, even though it was already pretty crowded round there.

It's only now I've started to understand what Dad must have gone through upstairs at the Regal when he was a boy. No wonder it took him so long to talk to me about it at all. And no wonder that, as a young man, he couldn't wait to get out. To escape. Terry Woodward got the best bit of luck he ever got when he met my mum. Jean was going to be the love of his life. And hers was a different kind of family altogether.

2.

I t looks like they had a nice day for it. My mum and dad got married in 1969. All smiles. And it looks as if they all nicked their button-holes off the bush behind them. Not that there'd have been much money about, but you can see they wanted to do things properly, can't you? Mum and Dad look pretty glamorous, anyway. Mum is standing next to Beryl and George. Next to my dad is my nana, Anne Stewart, and alongside her is Richard. Later on, when I was growing up, we called Richard 'Grandad', even though he wasn't my mum's father. In fact, he wasn't the father of any of Anne's children.

My nana was one of the most amazing women I've ever known. She had eleven children: seven boys, four girls. All of them had the same father – and they had his surname, Stewart – but none of them knew anything about him. He must have just turned up, fathered another child and then done one each time: incredible, really. Him and my nana were never married or anything. He didn't live with them; had nothing to do with them. He wasn't a part of their lives at all. So Anne brought eleven children up on her own, all of them squeezed into a three-bedroomed house in Burnage.

Anne found someone in the end, though. In the late sixties, she met Richard Bryanston, who's the lovely guy with her in the wedding photo. They lived together and I knew him really well. But, before that, all those sons and daughters she brought up on her own. And they became my aunts and uncles; their children became my cousins. You'd have thought, with that many kids and a single mum short of money, no father around, there'd have been problems. But it was the opposite. Maybe all being in one little house, older ones having to look after younger ones, was what bound them together.

Some of them have scattered now – I've got an auntie who lives in Australia – but they'll come together for family occasions every now and again and, in all those years, there have never been cross words or fallings-out. They're still close after all these years. My Auntie Elaine still lives round the corner, spends lots of time with my mum since my dad passed away. And I was part of it – this big, supportive extended family – while I was growing up. One of Mum's brothers or sisters or their children always seemed to be around. Mum's family was like a whole world for me when I was a little boy.

My nana must have done something right: all those children; all of them growing up to be settled, with jobs and marriages and children of their own: good, respectable people. She loved us grandchildren, too. Nana was a feeder, just like my mum is now. As soon as you walked in the door, she'd be straight into the kitchen, getting you something to eat. I was really close to her but I bet my sisters and our cousins would all say the same. She did everything with us. She was where the bond in our family began.

Of all people, Nana deserved the kind of happy ending you can see in a wedding photograph. She'd brought up her children the right way and now they were making lives of their own. But evil and darkness sometimes come without reason and without warning. The very worst came to the Stewarts – to Nana, to my mum and to my uncles and aunts – just a year or so after my parents were married. That wedding photo feels to me like innocence and contentment. But, only a year later, all that got broken for ever. I never knew my Auntie Lynda. But what happened to her became a huge part of my life as well.

~

Lynda was my mum's older sister and had always worked as a shop assistant. She was a very pretty girl and I think my mum really looked up to her. In 1970, Lynda was twenty-two, still living at home, and was seven months pregnant. She spent most evenings with her boyfriend but, this particular Friday evening in November, Lynda had been out for a drink with a friend, down in Fallowfield at the Princess Hotel. The two girls missed the last bus back to Burnage and had to walk home all the way up Mauldeth Road.

Lynda and her friend split up on the corner of Kingsway, the dual carriageway that runs out to Cheadle and Wilmslow. The next morning, Lynda's body was discovered in the garden of number 285. She'd been dragged through a hedge, raped, bitten and then beaten to death. It was shocking, absolutely horrible, what happened to her. She was just a few minutes' walk from home. What must it have been like when the police turned up on the doorstep the next day to tell Nana what had been done to her daughter?

It was a really big case at the time, because it involved a young woman, because it was so violent and because it seemed like there was no explanation for it. It was random and unbelievably savage. An unborn baby died that night, too. My mum still gets upset whenever she thinks about it. She's always been nervous of the press as well because there was so much publicity about the murder at the time. The police had to make a lot of public appeals to try to find out who'd done it. They even had a van covered in posters parked up on Kingsway for a few days. But Mum said the police were very good with the family, especially the superintendent in charge of the case. She remembers him being a very considerate man.

In actual fact, the police did a fantastic job with the investigation. It was a completely unprovoked, opportunistic attack. The guy was a psychopath, no question. But they found him: they traced a ring that was left at the scene and matched up forensic evidence like boot-prints and teeth-marks. Once they tracked him to the factory where he worked – he'd made the ring himself – he admitted to everything. Only eighteen, the bloke, but he was already a monster. He went to court three months later and was sentenced to life. One of my uncles was there and got a punch on him before he went down.

It's natural: for Nana and for my mum – and for the rest of the family – Lynda's murder was a memory that none of them could escape.

My older sister, Lynda, was named after her but none of it was talked about at all when we were young. What could anybody say? The details of what happened were so awful nobody would have dreamed of telling us children, would they? It was as if evil had come into all their lives and they could never make it go away. So they just tried to bury it. Maybe they hoped him being locked up would be the end of it. We all found out later that it wasn't at all.

3.

O h, we thought we'd really made it when we moved into that house. A garden, double-glazing and room for all of us. And it was in Cheadle Hulme, where even the council estates were tidy little houses, not high-rise blocks of flats. Not posh, maybe, but definitely posher than anywhere we'd been before. Spiderman must have been eight or nine when that picture was taken because I'm ambushing my younger sister, Louise. I was five when we moved to Cheadle Hulme, in time to start primary school. I bet Dad was laughing at the two of us when he took it.

My older sister Lynda and I were both born in Offerton. Mum and Dad bought a little house there, near where Gran and Grandad lived. I'm not sure they could ever afford to keep up the payments on it. I remember them having rows about money. And I remember the bailiffs knocking on the door and us hiding in the upstairs bedroom, pretending nobody was home. At three years old, I thought it was quite a good game. We used to have the electric cut off sometimes, too, which meant evenings in candlelight, the four of us huddled together in the lounge. Eventually the house got repossessed and we had to move in with Nana, Mum's mum, who by now had a two-up two-down in Handforth.

We stayed with Nana for ten months or so. I went to nursery school there. We were on the council list and they probably had us down as homeless: there wasn't really room for us, another family, at Nana's. And Mum had just given birth to Louise. Anyway, our name came up and we moved into the rented house in Cheadle Hulme, where my mum still lives now. Back off the main road down a cul-de-sac, new and neat and quiet. Like I say, we thought we'd landed on our feet.

The house itself doesn't look that much different now. Same white cladding. It had three bedrooms: two doubles and my little single bedroom looking out over the front. The only thing really that changed was that Dad knocked through the lounge and the dining room so it was one big room downstairs. And the kitchen was tiny, so he built this kind of wooden lean-to at the back of the house to give us a bit of extra space. Dad was clever like that: Mum was sure the thing would leak but it never has. He designed it and put it together himself. He knew what he was doing all along.

Even when we moved away from Offerton, Mum kept working at the Regal. She had a day job, as well, on the pharmacy counter at Boots. Money was always tight. Dad was an engineer. And quite specialised: he worked on engines that drove the machines for milling flour. He'd go all round Manchester, looking after these machines and installing new ones. He worked for a big company based in Stockport called Mirrlees, but ended up getting laid off.

Dad was out of work for quite a while and I know it was hard for him. He hated being on the dole. When he finally got another job, it was just shifts as a baggage handler at Manchester Airport, down the road from where we were living. It was only years later that he went back to what he was good at – the milling machines – when he got taken on by a Japanese firm, Satake, who had a factory in Cheadle. He stayed with them until he retired.

Back when it was difficult for us financially, though, we had this really flash car. Well, we thought it was flash at the time. My grandad George won the pools when I was about three and he bought us a Mk II Cortina: yellow, with a brown vinyl roof. Brand new. Believe me, back then everybody wanted a Cortina. So we'd drive around in style but with my parents worrying if they had enough spare to put a couple of quid's worth of petrol in the tank.

Dad was good with engines, of course. When the Cortina packed up, we didn't have a car for a while but, later on, when I was playing football regularly and he and my mum wanted to come to all the games, Dad bought this old green Fiat. It was a proper wreck. I think he paid about fifty quid for it. Mum thought that was fifty quid wasted but he promised he'd get it going. He lifted the engine out and stuck it in the dining room at home, laid out on newspaper. Took it all apart, put it all back together: we were amazed. He actually got it running again.

If you ask anyone who ever knew him, they'd say Dad was one of the nicest men you could ever hope to meet: soft, gentle, funny. He'd wind us up with tall stories all the time. I remember he told us he'd been the UK table tennis champion and we believed him for ages. I think now about what he went through when he was growing up. He was the complete opposite of his stepfather: joking with us, great with kids and loving us to bits. And he never hit any of us once. He could be stern – he and Mum taught us manners and respect – but he would never have dreamed of laying a finger on me or my sisters.

Probably his own experiences as a boy came through in how protective Dad was towards his own children. To the point of being a bit neurotic, really. But we were his world, I think. He wanted to keep us safe. He loved me playing football, too. When he was young, he'd played for Stockport Boys like I did later on. I don't know which team but he played a bit of semi-pro, too. But I think his stepdad put a stop to it; told him he needed to go out and get himself a full-time job.

Dad was so different to Grandad. But my mum was almost a mirror image of my nana. Maybe that came from having to look out for younger brothers and sisters when she was growing up. She looked after everybody. Every meal made, every bit of school uniform pressed. She did everything. And she was even more protective of me and my sisters than Dad was. I remember if I went out to ride on my bike, I could only go up and down outside the house. Mum would want to be stood at the front door, watching. We had rows about it: *Why can't I just go and play with my mates around the estate?*

I have so many happy memories of being a boy in that house in Cheadle Hulme. My sisters and I got on really well together. They weren't getting dragged around football matches back then! That would come later. Mum and Dad found ways to make Christmases and birthdays special, however little spare cash they had. There were always people calling round: aunties and uncles, their kids. There was always something going on. Thinking back, my parents had a social circle that was completely to do with family. They didn't really have friends from outside that circle. It was a charmed life, in a way, for us kids: I didn't have a care in the world. There were no sharp edges in our family. I didn't have to fret about growing up. It seemed to me I'd be able to pretend to be Spiderman for as long as I liked. It was close-knit. Maybe, with Mum having grown up in a house with all those brothers and sisters, family felt like all they needed. There was one person, though, who wasn't a relative but who was round at our house a lot: Pete. We understood Pete was a friend of my dad's. He'd turn up on the door-step, drunk, at all hours. Mum or Dad would say: *Oh, he's here again!* But they'd make Pete welcome and he'd usually end up sleeping on the sofa. Really, he was an alcoholic. He'd wake up next morning and start drinking again, whatever my dad said to him about leaving the booze alone for a while.

Pete's dead now and it was only much later I found out what the connection with our family was, why Dad always seemed to want to look out for him. Pete was actually the boyfriend of Lynda, my mum's sister, who was murdered. It was Pete's baby she was pregnant with at the time. And he never recovered. Alcohol was his way of dealing with what had happened. Or not dealing with it, I suppose. Back then, all that mattered to me was that he was Dad's mate. And he was always friendly and fun with us kids. As a boy, there wasn't anything else I needed to know.

At the time, I never gave it a second thought, how overprotective my parents were towards me and my sisters. They were so loving and so warm, it just felt like a natural thing. I understand now that it must have been what had happened to them when they were younger that made them that way when we were kids. And I sometimes wonder whether things might have been different for me – and for Lynda – if they hadn't been like that. I don't know. But, with Mum and Dad looking out for me every minute of every day, maybe I never really learned how to look out for myself.

4.

D ad was always taking photos. That was on The Warren, a beach
in Abersoch in North Wales. It's quite upmarket these days but
my nana had a caravan on it back then. Our first summer holidays
were down there: drive out along the A55 – in the yellow Cortina –
through Caernarfon and past Pwllheli. Maybe I'm four in that picture,
with the beach ball that's almost as big as I am. We went to Abersoch
a few times when I was young but then Nana got herself a caravan in
Rhyl and we started going there instead. She'd come with us, too, and
uncles and aunties and cousins would be there at the same time.

Those were fantastic holidays. All of us messing about on the beach,
playing football. We used to play in the penny arcade, go to the pub
with the grown-ups and eat chips for a treat. I was surrounded by
family: safe, happy, laughing all day long. Back home in Manchester,

we used to do the same but on day trips. Ten, even twenty of us would load up in cars and head out to somewhere like Buxton or Styal; all park up and have a picnic together and me and my cousins could just run wild in the fresh air. It was perfect; seemed perfect to me anyway and still does, thinking back.

And, in the Abersoch picture, I've got a ball, of course. Football was always in my life: watching World Cups with my dad, listening to his stories from when he used to play. Now and again, he had a special treat for me: we'd go off to Old Trafford to watch Manchester United on Saturday afternoons. We had a little back garden in the house at Cheadle Hulme and I'd be out there, kicking against the wall, until my parents got fed up with the thudding of it: *Will you put that ball away for five minutes, Andrew?* My first memories of actual games are from primary school, a place called Bruntwood that got pulled down about ten years ago. It's a new housing development now. But those are the first games of football I remember, either on the tarmac by the school building or on the grass field at the back.

Sometimes Dad would take me out onto the big field at the back of our house that belonged to the local secondary school. By the time I was about seven, they'd let me go off there on my own. You could actually see through to the field from our back window. So, during the holidays, if there were other boys from the estate playing, I'd be out there all day. There were always three or four of us wanting a game: Wembley, World Cup, headers and volleys. And then, a little bit later on, we had a team at Bruntwood. We'd go round and play against other schools.

I was a boy with a soft, gentle temperament, a bit like my dad, maybe. But, when it came to football, I was competitive even then. Wanting to win at everything I did. Maybe that came from Dad, too. I don't know what he was like as a footballer but I can remember him at our house with my Uncle Dave. They'd play darts for hours on end. Dad got that Pong game, the very first home computer game, and him and Dave would be up till three in the morning sometimes: *Just one more game!* Dad wouldn't stop until he'd won. I was like that with the school team. And not just football: I wanted to be the best at cricket and rounders and everything else, too.

The next step up for a young player in Cheadle Hulme was playing for Stockport Boys. I was about ten. The headmasters at different schools put their best players' names forward. We had to go for District trials, at another school pitch somewhere in Stockport. There were boys from everywhere. I seem to remember we played eight-a-side games, with the coaches watching and then picking out who they wanted. It was quite ruthless, really: we were all standing in a big circle and they just read out the names of the boys they'd selected. Anyway, I got chosen and that was all that mattered. I was desperate to play for that team.

When I was at primary school, I was a really confident boy. I was good at football. I had my mates. Quite a few of the girls at Bruntwood fancied me. So the trial for Stockport Boys wasn't something that scared me. It was a chance to go and show how well I could play. And, of course, Mum and Dad were there, too. Dad loved that I was playing; Mum was excited for me and she always did everything with my dad anyway. It all started back then: I don't think I ever played a game when both my parents weren't there to watch.

Playing for your town – your district – was quite a big thing. An adventure as well. We'd play other teams around the north-west like

Manchester Boys, Tameside Boys, Runcorn Boys. I was playing for a local club at the same time, too. I think Dad had started looking around and he found a team in Cheadle Hulme called Juno United. I went down to training and then started playing for them on Saturday mornings. I still bump into some of the lads from that team now and one of them, Gareth Whalley, was a really close friend all through my teenage years. His family lived round the corner and me and Gareth went on to play first team together at Crewe.

The very first game I played for Juno was on the grass pitch at my primary school. Although me and Dad were United supporters, my hero was a Liverpool player: Alan Hansen. A centre half who could do everything: tackle, pass, head the ball, even get forward and score goals. So, right from the start, when it came to picking a position, I played at the back. I loved Juno: the structure, the training and regular games. And the people who ran the club were great. Just parents, really, wanting us to have a good time. I was a big, strong boy and I could kick the ball a long way. That first game, I remember whacking the ball into the goal from near the halfway line. Dad ran on the pitch and gave me a hug! That's still one of my favourite memories of him: how proud and happy he looked, jumping up and down that first Saturday morning, me playing for the local team.

I already knew by then that football was something I just had to do. We had a really good team at Juno United. We won the league. Won the Cup, too. I've still got an old VHS of that game somewhere. I can't remember who we played but we won 7–0. Lovely warm day, all the boys and the parents celebrating after. Such a great experience: I felt so free.

It's a kind of therapy for me now: I think about the circle of fathers and sons, the generations through a family. I know how proud Dad was of me playing football. I actually feel the same emotions myself now: my son Izaak is in his early teens and plays rugby league and it's great watching him play. I'm sure he'll be good enough to make it as a pro if he wants to. He'll message me after games to say how happy and confident me being there makes him feel. I felt the same back in the day, knowing my parents were on the touchline watching my games.

I remember one match, down at Heath Bank Park in Stockport. Must have been the middle of winter: it was absolutely freezing. Wind blowing, rain lashing down. Some of the boys were crying. They just wanted to be substituted. It was such a horrible day. My parents were standing in it on the touchline, of course. I can still remember Dad coming into the changing room after, rubbing my hands in his to try to get me warm. We jumped in the car and he drove as fast as he could to get home. Chucked me in a hot bath. They must have been freezing themselves but all they were bothered about was me being all right.

My parents made my childhood a really happy place to be. Despite everything that's happened since, I can still remember the joy we experienced together, me and Lynda and Louise: off on car journeys, singing songs, board games at home and Dad telling his ridiculous stories. Stories you sort of knew weren't true – he hadn't really ever got lost in the woods and been chased by a bear! – but you still wanted to hear how they turned out in the end. He knew how to make us laugh all the time.

I don't remember my parents going out all that often. If they did, one of my uncles or aunties would babysit. When I think about that time – late seventies, early eighties – the memories are of us all doing stuff together as a family. We always ate together. We'd watch TV: *3-2-1*, *Dallas*, *The Dukes of Hazzard*; at the weekend, the pop van would come round the estate and we'd be allowed a bottle of dandelion and burdock; the same day, the video van would come past, too, and we could choose a film. Saturday night, that would be the five of us, having a film night in: my parents, my sisters and me.

Mum and Dad were like the best of friends. Don't get me wrong: they had their rows. And when they did, Mum would lose the plot completely: she'd start throwing things at my dad. He'd come back to her with a sarcastic remark, *You're mental, you are!* And that would set her off even worse. But they never slept on an argument, always sorted it out there and then. I know how much we were loved. Their lives revolved around us, my sisters and me. We were safe and sound. Every night, Mum and Dad would both be there: *Goodnight. Sleep tight. Love you. See you in the morning.* It was as if, outside the family, we didn't need anyone else. It was perfect. And that only makes the thought of what happened later hurt all the more.

5.

It was all I ever wanted to do. It was the only thing I ever thought I *would* do. I can remember sitting watching football on the telly with Dad: *I'm going to be a footballer. I'm going to be on TV.* I don't know if he really believed it or was just humouring me, but he'd agree: *Of course you will, son. You're good enough, aren't you?* I didn't have the faintest idea what had to happen for it to come true. And neither did my dad. But that didn't stop me being sure that becoming a footballer was what lay ahead. In my imagination, I was already halfway to *being* Alan Hansen: tall, slim, dark-haired and the most stylish player on the pitch.

Look at me in the picture: nine or ten years old. I must have fancied my chances. I'm wearing an England tracksuit. On top of the telly in the front room, where me and Dad used to watch Cup Finals and

Match of the Day, there's a photo of my sister and me, all smart and all smiles. Don't know what that was on the windowsill. Somebody must have given it to Mum and Dad. Maybe that was part of my plan: it was a genie's lamp and all I had to do was rub it to be sure I'd become a professional player when I grew up.

At ten years old, I was playing football for Juno United on Saturday mornings and I'd started turning out for Stockport Boys whenever they had a game, too. Before those District games, we used to train on a playing field at the back of Parrs Wood High School in East Didsbury, between the school and the Mersey Canal. Just along the road from Burnage, where Mum grew up. I was playing every chance I got. As I was tall and strong, they played me in defence but I'd go charging all over the pitch, trying to make things happen, trying to be involved in the game.

I suppose I wasn't the only one in that Stockport Boys team who had ambitions when it came to football. But I don't remember that getting talked about much. Nowadays, at junior games, I think there's always gossip about who might be watching, which boys might end up in professional academies. Thirty-odd years ago it was different, more innocent perhaps. I don't remember people talking about clubs being interested in boys. We definitely weren't thinking about how much money might be sloshing around if we ever got pro contracts. And neither were our parents. We were only ten years old. It was all just about enjoying the game.

One particular drizzly Saturday morning in October, though, was unusual. The Stockport Boys coach announced that there would be a scout from Manchester City at the game. We shouldn't be put off by it but, obviously, we should play as well as possible. *You never know what might happen.* I didn't know how these things worked but I remember my stomach turning over with excitement. This was my big chance, wasn't it? I had to make sure I played the game of my life.

I can still remember the guy arriving on the touchline as we lined up for kick-off, standing alongside the line of parents watching their sons play. He was wearing a dark blue Adidas jacket with a sky blue shirt underneath. Manchester City colours, for sure. I knew straight away: *That must be him!* He was holding an umbrella to keep the rain off. And he had two young boys with him, maybe eleven or twelve years old: a little older than me, anyway. I didn't even notice what he looked like. All that mattered was that he was wearing stuff that made it obvious he was from a professional club.

It was the same when I became a professional player: the big games, where there was most pressure, were the ones when I played my best. That Saturday morning in Didsbury was one of those perfect games, where everything you try comes off. I was happy with that and didn't give a second thought to who'd been watching. Straight after the game, though, the scout went up to Mum and Dad. He must have found out who I was and who my parents were during the game:

Hello. My name's Barry Bennell. I'm a scout and a coach. Wonder if your son would be interested in coming along to a trials match next weekend?

He explained that he worked for Manchester City but also had some kind of relationship with Crewe Alexandra. My parents knew as little as I did about how this whole business worked, but they gave him our number at home and said they'd talk to me about it. I didn't meet the bloke at all after the game.

To understand what happened to me later on – to understand why it was possible for it to happen – I'm trying to put into words what it felt like to be told by a coach from a professional club that he wanted me to try out for the team he ran. It suddenly felt like anything I wanted to happen was possible, within my reach even. My mum and dad knew what football meant to me and I think they were as excited as I was. It was like I'd been given a golden ticket, the big chance every young would-be footballer imagines he needs. The thrill of it made my head spin.

The phone call from Bennell came quickly, maybe that evening. Even though he'd introduced himself as a scout working for Manchester City, the trial game was going to be held at Crewe's home ground, Gresty Road, the following Sunday. Dad came off the phone so proud of me. I know now, as a parent myself, that there's nothing so intoxicating as things working out for your son or your daughter. The lot of us were dizzy with it all week. I don't know how many times I got my boots out and polished them till they gleamed. Don't know how many times Dad dug out the road map to check the route for the short drive to Crewe.

Saturday morning, I wasn't playing for Juno United. I can't remember if we didn't have a game or I was saving myself for the trial game the next day. Either way, I was at home with Mum, Dad and Louise when the knock on the door came. It was a policeman, asking to come inside. Just a short way away, on Cheadle Road, Lynda had been messing about with mates, run out into the road and been hit by a car. She'd been flipped onto the bonnet and the windscreen and then off again. The policeman didn't know what her condition was but she'd been taken to Stepping Hill Hospital in Stockport.

It was such a shock. Later on in life, I became a policeman and would sometimes have to deliver that kind of news to a family. People react in so many different ways: faint, scream, freeze. We all just burst into tears that Saturday morning. I'm not sure I'd ever seen my dad cry but he was in floods all the way, driving to the hospital. The four of us rushed into Accident and Emergency. As it turned out, Lynda was unbelievably lucky: the driver was a learner, which meant the car had been going a lot slower than most cars. And she'd rolled off onto the pavement side rather than into the road and oncoming traffic.

She was still pretty bashed up. We hung around Stepping Hill most of the day and then she was discharged that evening. It was a really scary day. And the next morning, I didn't want to go to Crewe. I wanted to stay at home with my sister. The drive to the hospital, we'd all been thinking we might have lost Lynda. And now, the following morning, I just didn't want to leave her.

Looking back, it was maybe one of those moments in your life when the choice you make decides everything that follows. What if I had stayed at home? If I'd not turned up for the trial game? Things might have turned out completely differently, not just for me but for Lynda as well. She was dead set on me going, though. Mum and Dad, too. So Mum stayed with her and Louise. Me and Dad set off for Gresty Road. It's strange: the rest of that day is almost a complete blank, like I was sleepwalking through it.

All I really remember is being with Dad. On the way over, he was reassuring me. About Lynda and about the game. *I'll be there watching. Just do your best.* The team I was in was in the home dressing room at Crewe. It was really quiet in there while we waited to find out what would happen next. Everybody was probably terrified: a room full of ten-year-olds, before a professional trial. I didn't know anybody, not even by sight. They'd come from all over: Manchester, Runcorn, Liverpool, Crewe.

I think it was Bennell who came in and gave us kit to wear. He seemed to be the only person around all day. After that, I don't remember anything about the game but Dad was pleased afterwards and told me on the drive home that I'd done really well. *You couldn't have done any more.* He said I'd been brave to play after what had happened to Lynda. And then the phone call came later on. I'd been selected. Bennell needed me to turn up for training, on the Tuesday evening, at Manchester City's training ground in Platt Lane.

6.

That first night, I was so excited. Mum and Dad took me down in the car. They never missed a training session or a game from then on. Platt Lane: the same place Manchester City's first team trained. We turned in off Yew Tree Road. There was a car park right in front, where the main building was, and another overflow one off to the right. On the corner with Platt Lane itself was a full-sized grass pitch. Behind the main building, there was a six-a-side pitch with floodlights and boards running round it. And then, stretching off to the right, was a big area maybe the size of two pitches, AstroTurf with fencing all round and floodlit, too, with a gap alongside where parents could stand to watch their boys train. Behind that was Platt Fields, the park and the trees, with a gate you could go out through if a ball went over the fence.

You went into the main building – it had two storeys – and there was a little reception area. You'd go through there to the dressing rooms: four or five of them each side, along a corridor. That first evening, I was told which changing room to go to. There were other boys waiting, boys I recognised from the game at Crewe on the Sunday. Kit was already laid out, hanging on pegs and folded up on the benches. Everything: tracksuits, shorts and shirts, socks, AstroTurf trainers. I don't think any of us could believe what we were seeing. This was the real thing, real football. Proper kit and everything. For ten-year-old boys, used to washed-out old stuff from junior football, I can't tell you what a thrill that was.

The photo at the start of the chapter wasn't taken that first night at Platt Lane. But I know it wasn't taken long afterwards. It says everything about the control Bennell had over us right from the start, even when it came to taking a team photo: all of us lined up, excited eager to please. Bennell was in his early thirties, younger than my mum and dad. Tanned, athletic: he looked like a player. A footballer's hairstyle, pure 1980s. That first evening, he came into the dressing room and told us we could get changed. *I think I've got your sizes right. If any of you have trainers that don't fit properly, don't worry. I've got loads more, all different sizes, in the boot of my car.* Straight away, I felt like I'd taken a step into the world of professional football. And, straight away, I felt like it was this coach, Barry Bennell, who'd made it possible.

Once we'd got changed, we went out onto the big Astro pitch. There was an older group finishing up. We used to swap over with them every week. I'll never forget the first session. It was completely different from anything I'd ever done before. Dribbling, ball skills, all technical drills. Working in and out of cones. A lot like the stuff young players do today. But back then? It all seemed completely new. It was to me, anyway. And, at the end of the session, there was a game that Bennell joined in with. He was so clever with the ball. He had all the tricks. I can remember him running along with the ball balanced on his forehead and all us kids chasing him, trying to get the ball off him.

It wasn't just me. It wasn't just the boys. The parents were mesmerised, too. This amazing training session and then the game at the end, all fun and laughing, all of us following on behind him it seemed. By the time we came off the pitch, all of us – boys and parents – were just thinking: *Wow!* I left the session buzzing. Went off home with my mum and dad still wearing this brand-new kit I'd been given. Quite a few of the boys I met that night I went on to play with for years, one or two right into professional football. They were the best of the best, it felt like. Bennell himself said later we were the best team he ever took charge of.

I was back at Platt Lane on the Thursday night. At first, we didn't play any matches but we trained twice a week. At the time, it seemed like a chance for Bennell to look at the players, work out positions and tactics. In hindsight? It was his chance to study us boys and our parents while we were all still fresh and excited about what was going on. Where should he start? Which boys were the vulnerable ones, the ones he fancied? Which parents were the most enthusiastic and the most trusting? He'd go round and talk to the mums and dads while the session was going on, working them out. Where could he spot an opportunity, for now or for the future?

As a coach, Bennell was quite strict. With the coaching drills, he made sure that we were doing them properly. If you couldn't get it, he'd take you and show you, touching you as he did it. A hand on your back, an arm round your shoulder. Pulling gently at your hair. But at the end of every session there'd be the game, which was where the real fun was for us, chasing around trying to get the ball off him. And during those games, again, there was quite a lot of physical contact involved with some of us: he'd hug boys, lift them up, chuck them up in the air and catch them. I was one of the boys he'd do that to a lot. I think he got a sense of how boys would respond; which ones drew back from him and which ones just took it as a natural part of the game. For me, it just seemed like fun. It never felt for a moment as if there might be anything wrong.

It was a slightly strange situation all round. Bennell had the run of Platt Lane. He had the run of Maine Road, City's stadium, too. If he ever took any of us down there, he'd just walk straight in and people would see him and it'd be *Hi Barry.* The older group of boys who he coached before us on a Tuesday evening were definitely a Manchester City team. But a little while later, he told us we were going to be called Railway Juniors and that we'd be a feeder team for Crewe. In fact, over time, he'd sometimes change our name again to get us into a particular league or cup competition.

Some of the boys who were at the first training sessions didn't come back. Over the weeks, lads would drop out or, more likely, Bennell got rid of them for whatever reason. Other boys would turn up and start training with us instead. It was at least a couple of months before he registered us as Railway Juniors and started to organise fixtures. But it didn't take as long as that for him to get into me. Or, specifically, into my parents. He always talked to them those evenings at Platt Lane and would sometimes just turn up at our house. He'd say he had been in the area anyway and thought he'd drop by for a drink and a chat.

Give you an update on how Andy's doing, you know. Is that all right?

Yes, of course. Come in. What would you like?

He never drank hot drinks and never touched alcohol so it would always be juice or a squash. It all started so quickly. I'd only been training with him for maybe three weeks. He'd sit in our lounge, talking about himself, asking questions about the family. He told them he'd been a young player at Chelsea but had to stop because of injury; how he'd been at City for a number of years. He'd reel off the names of players he'd brought through. With me there as well, he'd tell my parents that he thought I had a real talent, that I had a very good chance of making it as a footballer.

And then, one night, after training at Platt Lane, Bennell came up to my parents and said he'd had a great idea. If I wanted to – and if Mum and Dad were happy with it – I could go and stay at his house at the weekend, get dropped off on a Friday night and then picked up again on the Sunday. The plan was we'd go and watch games together, talk about football and do extra training. Bennell reminded them that he was convinced I had this talent; weekends with him could make me develop even quicker.

And that was where it began. I was excited. This was better than anything I could have imagined. Mum and Dad were swept away by it, too. They were mesmerised. They'd been to the sessions. They'd seen what a good coach he was and how much I enjoyed what we were doing. They were completely taken in by the man. It's incredible when you think about how protective they'd always been towards me and my sisters.

I know it seemed to them like such an amazing opportunity for their son to be offered. Especially as I was so chuffed about being singled out. Bennell was the most amazing person I'd ever met in my life. It was like a dream. He seemed to me like everything I wanted to be in terms of becoming a player. Right from the start, he was the man who could make it all happen. I was in awe. When it came to football, this guy seemed like God. And him focusing on me, which he started to do during training sessions, made me feel I was special straight away. I'd be the one he picked out to show everyone whatever it was he wanted us to do.

And, of course, Bennell reassured Mum and Dad. They'd never had any kind of dealings with the world of professional football. He made them feel like he was a friend, a mentor. And that all he wanted was the best for their son. He always said the right things.

He can try it, can't he? He can come along for a weekend, see if he enjoys it. If he does and if he's getting something from it, then we could even think about making it a regular thing.

7.

S ome people have that gift for talking to people. Bennell had it:
he'd seem so warm; softly spoken and gentle, making the person
he was talking to feel as if they were special. He knew how to laugh
and joke and make people feel comfortable, the parents as well as the
boys themselves. You can see it in the picture. He was good-looking, a
charming and very charismatic man. And he knew who he wanted; me
and Paul*, the boy on the left in the photo.

Bennell had spent those previous weeks getting to know us as players
and getting to know us as boys. He'd been working out which of us
would be open, which of us would freeze. He did exactly the same with
our mums and dads. He could tell which ones would resist and which

---

* Consent for inclusion has been given, the name has been changed.

38

ones he'd be able to beguile. It was very powerful, the way he had, and hard to put into words. Anyway, us and our parents, he sucked us all in.

After he'd talked to them at Platt Lane, my mum and dad asked me if I'd like to go to Bennell's house for the weekend. I'd never spent the night alone anywhere without them, not even at my grandparents'. But I'd never met anyone like Bennell, so I said yes straight away. He'd told them that he'd often done the same thing with promising young players from his teams, trying to advance their development as players when he believed they were particularly good and had the chance to make it as pros. I'd only known him for a few weeks and he'd picked me out. I was unbelievably excited.

I got my bag all packed and, on the Friday evening, we drove over to Dove Holes, where Bennell lived, after I got home from school: out on the A6, past Whaley Bridge and Chapel-en-le-Frith, towards Buxton. Dove Holes is a little village and his place was on a bend – there's a roundabout there now – with a couple of other houses on the edge of the village.

It was an old, dark-coloured stone-built cottage. Holmleigh it was called, the name carved on a piece of stone stood on the front wall. With evening coming down, I remember, there was something a bit spooky about it all. There was a bare hillside up behind the house in the gloom. The busy road snaked away up the hill towards a railway bridge and the woods beyond.

There was one other boy, Paul, coming that weekend too, but we were the first to arrive. I went up and knocked on the big wooden door. Bennell answered, stood there smiling from ear to ear. He waved at my parents. *Come in. Come in!* I stepped inside, into what must have been a dining room originally. It was the only part of the house he showed to my parents.

Anyway, I looked around and straight away saw there was a full-size pool table. A fruit machine against the wall. And a jukebox. *Wow! Look at this!* We sat around for a little while. Bennell chatted to Mum and Dad. Lynda and Louise were there, too. *Don't worry. I'll look after him. Come and pick him up Sunday night.* They asked him if I'd need any money and he said no. *That's fine. I'll look after him.* They gave me a kiss and that was it. Off they went.

From the room we were in, there was a door through to the kitchen. To be honest, it was disgusting in there: filthy plates and pans everywhere; a hole in the ceiling. To one side, there were wooden stairs with two handrails going up to the bedrooms and then another door that went through to his lounge: a sofa against the wall, facing a fireplace and, in the corner, a big TV, a gaming console and a video recorder. All the electronic stuff was brand new. Against the other wall was a fish tank, a big marine tank with salt water. There was a dartboard hanging on one of the walls, too.

It was an old cottage, scruffy and not looked after. Completely different to our house, which was new and which Mum kept spotless. Here, nothing was really properly clean. Old, damp; it was a bit eerie. He had a dog: an Alsatian. There was a little yard at the back that was full of dog shit. The Alsatian was big enough that being in the same room with it made me nervous but that seemed to amuse Bennell. *Just sit on the sofa and watch the telly. Relax. Paul'll be here in a bit.* My parents were so protective towards me but they trusted this man to look after me, so I had no reason to be worried about anything, did I? Especially after Paul showed up.

All I can recall about that first night at Bennell's house are little fragments. He used to do magic tricks. That evening, he had a red handkerchief that he stuffed into his clenched fist. Of course, when he opened his palm, the handkerchief had disappeared. To a ten-year-old, this wasn't just clever; it was unbelievable. I remember the three of us sitting together on the sofa, watching a film: Paul on one side of him, me on the other. And he had his arms round our shoulders. That didn't feel uncomfortable at all. He'd got us used to the idea of him touching us during those Platt Lane training sessions. It just seemed like he was being friendly.

We slept upstairs. There was a room straight off the landing with bunk beds and a single bed. Next to that was another room. I'd never seen anything like it: it was stuffed full of football kit. Boots, trainers, shirts, tracksuits. Boxes and boxes of the stuff. All new. I mean, you couldn't see the floor. It was incredible. A wardrobe to one side, full of gear too. It was like the stockroom at a sports shop. Then there was his bedroom at the back and, next to the stairs, another room. He opened the door.

Look in here. D'you want to see what I've got?

There was a cage, floor to ceiling. And inside was this little monkey. I think they call them marmosets. It was really tame. He opened a grille in the cage and the monkey came over, sat on Bennell's arm and then on his shoulder. He gave us little bits of apple so we could feed the thing. To be honest, I couldn't believe any of this. It was like another world. Anything a kid could ever want: the pool table, the fruit machine, the big telly, all this football kit. And, now, he's got a pet monkey as well.

That first weekend, nothing untoward happened. We had a brilliant time. It was all an adventure. We went to two or three junior games. Bennell seemed to know who was playing where and when and he always seemed to know people as well. He had a ball in his car boot and we got it out and did a little bit of training on the pitches, just me, him and Paul, after the games had finished. He was laughing and joking the whole time, making sure we had fun. Then we'd get in the car and head back to Dove Holes. We'd stop for fish and chips. Even that: for me, a takeaway seemed like a treat.

Come the evenings, we watched films he'd brought from the video shop. Scary ones, 18 certificates. We huddled up together on the sofa. I think the first Saturday night we watched *A Nightmare on Elm Street*. You know, the first one with Freddy Krueger. I had nightmares about it later but, watching, I couldn't let on I was scared. Him with an arm round me was a bit of comfort, I suppose. I think, as well, I was already desperate to impress Bennell, this bloke who was the gatekeeper to everything I wanted. I'd go along with anything he thought would be fun. I couldn't cry or let him think I didn't like the film, could I?

Mum and Dad came and picked me up on the Sunday. All the way home in the car, I was just chattering on about what a fantastic time I'd had: the house, the monkey, the magic tricks, the football. But it's strange, isn't it? Even then, for whatever reason – I must have known instinctively it wasn't right for me and Paul to be watching them – I didn't mention the horror films or being sat on the sofa with Bennell. Anyway, Dad wanted to know if I'd like to go and stay again.

Of course. Please, please. Let me go again next weekend.

I felt so happy, so excited. I felt safe. It all seemed so innocent, I suppose. Bennell was going to make sure all my dreams came true, wasn't he? That Sunday evening, I couldn't possibly have imagined I'd never experience those sweet, uncomplicated emotions ever again. Thinking back, those first ten years of my life were like my own version of a perfect childhood. All smiles. Just look at the pictures. But all that was finished now. Finished for good.

8.

It's where it all started. It's where childhood ended. I took that picture myself a little while ago. I've been up to Dove Holes once or twice. Trying to take back control of my memories, I suppose. That picture's taken from the woods up by the railway bridge, heading into the village. You look back down the valley and there sits Holmleigh. I've got no idea who lives there now.

Nobody at training knew that me and Paul had stayed with Bennell the previous weekend. I think I told friends at school about it, though. I'd stayed at the coach's house and he had all this amazing stuff there. He even had a monkey. That was what fascinated us, ten-year-old primary school kids. *A monkey!* It had been a completely unbelievable experience, like a fantasy world. I couldn't wait to go back. And I did, the following weekend. So did Paul.

The Friday night, after our parents dropped us off, we ended up in the lounge, watching another scary film. As we were going upstairs to bed, Bennell had an idea.

That was fun, wasn't it? Shall we watch another one? We can watch one in my room.

He had a double bed in there, pushed up against one wall. At the foot of the bed was a telly, with a video recorder underneath and a load of films lined up neatly alongside. We got onto the bed. I was nearest the wall and Paul was on the other side, on Bennell's right. He put the film on, whatever it was, and he cuddled us up next to him. But I know nothing happened. Me and Paul were both still in his bed when we woke up on the Saturday morning.

The next day was like the previous weekend, on repeat. The football, the messing about, the magic, the monkey. It was fun. As much fun as I'd ever had in my life. A takeaway and then back to Dove Holes, watching a horror film in the lounge. And then: *Shall we watch another one in my room, like we did last night?* I'll tell you what was different, though. It still fucks me up to this day, the memory of it. The smell. Bennell had a bath. He came in, wrapped in a towel, put on Kouros aftershave and then a load of talcum powder down his shorts. If I smell those things now, especially the Kouros, I retch. The memory of that first night comes flooding back.

We watched the film. It was really frightening: *The Exorcist*, I think. Again, I was on the side of the bed by the wall and Paul was on the other. Bennell turned the telly off and it was suddenly pitch black in the room. He didn't say a word. But he started stroking me, my head and my chest. The three of us were just wearing football shorts and we were still squeezed up close to one another in his bed. I froze a little. Even at that age, maybe I was instinctively aware that this wasn't right. But he just said *Relax.*

I could sense he was doing the same thing to Paul with his other hand. After a couple of minutes, he moved his hand down between my legs and I flinched, sort of half turned away from him towards the wall. But he said *Relax.* I don't know, to this day, what was going on in my head. Was I afraid? Afraid of him? Or more likely: *It's Barry. So it must be all right.* Paul was there, too. *It must be okay.* This amazing man; this amazing coach. We're here in this house, this kids' palace. *This must just be a part of it.* I wasn't thinking anything, of course. How could I have been? This was just what was happening.

His only words then: *Follow me.*

That's all he said. He put my hand on his chest. And I had to do whatever he was doing, like a mirror. Whatever he did, I did. And Paul had to do too. *Follow me* was to both of us. I could feel Paul's hand moving. Bennell had shorts on. We both had shorts on. His hand went under my shorts and so I had to follow. My hand went under his shorts. So I was touching him down there. Paul was, too. And he was touching us. I don't know: why didn't I pull my hand away? I didn't. Nor did Paul.

It was Bennell's thing: he always started with two boys. *It's okay. If Paul's doing it, then I should do it.* It made it seem normal somehow. Thinking back now, it was almost as if I was hypnotised, as if this was happening in a dream. And, that time, it didn't go on for long. He didn't ejaculate or anything. It stopped. He went to sleep. I think Paul did as well. I put my back against the wall so I was facing Bennell. I was wide awake, trying not to let him or Paul know I was upset, that

I was crying to myself. I was confused; I was scared; and, even though I didn't really understand what had just happened, I felt something that I know now was shame.

I was ten. I look at a ten-year-old now, at one of my own children, even. Ten years old, they're still babies, aren't they? How could I possibly have processed what Bennell had just made us do? It was the first time in my life I'd had an erection and I beat myself up about that for years afterwards. *How could I have had an erection?*

At the time, I didn't even know what that meant. This was something so outside the protected little world I'd grown up in. I didn't understand at all what had happened. Now I know: I was a victim from that moment onwards. And, for all victims, shame is the poison that seeps into the rest of your life.

Bennell was this man who everybody loved, who parents trusted, who had become so important to me and so quickly. I was the one he'd chosen and now he had my future in his hands. He'd brought me to this amazing house. He could do magic. And starting that night, I struggled with the thought: *If I had an erection, does that mean I enjoyed what he did? Did I want it to happen?*

But, ten years old, I had nothing to compare this to, no way of knowing whether this was wrong or right. There'll be people who've had the same experience who still won't be able to come to terms with it. It's taken me a lifetime to stop blaming myself for something that, actually, was just something that happened to me: physical sensations, in the dark, with not a word being said.

There wasn't a word said between me and Paul the following morning either. You know, that night, both our lives changed for ever. But we didn't speak about it. And we never have since. Bennell woke up and it was as if nothing had happened. *Come on, lads. Let's get up. We're going to a game. Your parents'll be here later.* He was happy, in a really good mood. He went downstairs and made us breakfast. *Are you having a good time?*

Sunday was another day: watching football, playing football, talking about football. Bennell didn't mention the night before. Mum and Dad picked me up and, of course, I didn't say anything about what had happened. We got home and I was asleep straight away. I hadn't slept at all on the Saturday and I was exhausted. And, that evening, sleeping was the best way I had of hiding away.

Bennell had said nothing to me about what had happened. If he had, maybe it would have unlocked something. If he'd said something, maybe I would have as well. But, instead, he'd buried it under all the *This is fun, boys* of a Sunday out around Derbyshire. He buried it. Paul buried it. And I did too. Or, at least, I tried. For the first time in my life, here was something I couldn't talk about; a secret that my fear and shame told me I couldn't share with Mum or with Dad or with anyone.

There are so many ifs and buts, aren't there? I've turned them over in my mind ever since. When it came to going back to Dove Holes the following weekend, I'd been upset by what had happened on the previous Saturday night but I still wanted to go. Everything else had been amazing. It had just been that one unsettling, confusing bit. But it hadn't hurt me, had it? Maybe it wouldn't happen again.

I couldn't let on there was anything wrong. If I'd said to my parents that I didn't want to go back to Bennell's, they'd have wanted to find out what had happened. Instinctively, I knew not going back to

Holmleigh would have meant the end of the story for me as a footballer. Thinking about it now, a first little disconnect opened up between me and my parents that Sunday evening. It had never happened before. I had a secret I couldn't tell Mum and Dad. And, if I couldn't tell them, then I couldn't tell anyone.

We trained on the Tuesday night at Platt Lane. It was as if the previous weekend hadn't happened. And by the following Friday I was excited to be going to his house again. Excited about most of it, anyway. When Mum and Dad dropped me off, Bennell came out to the car and chatted with them, laughing and joking. Putting them and me at our ease. But I had this little knot of apprehension in my stomach. Was I worried he was going to touch me again? All I was aware of was thinking: *Where am I going to be sleeping tonight?*

That weekend, Bennell had something different for us. We watched a Bruce Lee film and he announced that he was a martial arts expert as well. Me and Paul just sat there and he dug out these nunchucks: two wooden handles with a little chain link between them. It was astonishing: he spun them round, cut them back across, all lightning-quick. Scary. It was as if he could do anything with them. I've no idea how or why he learned how to use them but, for us that weekend, it was another thing that left us in awe. Something else about him that seemed almost incredible.

I remember being fascinated by his marine tank, too. We stood next to it for ages, looking at the hermit crabs burying themselves in the sand at the bottom. Then he went upstairs and fetched the monkey down and got it to sit on my shoulder while he fed it bits of cucumber. All this new stuff distracted me from the fears I'd had beforehand. It was like one of his magic tricks: these new things made it seem amazing being at Barry's house all over again. As soon as my parents drove off and the front door closed, it was like stepping into wonderland.

Bedtime, though, and I got that knot of fear in my tummy. *Why don't you come and sleep in my bed, like we did last week?* It seems incredible to me now, but neither Paul nor I said or did anything. We didn't even exchange a glance. No emotion whatsoever. That was Bennell's power, the strength of his will: it was like we were frozen, helpless. As if we'd been given a drug or been put into some kind of trance. Both of us were too young to work out what was happening to us. To know what it was Bennell was doing.

Two little robots: up we went, shirts off and just wearing shorts. All exactly the same, me on the left of him on the bed, Paul on the right. And then: *Follow me.* The same movements. The same touching. Only this time he ejaculated. And I had an orgasm, too. Although I didn't have the faintest idea what that was. *What the fuck just happened?* It scared me. Turned into another thing to haunt me. For years, I was completely messed up about it. *Why? Why did it feel like that?* I know I'm jumping ahead but it's important for me to remember this now.

As a teenager, I'd have flashbacks to that night. Had I enjoyed it? Well, I'd enjoyed the physical sensation of an orgasm, which I'd never experienced before. What did that say about my sexuality, though? Maybe I'd liked it, after all. It didn't make me cry like the first time he'd touched me. At seventeen or eighteen, I couldn't strip it down to what it had really been: impersonal, unemotional; just a physical sensation. Or recognise it for what it was: sexual abuse; Bennell getting what he wanted. Instead, the shame bit into me. I tried to lock it away. From myself and, definitely, from other people.

I don't know exactly what happened to Paul, whether he had the same experience I did. But I know that the following evening, Saturday, when Bennell said we should go upstairs, he didn't have to ask either of us. We went straight into his bedroom, as if that was a normal thing. What he'd done hadn't hurt me. That probably made it easier to just do what was expected of me. It worked for Bennell, too, what was unspoken between me and Paul: *Well, if Paul's going in there, it's probably okay.* Even: *If I don't go in there and Paul does, I might miss out.* This man was in charge of everything, including our futures. There was nothing he couldn't do. *If I don't go in, I might get left behind.*

All of that going on over the weekend, I can remember so vividly. It's weird: the other thing that really sticks in my mind. On the Saturday, after we'd been to a game over that way, Bennell took us to a McDonald's in Macclesfield. I think it had only just opened and I'd never been to one before. I had chicken nuggets and chips, with barbecue sauce. I'd never tasted anything like it. And I'm still addicted to that barbecue sauce. Why would I remember a McDonald's so well? Probably because it was all tied up with the other stuff. Bennell sat there and looked at the pair of us, munching away. He'd just stolen our lives. That grin on his face: a Happy Meal was supposed to be our reward.

9.

The boy on the left is Gary Cliffe. He was fourteen when I first met him at Dove Holes. You look at me, crouched at the front and you can see my excitement. Just turned eleven, playing football, convinced I was going to make it as a player. I'd been chosen, hadn't I? Picked out as a special talent by the man who could make it happen?

Then you look at Gary. When that picture was taken, he was coming towards the end of four years of abuse by Bennell. He'd been chosen, too. And he already looks as if it had all but destroyed him. You can see all those emotions I'd only just begun to experience: the fear, the hurt and the confusion. But you can also see how Gary had coped: by shutting down, withdrawing into himself and into silence.

Gary came to Bennell's house one weekend not long after Paul and I had started staying there. He was already turning out for Manchester

City junior teams. He was where I wanted to be or, at least, that's what I thought at the time. Paul and I were still bubbling. This was all new and, for the most part, these weekends were about football, about our dreams coming true. Gary was different, though. He was quiet, serious; blank, somehow. Of course I had no idea why. As far as I was concerned, that was just how Gary was.

Bennell introduced us. Told us what a great player Gary was going to be. When we went off to watch games, Gary came, too, and joined in with the little training sessions after. At the time, it felt as if he was sort of taking us under his wing. Bennell never cooked. He seemed to live off takeaways. But Gary would go into that horrible kitchen, surrounded by dirty dishes and leftovers, and make us food, even if it was just heating up a tin of beans on the ring. He never spoke to us, though, about what had been happening to him or what was now happening to us.

On nights Gary stayed at Dove Holes – he wasn't there every weekend – he would go in and sleep in Bennell's bed. I have to try to be as honest about this as I can: in a way, I felt relieved when Gary was with Bennell because it meant I might get left alone; but, at the same time, I felt something a little like jealousy, as if I was missing out and maybe wasn't so special after all. That said, Bennell would often come into the room with the bunk beds later anyway and abuse me, even though Gary was in the bedroom on the other side of the landing.

Gary and I have talked since about those weekends in Derbyshire. I think we both understand ourselves – and Bennell – better now as adults. We understand there was a pattern to what he did: picking boys at ten or eleven and then easing them out of his life at fourteen or fifteen to make room for younger ones. I know Gary has felt huge guilt. He looked after us when we were at Dove Holes as far as cooking food and the rest was concerned. But he never did anything to stop what Bennell was doing or to warn us about what lay ahead.

By the time I was the age Gary was when we first met, I felt that burden of guilt, too. I never said anything – did anything – either, when I saw Bennell start abusing younger boys. Both of us have tried to get past blaming ourselves but that's much easier to say than to do. To be able to share our thoughts now, though, and talk about our experiences is a step in the right direction. I'm glad I've been able to have those conversations with Gary: I can't tell you how much I respect and admire him, as a man and as a survivor.

It's frightening to think of now: how quickly things moved on for me. And how quickly the idea of what was normal changed. Being with Bennell and him being the centre of everything was something that developed over weeks, not months. I think about it now: for ten years, my life revolved around my parents, my sisters, our family. But then he came along and it was almost as if I was pulled out of childhood's orbit and into his. What Bennell offered – football, adventures and dreams coming true – was too powerful for a ten-year-old to resist. He didn't have to tell me. He was my future now: *And we won't say a word.*

The bond – the intimacy – with my parents, just a few months before, would have seemed like a permanent thing. Home and family would be at the heart of everything for ever, for me like it always had been for them. Was it my innocence or theirs? Both, probably. We just gave up what we had, handed over my dreams to a man we hardly knew. For me, it was the promise of life as a footballer. That was all that mattered. Mum and Dad would watch from the touchline. Bennell told them I could be a special player and they could see it happening. They could see how I came alive during games. I think they really believed that he could make me a star.

It wasn't long at all after Paul and I started to stay at Dove Holes that Bennell started phoning my parents on the Sunday: *I've got a load of things going on this week to do with football. Be great if Andy could be around. I can bring him back to Manchester in a day or two.* Mum and Dad must have thought this was all a good idea. They had no reason not to. And they must have phoned school and made my excuses. It meant Paul would go home on a Sunday evening and I'd be left in Dove Holes with Bennell on my own. Bennell was in control and that always meant he'd push things further. Once he had me at the house on my own, the abuse went into a new phase. He would push my head down between his legs and put himself in my mouth for oral sex. Like I say, I still gag at the smell: Kouros and talcum powder. My mind flashes back: the confusion. It only took a minute – less, maybe – and he ejaculated. I didn't know what the hell it was, this taste in my mouth. He did it to me as well.

Weird, too: I don't know if any other boys experienced this with him, but Bennell started behaving as if he felt affection for me. He started kissing me, opening his mouth, like people kiss when they're in a relationship. I was passive, offered no resistance, let all this happen. It was instinct that took over: I couldn't fight or fly, so I froze.

When it came to training, me staying at Bennell's house didn't mean I was treated like some kind of favourite. The opposite, really. When we were doing our drills he'd be really encouraging to most of the boys when they did something well. But he'd never say anything to me. I never got that encouragement or any compliments.

It was almost as if he'd decided to separate me from the group even though, once we started playing fixtures, I'd always be in the team. I used to get upset that he behaved as if I didn't exist. *Wasn't I good enough?* Bennell made the conscious decision to ignore me; sending me a message, I suppose, and sending the other boys a message, too.

It was after a couple of months that we became Railway Juniors – a proper team – and started playing matches. Obviously the 'Railway' referred to Crewe, a big railway town. Crewe Alexandra's nickname was 'The Railwaymen'. Bennell took us all over the place, games he'd arranged against local junior clubs.

We always played against teams who were at least a year older than we were, sometimes two or three years older. The fixtures were usually on a Saturday so, of course, that meant Paul and I would arrive with him and go home with him after. That's probably when the rest of the boys realised the two of us were spending whole weekends with Bennell.

Around the actual matches, even though we were only ten and eleven years old, Bennell would treat us as if we were a professional team. He'd be very stern, very serious with us. It was all extremely regimented: kit clean, boots shining; all of us would go out onto the pitch together and he'd insist that our warm-ups were spot on every time.

The whole squad of players would come to every game and then he'd pick the team once we got there. He made sure we were all scared of losing our place: the team was that good and he was that good as a coach, us boys would do anything to make sure we were picked to play. It was absolute discipline, almost like a military thing.

It worked. We beat most teams, even though they were older than us. At the same time, though, training became less about having fun and more about getting things right. Bennell was pretty obsessive: endless drills, always ball work and ball retention, stuff that you'd take for granted now but which, back then, was quite ahead of its time.

If we couldn't get the hang of something, he'd run us: one or two laps of Platt Lane. *Now let's do it properly.* He worked us hard. But did we mind? We were winning all our matches and, for all of us, that sparked up the dream of making it as players. I still have no idea how I put that together with what he was doing to me out at Dove Holes. As far as football went, it felt – for us and for our parents – as if we were on to something with Barry Bennell.

10.

That van is parked outside Bennell's house. It was our first football trip away with him. The team had to meet out at Dove Holes, after school. You can see that parents were a part of all this: the dads are helping to load bags onto the roof rack. It wasn't just my parents: every one of us boys had mums and dads who were convinced Bennell was the best thing to have ever happened to them and to their sons. By the look of it, in that picture, us lads were already squeezed into the back. Bennell was taking us to Wales: to Anglesey.

For some reason, we headed off in the opposite direction, towards Buxton, and stopped for something to eat. Bennell paid for everything. Maybe he wanted to make sure we didn't get where we were going until it was already dark. When me and Paul were at Holmleigh, Bennell used to show us horror films. That weekend in Anglesey, he actually put all of us into one.

I don't know where we were when he stopped the van on a country lane and told us all to get out. *There's something I want to show you.* It was pitch black. He climbed over this fence and told us to follow him. We went down this long track. All of a sudden, Bennell let out a scream and went running back up towards the van. He was fit and fast and he had a head start. He got back and started the engine. We were all scared out of our wits, lots of us crying our eyes out as we scrambled to get back in our seats. One lad lost a shoe on the road and had to reach down to grab it. Before we'd even got the door closed properly, Bennell drove away, laughing his head off.

We got to where we were staying, some kind of hostel in a big, old house. It was creepy: still makes me shudder when I think about it. There was nobody on the reception, just a book left open on the counter to write down names of people who were staying. The place was empty apart from us. There was just one room to stay in, which had long rolls of matting laid out on the floor. We were going to sleep in our sleeping bags. Bennell put his sleeping bag down and I remember him pointing to a space next to him: *Right, that's where you're going to be.*

We all got laid down and settled, lights out. All of a sudden, though, you could hear this creaking and groaning. Bennell said: *Did you hear that?* Of course we had. It sounded as if someone else was somewhere in the house. *This house is haunted,* he said. These noises carried on, knocking and loud sighs. A room full of ten-year-old boys, all of us terrified. He told us to huddle up together, that he'd protect us. He started touching me and then I could feel him reaching around, touching other boys, too. He knew exactly what he was doing. I'd never been so scared in my life.

It seems incredible: it was probably three years later that he told me he'd had all those noises on an old cassette recorder. He'd just pressed Play and left it running outside the room. I can barely remember the football from that weekend. I think we trained and had a game. We went off playing in the woods around the house. Bennell would just disappear and leave us to it. The Saturday night, though, I'll never forget and nor will any of the other lads who were there.

We had some dinner and then all went into the big room with the mats to get ready for bed. One of the boys opened up his sleeping bag and there, inside it, was a sheep's head. A real sheep's head, cut off at the neck. We all screamed and ran out of the room. Bennell came out of the kitchen and asked what was wrong. *A sheep's head. There's a sheep's head!* He walked into the room, picked the head up and went to the front door. He just chucked it out into the night. *Wonder how that got there? Don't worry about it, lads. That kind of thing happens in haunted houses.*

Bennell thought it was funny. He got a kick out of 'that kind of thing'. The following day he acted as if nothing had happened. *What shall we do today, lads?* I mean, it's fucked up: we were ten- and eleven-year-old boys. After we got home on the Sunday evening, Mum and Dad came and picked me up. In the car, they were asking about the weekend. *What was it like? What did you do?*

I just said we'd trained and played a game. That we'd stayed in an old house. But I didn't dare breathe a word about any of the other stuff. To say anything would have meant breaking a spell. And this was what I wanted, wasn't it? To do what I had to do to become a footballer. If I'd mentioned any of the scary stuff, my parents would have put a stop to it all. They'd have wanted to know what else had gone on. On the following Tuesday night, a couple of the boys who'd been to Anglesey didn't turn up at Platt Lane. We never saw them again.

Paul and I were at training that Tuesday, though. So were our mums and dads. We never spoke about what was going on but I suppose Paul and I became quite close in a way. We were the ones going up to Dove Holes together every weekend. Our parents became friends, too. Bennell picked out the boys he wanted and he'd pick out the mums and dads he could control, too.

Paul's parents, like mine, used to be at every game and every training session. They thought the world of Bennell, were completely taken in by him. Their sons were dreaming about being footballers and they'd do anything they could to help those dreams come true. The game wasn't about money back in the early eighties; our parents just wanted to see us happy. They were as excited as we were about Railway Juniors and this amazing coach; as things turned out, their innocence meant our parents became his victims too.

~

I don't know what got said between Bennell and my parents and Paul's parents. I was never really part of the decision but I guess Mum and Dad just assumed I'd be thrilled with the idea of staying with our coach over Christmas. I'd only ever talked to them about the football, the pets, the treats and the magic tricks when I stayed at Dove Holes at weekends. As far as they knew, I always had a brilliant time. So that was the plan: me and Paul, just a few months after meeting him for the first time, were going to spend Christmas with Bennell at his house. When they told me, I didn't even think to say no.

Me, Paul and him in that cold, damp house with a kitchen floor spotted with dog shit. This musty, bitter smell hung in the air, trapped by the chill. But, when Bennell was in the room or we were tucked up close on the sofa, everything smelt of him. Aftershave, strong deodorant. He was always clean even though his house was filthy. I think Christmas Eve we watched Christmas films. Soppy stuff, really. But upstairs afterwards was the same as always. I'm not sure what we ate on Christmas Day but it definitely wasn't Christmas dinner. Bennell still never cooked. But I do remember the presents under the tree for us: trainers, boots, tracksuits, all football gear. Tons of it. More presents than I'd ever had for Christmas before. He was spoiling us, wasn't he? We went off to see a pantomime in Stockport the following day.

Apart from the presents, though, Christmas had nothing to do with football. I remember feeling sad that I wasn't at home. Christmas with Mum and Dad and Lynda and Louise was never a big do but my gran would come round in the evening. It was warm and it was about family. At Bennell's, it wasn't like that at all.

Paul and I were in the same boat: smiling, pretending this was a good time. And when I got home afterwards, it was no different. To tell my parents anything other than that it had been great would have been too much like telling them what was really going on. *And look at all the presents I got.* Mum and Dad couldn't believe their eyes when I came out to the car with all that sports gear.

You can understand it: why would they ask about what we'd been up to when they could see for themselves? I had my little smile fixed on my face as I slumped, exhausted, on the sofa, these piles of Christmas presents laid out around me. I didn't have to say anything and, of course, I didn't want to say anything. Yes, I'd had a brilliant time: just look at me. Look at all this stuff. *What a lucky boy.*

It was just like the football: Mum and Dad came to every game. I'd throw myself into it. I'd be everywhere: running, tackling, passing, scoring goals. And, of course, we'd always win. I must have looked so happy and fulfilled. And, during the matches, I was. Football took me over, took me out of myself. My parents, I suppose, would never have questioned that. They never questioned me. The surface of things looked so perfect. Why would they ever feel the need to look for what might lie behind?

That was the thing with Bennell, how he'd keep us on the hook. It worked on my parents, on all the mums and dads. On us boys too, me more than anyone. Magicians are able to pull off their tricks by distraction, by making you focus on something other than what's really happening. You look at the one hand and never notice what the other's doing. So, that Christmas and every weekend, he'd come up with new things to show us. Most of them were frightening; all of them were mesmerising.

He'd get you to hold out a piece of newspaper, stare straight at you and then swing his nunchucks round to slice the paper in two. He used to put razor blades in his mouth – real ones – and pretend to chew on them. He'd move them around in his cheeks, lay them flat on his tongue and show you them. He'd take us to the arcade to play table football.

I've never seen anyone who could play like he did: flicks, passes, trick shots and volleys. He could do anything. And then he'd take us out for drives over Snake Pass, driving at eighty or ninety miles an hour. He'd throw coins out of the sunroof so they'd hit the windscreens or bodywork of cars behind us, and then accelerate away.

Bennell was always pushing things further, always had a dare going on. He'd make you afraid but he'd always be in control. That was a power. Horrible stuff like on Anglesey but stupid little things, too. I remember going into a shop with him, at a garage. He went round getting what he needed but then, just before he went up to the counter, he tucked a magazine under his arm. He went to the till and paid for everything, but not for the magazine. As we walked out, I said to him: *You forgot to pay for the magazine.*

That was his little trick, he said. How he got his free magazine. *I can teach you how to do it.* We got back in the car and he just laughed his head off. This was all so different to anything I was used to, so unlike how we did things at home. He thought he was clever. And so did I, I suppose. I was impressionable enough to assume that it must be okay. Normal, even. All this was supposed to feel like fun.

Bennell was in charge and I got used to how things seemed to work while we were at Dove Holes every weekend. The same over Christmas and school holidays. What happened at night didn't make me happy but, the rest of the time, Bennell would always be making up things to do, things he knew would excite a ten-year-old. The only time I remember being upset was when his world – football, adventures and what went on at the cottage – came into direct contact with the world I'd grown up in at home.

Very early on, Bennell had made a point of dropping in on my parents: he was grooming them as much as he was me. Then, instead of Mum and Dad coming out to Derbyshire to pick me up, he started bringing me back to Cheadle on Sunday evenings. Out of politeness – out of gratitude, really – he'd always be invited in.

Before long, Mum had got into the habit of cooking him a Sunday dinner. We'd sit around in the front room. Bennell would talk about the weekend, about all the stuff he and I had done: games we'd been to, people we'd met, drills we'd practised. *It was great, wasn't it, Andy?* Of course I'd nod my head and smile, agreeing with every word. But I knew I didn't like it, that I wanted him gone.

Home was still a refuge for me and it upset me him being part of it. And he was: he'd sit there as if he was part of the family. Mum and Dad were completely taken in. He'd look across at me, making sure he caught my eye. A little smirk: *We've got our secret, haven't we?* And I'd say nothing. I didn't like Bennell being there but, at the same time, him talking got me off the hook. It meant I could keep that secret. He painted the picture for my mum and dad: the fun we were having, how happy I was being with him. How good I was at football. That meant they didn't have to ask me, question me. I didn't have to say anything at all.

Bennell was abusing me. He abused me in my own house, in the little front bedroom, with Mum and Dad cleaning up after him downstairs. I'd go up to get my stuff ready for school the next morning. I'd be in bed and then I'd hear him getting ready to leave: *I'll just pop up and say goodnight to Andy.* Steps on the stairs, and then he'd be in the room, pulling his trousers and pants down. Those

Sunday evenings, even though they didn't know it, he was abusing my parents, too. As if that was part of abusing me. Hiding in plain sight, he was getting away with it. And, for him, that was all part of the thrill.

11.

Paul and I had our secret, didn't we? A bond that neither of us would ever breathe a word to anyone about. As I say, we never even mentioned it to each other. All the focus was on our football instead, like in that picture. We were eleven, I think, and I'm not sure where it was taken. Railway Juniors were winning games most weekends. You look at the pair of us there, with our little cup and our awards, and I couldn't have been happier, could I?

I don't know who took the photo. It might have been my mum or dad: it might have been one of Paul's parents. Lots of the parents came everywhere with us, every training session and every match. Bennell fostered that feeling of us all being in it together: a family. He made as much fuss of our mums and dads as he did of us.

By that time – 1984 – Bennell had left Manchester City. None of us knew why. But he had joined up with Crewe Alexandra and we started going over there to train twice a week on the old Astro pitch that used to be next to the stadium in Gresty Road. We'd go to Crewe after school: I'd get home, have something to eat and drive over with Mum and Dad. They'd watch through the fence that went round the pitch; the sessions would run under floodlights. That was the first time I met Dario Gradi. He came to watch us train sometimes and even took the odd session. That was a big deal for us: being coached by the manager of Crewe.

The coaching was way ahead of its time: first touch, close control, triangles, passing and moving, making angles, in and out around cones. Endless repetitions. During my career as a pro, I saw those kind of sessions start to be put on at other clubs. I'd think: *I was doing this stuff when I was eleven!*

That was what we were like in games, too. Just pass, pass, pass. Other teams would get frustrated and try to kick us all the time. I remember Bennell used to have this thing, during matches, where he'd shout: *Keep the ball.* We knew what that meant. We wouldn't try to score. We'd just keep the ball between ourselves, rotating it, twenty or thirty passes at a time: defence to midfield to forwards and back again. Clockwork.

Football was that important to me that I never once didn't want to go to a training session or play in a game. But I do remember experiencing some very strange emotions around those training sessions in Crewe. Emotions I've really only understood much later on in life.

Most of the time, I'd just blot out what he was doing to me, just concentrate completely on football. But sometimes during training sessions, especially when Bennell would gather us round in a big circle to talk to us, I'd get this sick feeling, as if my stomach was turning over. I know now that was a physical reaction to the gap between what was happening on the football pitch and what was happening at Dove Holes.

The feeling came when the focus was on him instead of the football. Deep down, I couldn't put Bennell the football coach and Bennell the abuser together. I couldn't reconcile the best thing and the worst thing in my life being bound up together so completely. It wasn't anger exactly, but anger is what it became later on: all through my professional career, I'd have moments when a coach gathered players round and I'd just feel like rushing across the circle and punching him. The coach wasn't Bennell any longer, of course, but the same conflicting emotions would suddenly overwhelm me, flashbacks to those private moments of crisis on the Astro at Crewe.

We played some matches in Crewe, at a pitch that was associated with the club. I remember it was next door to an abattoir where they used to slaughter pigs. The rest of the time, we'd be off all over the place: Derbyshire, Manchester, Liverpool. Bennell would have had to let parents know where the games were so they'd get their boys there in plenty of time. He'd have let my parents know, too, because they never missed a game.

It was different for me and Paul, though. We were already at Dove Holes. We'd have no idea where we were going or who we were playing against. *Doesn't matter, boys. Just get in the car.* I don't know if Bennell did it on purpose but it made the weekends even more disorienting somehow. Me and Paul were just in this weird bubble. *Special.* I sometimes wonder how the other boys felt about that.

Even in that first year together, the team was amazing. From that point of view, it was really exciting to be a part of. It wasn't just us winning all the time. It was how we played: under-elevens and we'd be stringing fifteen or twenty passes together, humiliating other teams. I loved being involved, of course, and I always played. But, from very early on, I began to feel isolated, different.

I was going to stay at Bennell's at the weekends. I was the one he said was special. But that didn't mean he treated me like some kind of favourite at all. I felt I had to try harder all the time just to please him and to be sure of playing on Saturday. It wasn't any longer about making Mum and Dad feel proud. Without me even noticing, it had become all about him instead.

I wasn't aware of it happening at the time but it wasn't just the other lads I began to be isolated from. I spent so much time with Bennell and every day, every weekend, I was at Dove Holes drew me closer to him and loosened my ties to my own family. I spent less and less time at home, less and less time doing stuff with Mum and Dad and my sisters. I wouldn't see my nana, my aunts and uncles or my cousins, sometimes for weeks at a time.

It's weird. I was growing away from my family but, really, none of us noticed it happening. My life was completely bound up with football – with Bennell – and Mum and Dad weren't cut off from that. They came to watch me train. They came to watch every game. They still felt a part of it. A part of my life. And they were: he made a fuss of them, like he did all of our parents. Mum and Dad could tell the rest of the family how well I was doing. Me being a footballer, me being special, probably made them feel special, too.

Bennell gave me no encouragement at Railway Juniors. Even back then,

I think I started to withdraw into myself, putting myself under pressure. It was like I had to prove myself to Bennell at every training session and in every game. I can remember at least one game, over near Buxton, when the team didn't play well for a half. He got really angry and ripped into me, out on the pitch, in front of all the players. Even though the whole team had been underperforming, he turned it all on to me.

The strange thing is that I think learning to cope with that pressure as a kid maybe helped me cope as a pro later on. On the pitch, anyway. Despite everything and despite how I was feeling, I could go out and play really well. It was already like that when I was ten or eleven, turning out every weekend for Bennell and for his team.

Clare* was Bennell's girlfriend: in her twenties, blond, friendly. He could be so charming and charismatic, I can understand that a young woman would fall for him. Clare started to come and stay with him out at Dove Holes at the weekends, probably about six months after I started staying there. I spent quite a bit of time with her. She seemed nice although I didn't really know anything about her. I still don't: don't know what happened to her or where she might be now.

When she was around, Clare would tidy up the house and sort the kitchen out but Bennell didn't make any sort of compromises. He was how he always was. Now, I'd describe him as very controlling towards her. I'm sure she was afraid of him as well as being in awe of him, same as us. And he'd still sit on the sofa with his arm round me or Paul with Clare in the room.

I remember her arguing with Bennell sometimes. About us lads

---

* Name has been changed.

staying and about how he seemed to pay more attention to us than he did to her. When Clare was at Dove Holes, she'd be in his room. Me and Paul would be in the other, the room with the bunks and the single bed. He used to still come in to us, though, during the night. Who knows what Clare knew or thought about that.

Those nights moved things on in a way. With me, it moved on from touching to sucking a lot of the time. As well, instead of me and Paul being in his bed with him at the same time, we were in separate beds. He'd do whatever he did to us one at a time instead of both together. But we'd both be in the same room, so I'd be aware of Bennell abusing Paul. And Paul would have known what he was doing to me, too.

It's difficult but it's all part of it and I have to be honest. Bennell knew how to exploit the different psychologies of two young boys. He made Paul captain of the team; he gave me a really hard time at training and around games. But I was his obsession. He went further with me than with anyone else. If Paul and I were both at Dove Holes, though, he would never abuse just one or the other of us. He'd always want both.

At first, the fact that Paul had been there had meant I wasn't so scared about what Bennell was doing. *If it's happening to Paul, too, it must be okay.* Now, when he was doing things to Paul, I can remember feeling confused about it. Insecure. *That's what he does to me. I thought I was special. So why is he doing the same thing to Paul now as well?*

12.

T hat's a group of us at the end of our first season together, maybe eight or nine months after I'd first met Bennell. We're off to a training session by the look of it: he always made sure our boots were spotless. It's a sort of holiday snap, I suppose: Bennell took us away to Butlin's in Pwllheli. Another trip in the old blue van. None of us had to pay anything. He just told our parents to let us have a little spending money.

I know now that he used to do some coaching in the holidays at Butlin's but, at the time, it seemed incredible that he could arrange all this. We tipped up and he just wandered into reception and came out with a load of keys. We were all together in a row of those little Butlin's chalets you can see behind us in the picture. Of course, though, it was Bennell who decided who would be sleeping where. *You and Paul are in my room.*

This was the summer of 1984 and, to be honest, the camp was pretty dingy and run-down. Our chalets were probably the worst in the place. All the furniture and the curtains were grubby, falling to bits. But he knew everyone there, all the staff, so he'd get us free drinks, get us a big table together when the shows were on.

We'd go on the roller coaster because Bennell loved it on there. We were together the whole time and had to be on our best behaviour. There were lots of other kids and their parents around the place on holiday. Then there was us, like a little group of North Koreans, on our training camp.

I think we stayed for three nights that first time. He had us all kitted out: tracksuits, shorts, T-shirts, rain jackets. All the same, even the same brand of trainers. When we went around the camp, it'd be as a group, whether that was to go and eat or watch a show or whatever. Behind the roller coaster, there was a big playing field and that's where we trained. He'd brought cones and balls and everything; these were proper sessions, not just a runaround but two or three hours at a time. Military-style exercises as well: push-ups, sit-ups, all done in unison. To look at us, it was as if we were a group of miniature professional players.

He was at it with Paul and me every night. That goes without saying. He had other stuff going on with the whole group, too, though. Up behind the camp, there were little hills. If you climbed up them, you'd reach these rocky outcrops overlooking the sea. He knew what he was doing. He took us up there at high tide and got us to sit on the rocks, with our backs to the water, all holding hands. Because the sea was up, the waves were crashing into the rocks and splashing up over our heads. We were all soaking wet. Scared, too: it felt as if the water could drag you off the rocks and into the sea. He was sat there laughing. *Isn't this fun?*

I was with Bennell the whole of that summer. In fact, from then on, it was every weekend, every Christmas, every school holiday for the next six years. And there wasn't a single night in all that time when he didn't do something to me. Over that first summer at Dove Holes, my life changed completely and for ever. By the end of it, I was trapped: by my dreams, by my secret, by Bennell.

This fantastic football team I was part of and what he was doing to me: his trick was that those two things became completely bound up together. I felt as if I couldn't have one without the other. My parents had no idea whatsoever. As far as they could see, this man was going to make me a star. I would never at any point have been able to say to them: *This is what's happening. I don't want it to happen any more.* Everything I said and did was telling them the opposite. I loved Mum and Dad. I missed not seeing them. But this whole secret world lay between us now, cutting me off from them and from home. My parents trusted Bennell completely. Even though they weren't inclined to trust anyone outside the family. They were always very protective but, from their point of view, it was as if I was on a special kind of holiday. And as if Bennell was part of our family. They wouldn't have been able to afford to take me away. Mum was still working at my grandad's chippy and Dad was doing shifts as a baggage handler at Manchester Airport. They might have been able to go to my nana's caravan with Lynda and Louise for a weekend, but nothing more. I'd speak to them on the phone – from Dove Holes or wherever we were – every couple of days. *Everything's fine, Mum. I'm having a fantastic time.*

Some of that summer, Paul was at Dove Holes, too. Some of the time, Clare was there. I'm pretty sure Gary Cliffe came by a few times as well. I was there for the best part of six weeks, though, and a lot of it was just me and Bennell. For all I know, that's what he'd been planning for all along. The more I've thought about what happened to me back then, the more I've come to believe that none of it happened by chance.

There's an idea, I think, that sex abusers just take opportunities when they present themselves. Do what they do and then whisper *Don't tell anyone what just happened.* That's not how it was with Bennell. He was so clever and so patient. So in control. He knew exactly what he could do and when he could do it. How best to get what he wanted. He had all the tools he needed: fear, excitement, flattery. The secret. Bennell gradually drew me into his world and, at the same time, loosened whatever hold I might have had on any kind of life away from him.

We were in his bed one night, just the two of us. Watching a scary film on video. It was how every day ended up; it was what was expected to happen. This night was different, though. He was touching me, getting me to touch him. Then, slowly, he rolled me over, towards him, so I was lying on my front. Still stroking my hair, that smell of after-shave and talcum powder hanging over us. I didn't know what was happening, of course. Usually, he didn't say anything while the touching was going on. But now, he said *Just relax.* He sort of moved my legs apart a little with his knee. What was happening now?

The first thing I knew was the pain when he stuck himself inside me and started pushing down on me. It hurt, really hurt. Nothing he'd ever done had hurt me before. But I didn't shout out. I didn't ask him to stop. This wasn't like anything he'd ever done, all the other stuff that had been confusing at first, the physical sensations that I hadn't understood. This was different, straight away. I felt really afraid. He finished what he wanted to do, ejaculated inside me. He didn't say a word.

For me, it was as if I realised then what being completely powerless felt like. The fear set in and, from that night onwards, it never really went away. Not just fear of what he'd actually done; fear of the power it meant he had over me. Rape is someone having complete power over you, isn't it? Bennell had crossed some kind of line: if he'd do that to me, then what wouldn't he do? He'd taken me somewhere there was no turning back from. *You're mine now.*

Being raped by Bennell that first time left me feeling completely lost, as if somehow all the threads that might keep me connected to the rest of my life had been cut away. There was nothing but him now. Nothing but what he wanted and no way out for me. I was a little boy and a fully grown man had lain on top of me, forced himself into me. It had hurt and it had been terrifying and it had felt like there was nothing I could do.

I didn't sleep. I lay with my back to the wall, trying not to cry. Just wishing, somehow, Mum and Dad would be there and take me away. There was nowhere for my emotions to turn other than in on myself: pain, fear, shame, helplessness. It was like drowning. Fighting for breath, choking on my own feelings. Not just that night: that's how I was going to feel for the next thirty years.

Bennell didn't rape me again the following night. Or the night after that. He didn't say anything but he knew I was sore. He waited. He went back to touching and to oral sex and, because those things didn't hurt, I was grateful to him in a weird sort of way. Grateful he wasn't raping me. That's how it worked. It made the other abuse easier, I suppose. By now, though, I don't think it was just a physical thing for him. He was starting to do things that would be normal in a grown-up relationship: kissing, stroking, being gentle after he'd done what he wanted to do. I didn't understand what any of that meant back then. I think I understand now.

Bennell abused hundreds of boys as he abused me. Hundreds of times. I don't know about any of the other lads; I can't speak to their experience. But I know, from that first rape onwards, Bennell wrapped me up in something else as well. Something that went beyond getting his sexual fix. He penetrated me emotionally as well as physically; took control of me emotionally as well as physically. He had that power and all that mattered was what mattered to him. How he behaved when we were alone together at Dove Holes seemed to change. Makes me shudder: if I had to put it into words now, thinking back, I'd say it was as if he was falling in love.

13.

This is part and parcel. This is what I have to go through. This is my present and probably my future. How does a boy, just turned eleven, deal with the stuff that's happening to him? He learns to block out the bad stuff; he stops admitting to emotions. He shuts down on everything that hurts. In my case, that meant weekend after weekend – and in between, too, of course – learning to put on a mask. Never mind what's going on: give Bennell what he wants. Give everyone else the look on your face they'd expect from a young lad chasing a dream. Fishing? I don't even remember ever going fishing. But that's one of Bennell's jackets I'm wearing. And my own little smile frozen in place.

Bennell dressed all his players up in sports gear: new tracksuits, new trainers. He wore the same gear himself, too. He used to take me down to where he got it all, a place in Cheetham Hill, opposite Strangeways

Prison, just north of Manchester city centre. There was a whole row of sports shops: it being Cheetham Hill, probably a lot of the stuff sold there was knock-off.

One shop, they'd lock the door behind us when Bennell turned up. It was owned by a man I later found out was named Frank Roper: a youth coach at Blackpool, who was also a sex abuser but died in 2005 before he could appear in court. We played against his teams quite a lot so I'd see him at games. Roper and Bennell, back then, were really good mates.

Anyway, Bennell would buy loads of gear on a Sunday morning and stuff it into black bin bags. Sometimes he'd steal a bagful as well – couldn't resist – even though these people were supposed to be his friends. I think he used to sell kit on. He had his fingers in all sorts of shady stuff. He also made sure he always had plenty to give away to his players. Ten-year-olds would be bowled over by that.

He'd always pay cash in Cheetham Hill. He used to keep the rolls of notes stuffed into his underwear. He owned a couple of video shops: one in Furness Vale, one in Chapel-en-le-Frith. They were always busy. He had a sports shop over in Crewe. They were cash businesses. So I'd be with him sometimes: he'd go into one of the shops, lean over the counter and just take a big wad of notes out of the till.

He seemed to know people everywhere we went. Around the village, everyone seemed to recognise him: *All right, Barry?* But it was the same all over the Peak District: Glossop, Buxton, Chapel-en-le-Frith, every game we went to they'd know him. It was as if he'd built this network around junior football in the area. I know lots of the boys he took to Manchester City had come from towns and villages round there. He'd run teams in places like Glossop before he moved on to Crewe. He even had a job at a boarding school up that way. If I was off school and staying at Dove Holes, he'd take me with him and leave me sat in his Volvo while he trained their boys. He'd disappear into the school afterwards, too. Into the boys' dormitories.

Some of the things we'd do together might simply look like craziness from the outside. But with Bennell it was always to do with power and control. He had an air rifle and we would go out in his little back garden, tiptoe round all the dog shit and fire at these targets he had set up. *An air rifle! Wow!* Then one day we went up the main road and over to the woods on the other side of the railway bridge, where there was a little stream running through.

Bennell was firing at trees and getting me to have a go. Then he shot a bird – a duck, maybe? – and he told me to go and fetch it. As I crouched down over this thing, I heard a whistle past my head: a pellet. Then, as I stood up, another one. He was shooting at me but to miss, obviously. And laughing. If he thought it was fun, I couldn't show any fear, could I? I was terrified: he was putting me in the way of danger but forcing me to trust him at the same time.

We played our games. We trained. That was fantastic. And the holidays and the weekends at Dove Holes almost became a routine. During the days: the adventures, the football matches; trips to Blackpool, to Alton Towers; boys having Bennell's idea of fun. And then at night: you know, the more something happens, even a bad thing, the more it comes to seem normal. The more shutting it away becomes a habit.

I didn't like what he did but I wasn't scared by it like I had been. I'd gone way past the point where I could talk to anyone about it anyway. It was what went on. Life before Bennell already seemed like ancient history. I still had my heart set on becoming a footballer. Consciously or unconsciously, in my mind, the abuse had become the price I had to pay. I would wake up every morning and bury the thought of what had happened the night before. For me to carry on, every day had to be a new day.

I loved my time at primary school, even though towards the end I started getting a bit of grief off some boys there who lived nearby on our estate. I had a Mediterranean complexion, like Dad, and they'd call me names because of that. Threaten to beat me up on the way home from school. I think it was a couple of things: one was the football and me getting away with stuff at school because I was playing for Stockport Boys; the other was that a few of the girls used to fancy me. I was half-decent-looking and I already had a reputation as 'Andy, the foot-baller', even at eleven years old.

Mum and Dad knew I was getting bullied a bit so, when it came to going to secondary school, they decided it would be better not to go to the local school, which was just at the back of our house. Instead, they sent me off to the school at Woods Lane, which was a bus ride or a very long walk away. I know that decision was made for the right reasons but it meant I was at a different school to Lynda, who was at the local. Louise went there, too, later on. And it meant I was separated from all my mates from primary school.

I remember I found that really hard at first. Because of what was going on with Bennell, I felt isolated anyway and being at a new school on my own made it worse. I was away every weekend so I didn't carry on friendships with other kids from the estate. I saw a lot less of my own family as well. Even after games on a Saturday, I'd be going back to Dove Holes instead of home to Cheadle. The loneliness – not that I would have called it that back then – probably just drove me towards football all the more. It was what my whole life was about.

I suppose I was an odd one at my new school. I had this very different life and, even during my first year at Woods Lane, I wasn't right emotionally. I'd be upset on a Monday after what had gone on at the weekend. I can remember walking to school or waiting for the bus, crying to myself. Tired, miserable. Different. Then I'd be anxious by the Thursday, knowing that the next day I'd be going to Dove Holes again. That feeling – being different, remote – cut both ways, though. Football – and being a footballer – gave me an identity and a status with other kids and even with some of the staff at school.

Maybe it's because we lived then in a different time. Less aware, less questioning. Maybe it's because of the kind of family we were. Polite, self-sufficient. Decent people. We kept ourselves to ourselves. I felt very alone and my parents must have noticed me changing – speaking less, smiling less – even though I did everything I could to keep my tears and my anxieties private. That's what everybody did. You know: people back then – and our family, in particular – just got on with things. It was all about how things looked on the surface. Digging below that wasn't something it ever seemed a good idea to do.

People didn't used to say to each other: *How are you really feeling? Is there anything wrong?* Or, if they did, I'm not sure they really wanted an answer. If I said *I'm okay. I'm a bit tired. That was a tough training session*, Mum and Dad would take that at face value. Feelings and emotions were things you kept to yourself, like secrets. If you looked all right on the outside, that was enough. And the outside of me? Even if I was moody, withdrawn, a bit of a teenager at home, football trumped all that. On Saturday, out on the pitch, they saw me happy and fulfilled. And, despite everything, for ninety minutes at a time, that's exactly what I was. Football was the picture of me that everyone believed.

I played for the school team, the year older than me. It was like a free pass: the 'in-crowd' who might have bullied me were happy with me being around, taking my place up the back of the bus; the girls who might have been taking the mickey out of me if I hadn't been 'The Footballer' fancied me. *Come on, Woody. Come and sit with us.* Maybe that's why, as well, the school didn't make a fuss whenever I took time off to be with Bennell. They didn't pick up on me falling behind in lessons and with homework. I got away with it: extra time to catch up, sitting tests on my own if I missed doing them with everybody else. I was bright, too, so I ended up getting five 'C' grades at GCSE even though I missed so many lessons, off sick or off with Bennell. Just like my parents, nobody at school ever dug below the surface. I knew – and they all knew – what it was I planned to do when I grew up. Things were mapped out for me, weren't they? I had this talent and, you know, football just seems to turn people's heads. It always has.

I don't remember talking much to schoolmates about my life away from Woods Lane. Off away at weekends and at training sessions in the week, I didn't really see much of them. There was never time to have those conversations and I never thought I wanted or needed to have them anyway. I wonder now, though, what they might have made of it: for a kid, Bennell's place was like some kind of wonderland –

Neverland – with the pool table, the fruit machine, the monkey and everything else. At one point, he even had a puma roaming around the place. A puma! I've no idea where he got it but it arrived one day, a kitten about the size of a big domestic cat. It was absolutely beautiful: beige coat, big eyes. He let it wander around: the dog would be locked out in the kitchen or in the back garden.

I was scared of the thing, even though it was just a baby: if it didn't like you, it would hiss and growl. And it grew soon enough. It had proper claws and I think Bennell started getting nervous about it, too. He eventually took it to a zoo somewhere and left it with them. So, the puma left before it could do any harm. That still left Bennell's dogs. Over time, he had all sorts, including an enormous Pyrenean mountain dog. From the very first time I went out to Dove Holes, I'd always been nervous about his Alsatian. I just kept my distance but Christmas 1984 turned out to be all about that dog: Zico, I think Bennell called it.

As well as our local games at weekends, he used to arrange for us to play in tournaments all over the place: Southampton, Norwich, Ipswich. After we played a match down in Plymouth, Bennell invited a couple of the lads we'd played against – Steve Walters and Micky Fallon – to start coming up to Crewe to train during holidays and to play in the odd game in between. He'd drawn them and their parents in and the lads came to stay over Christmas as well.

There were the four of us there together on Christmas Eve: Steve, Micky, Paul and me. Steve and Micky were a year older than us. I still don't know what happened exactly but I remember Micky screaming: the Alsatian had gone for him and bitten him. He had a big gash in his cheek, blood pouring out of it. A proper, deep wound. Thinking back, the obvious thing would have been to go to the nearest A & E. Micky's cheek needed stitching but, instead, Bennell got us all in the car, his old Volvo, and drove us into Manchester.

It was already quite late and this was Christmas Eve but Bennell found a twenty-four-hour chemist that was open somewhere in the city centre. He bought bandages to cover up the gash, didn't even show the pharmacist what the bandage was for. He stuck the bandage on Micky's face and then we were back in the car to Dove Holes. Except we didn't drive straight back. Instead he took us down to the red light district around Piccadilly station and walked us round there. This was a really rough part of Manchester. I'd never been there before.

I remember it was freezing cold, might even have been snowing. Prostitutes on the corners, some nasty-looking blokes around. And he was trying to convince us that he knew these people. That, maybe, he was a bit of a gangster himself. Doing his best to scare us but laughing about it, like this was something we were all supposed to enjoy. With Micky holding this bandage up against the bleeding on his face the whole time.

You know how it feels, thinking back? Like this stuff Bennell did with us is the kind of stuff that would happen in dreams: it made no sense; it was just this nightmarish chain of random events. But that Christmas Eve, 1984, us four boys and Bennell: it all really happened. And Micky, for one, has had the scar on his cheek to remind him every day since.

14.

Maybe it would have been better if I'd fallen apart as a player. Bennell might have lost interest or I might have drifted out of the game and away from him. Instead, even though I was starting to really struggle with what was going on in my life off the pitch, on it I was going from strength to strength. So were Railway Juniors. Bennell always said we were the best group he'd ever had. Proof of that was that he kept coaching us all the way through, even after me and a few others signed apprentice forms at Crewe when we turned sixteen.

That picture is of me, ready for another game. That's a Railway Juniors kit. It's not got a Crewe Alexandra badge even though we were affiliated to the club. I guess Dad took the picture. And my poor sisters will have been around somewhere. They got dragged along every weekend. My parents wouldn't leave them at home. Mum's leaning over behind me, putting away my school uniform by the look of it. Like many of the other parents, she and Dad came to every single game. They loved it: me playing football was their life just as much as it was mine. Games were our family's time together, family events. Uncles would come along to watch sometimes. I'm sorry, really, that my nana never did.

I think some of the mums and dads were already thinking about the future and their sons becoming professional players. They urged their boys on and you could see they were quite competitive about it all. My parents, though, just wanted me to enjoy myself. Dad had an idea, having been a player himself, that I was good enough to have a chance of a career but he never put any kind of pressure on me. He and Mum had their fun watching me playing for the best team around and being looked after by the best coach around. They enjoyed the company of the other parents as well.

Was that why my parents – and lots of others – were completely unaware of what was going on between their sons and Bennell? Mum and Dad watched me play and train. What they saw was a boy living out his dream, excelling at the one thing he loved more than anything else. As far as they could tell, I was having the very best of times. I never gave them reason to think otherwise. I wouldn't have wanted to hurt them, of course, and I was scared of how Bennell might hurt me – physically, psychologically – if I ever breathed a word. But the real fear – the real shame – was turned inwards. I loved my parents being on the touchline for games. I enjoyed them feeling proud of me, wanted their admiration. What I didn't want was any of that to be questioned.

I had my own doubts about myself. The last thing I wanted was to have to deal with any Mum and Dad might have as well. I did everything I could to make sure they wouldn't have any. They were so protective of me when I was a boy; I know how much they loved me and cared about me. Instinct told me that, if my parents had any feeling at all that things weren't right, they'd snatch me away from Bennell. They'd snatch me away from football. And, by this time, I couldn't imagine life without either. Waking up from the dream: for me, that was scarier than anything. And it was their dream, too, wasn't it? The first mask I put on and hid behind was the one designed to keep the truth from Mum and Dad and I made sure it never slipped.

I was way past ever saying anything about what happened at Dove Holes, away on trips and during holidays. There was never a chance of me opening up but, even now, I sometimes wonder: what would Mum and Dad have thought if I'd told them, all those years ago, what had been going on? How could they have even begun to imagine the gap between how things seemed and how they really were? When they looked at Bennell, they saw an amazing, charismatic guy who was making all this possible. And when I looked at my parents I could see how happy I made them, how much they enjoyed being part of my football adventure. Me being happy – seeming to be happy – was the most important thing in the world for them. That just made it more unlikely that I'd ever say anything about what was going on or give them any reason to suspect things weren't what they appeared to be.

When we reached under-thirteens, Bennell entered us into a league for the first time. An under-fourteen league, of course. He always insisted we play against teams at least a year older than us. The West Derby

League was a bit of a shock to the system. West Derby is a pretty tough part of Liverpool. We played on pitches in parks with stones and dog shit – even glass – strewn around.

Some of the lads we played against were pretty rough, too. We won every game and the reactions would be fouls, elbows, even the odd punch when the ref wasn't looking. My mum and dad, on days out from our nice estate in Cheadle, discovered a different world as well. Parents on the touchline were pretty full on: mine weren't used to hearing twelve- and thirteen-year-old boys being sworn at all the way through games.

But Bennell chose that league for a reason. He said it more than once: he wanted to toughen us up. The whole thing was probably asking for trouble. We won the league but I remember there being some flare-ups with other managers and parents. We were entered as Railway Juniors but I think word got out that we were connected to Crewe and teams from professional clubs weren't supposed to be playing in the West Derby League in the first place. Bennell would argue with anyone, though, always pretending he was the hard man, so he didn't care. But we didn't hang about after games: into the cars and gone.

I really liked those games in the West Derby League: we played on Sundays, which meant I'd go home afterwards with my mum and dad instead of back to Dove Holes with him. Bennell used to get really moody about that. He was jealous, somehow, I suppose. Angry when he didn't get his way. Things got strange: he behaved as you might in a difficult relationship between two adults. We'd be driving somewhere and Bennell would suddenly start telling me he loved me. I was a twelve-year-old boy but he was saying: *You're different from the rest. It's not like with the other boys. You're so special.* I'd just sit there. What was I supposed to say? To be honest, he didn't need me to say or do anything. It was all about him. My part in those conversations wasn't to speak at all.

Other times he'd get angry or go into these really dark moods. We were still going to Butlin's sometimes, me and Paul and Bennell or just me and him, when he was coaching at their soccer camps. One time, when it was me and him in one of those grubby old chalets, he told me he'd had enough of everything and that he'd taken an overdose of paracetamol. *I don't want to be here any more.* I heard the tap running and there were a couple of tablets in the sink. It's crazy: remembering back, I got really upset. *What if he's killed himself?* You know, the bloke was abusing me, ruining me, but I burst into tears. And it was probably all put on anyway: the kind of emotional blackmail that happens in messed-up relationships. Like a scene out of a really bad film.

Bennell used to take us away to tournaments as well: Norwich, Southampton, Ipswich. All over. Our parents would come along but they'd stay in local hotels and just come to the matches. The players would all stay together. I remember in Southampton, we all slept on the floor of a school gym. A tournament in Ipswich was the one time I actually stopped Bennell doing something to me. We were in a hostel, I think, and there were other people around and that made me nervous. I was afraid of us being discovered even though, for him, that was probably part of the thrill. I pushed him away. He came again and I pushed him away again. There wasn't a word spoken.

The next morning, it was as if I didn't exist. Bennell completely ignored me. We went off to our game and when he named the team I wasn't in it. That was the first time that had ever happened. I always played. He didn't say: *Okay, Andy. You're sub today.* Just read out the team without me. I was devastated. He had the power to take away football, the one thing that had kept me going all this time. It was as if Bennell was saying *This is what happens if I don't get my way.*

It had nothing to do with football, of course. I was being punished out of spite, in the way somebody might try to punish a partner, hurting them as much as possible, in a dysfunctional relationship. Bennell was a grown man. I was a twelve-year-old boy. *What's this about? What are you doing to me?* What chance did I have of understanding what was going on? None.

What Bennell was doing to me, the sexual abuse, was difficult enough to deal with. But he'd taken me to a place that was even more demor-alising and traumatic: this hold he had over me psychologically, as if we were in some kind of relationship. Him taking football away from me, leaving me out of the team, was just shattering.

At the time, it was like a reminder of how important football was to me. Playing football was what kept me going: everything else was the price I had to pay for that. Looking back, I can see there was a flip side, too: if I wasn't allowed to play football, why had the abuse happened in the first place? I thought Bennell had picked me out because I was such a good player. But maybe the abuse was all there was; maybe football had nothing to do with it and my dreams were him kidding me – and me kidding myself – all along.

It was right around this time that everything changed for me. At twelve, thirteen, every teenage boy starts seeing the world in a different way and starts feeling new emotions that have got nothing to do with childhood. For me, though? Bennell had abused me for two years and more, weekend after weekend; holidays and Christmases, too. It had become a normal thing in my life, it happened so often.

Him raping me, though, took things to a different level: the physical pain, the shame, the fear of what was happening and what might happen next. An even darker secret. He kept doing it: the experience of being raped dominated my emotional life. I was crying to myself, vomiting, getting sick and missing school. My confidence drained away and I just withdrew slowly into myself. I was cut off and coming apart. *Is this who I am?* Me being so fragile made it even easier for Bennell to keep me under control.

How do we learn about life? What happens between us and our families, between us and our friends, is a big part of it. But I was around my family less and less. Even when I was at home, I was sepa rate, away in my own thoughts. If Mum said anything about that, I'd just tell her I was tired or that I had homework I was worried about. Either way, I'd disappear upstairs. Apart from when I was at school, I spent hardly any time with friends my own age. I was in this other world Bennell had created around me. I didn't know how to deal with anything else.

Even so, some of the girls at school liked me: they'd write me notes, that kind of thing. And one afternoon – I think I was just thirteen – an older girl said she'd walk home with me. She was fifteen. On the way, she started kissing me and said *Come round to mine. We can have something to drink.* She meant a glass of pop, obviously. But when we got there, her parents were out. She took me upstairs and I lost my virginity: we had intercourse. I just followed her lead.

She was older and she was in control but, for the first time in my life I'd had a sexual experience that I wasn't forced into. One that didn't come with a price. When I think back now, it's a nice memory. She was a really attractive girl and I like remembering her. I like the memory of having sex with her, young as we were. But that afternoon, I was all over the place. I actually got upset afterwards. She didn't understand why, of course. I'm not sure I did either. I couldn't process what had happened.

Even in that situation, I couldn't experience anything that didn't somehow connect back to Bennell. I had this vague sense of: *I've got to do this to prove I'm normal, to prove the stuff with him isn't really who I am.* Back then, kids wouldn't think twice about calling someone who was a bit soft or a bit different – a bit separate – a *homo* or a *queer.* I think I was too young, then, to really be thinking about whether I was gay. I wouldn't have had the words for it or a real understanding of what it might mean for me. But Bennell was a man, a grown-up man, and until now that was the only experience of sex I'd ever had.

It was another step towards him poisoning the rest of my life, really. After that afternoon in Cheadle, over the years, the sense of having to prove something in my relationships with women became over-whelming. It became almost an obsession: the starting point for all my relationships and my marriages. I'm only just beginning to understand it properly now.

Meeting a woman and wanting to prove to myself and to her that I wasn't who Bennell wanted me to be – that I wasn't a *queer,* that I hadn't wanted to be raped and abused, *I'm a normal boy, aren't I?* – was never going to be the way to start something good that could last.

Then – and ever since – it's been like I was acting out a part, trying to convince myself as well as other people that I wasn't the boy who was submitting to Bennell. Having sex, having relationships, but being outside and watching myself, at the same time. I balanced on a knife-edge, not knowing what was really me. That afternoon I lost my virginity – and in every relationship I've had since, probably – he was a part of it. A shadow. He was the secret I couldn't tell. And anyway, come the weekend, I knew I was going to be back at Dove Holes.

15.

That picture is from the first trip away with him that had nothing to do with football. A summer holiday on Majorca, an apartment block in a resort called Santa Ponsa. It's a beautiful place, the rocks and trees up off the side of the beach. We only went to Majorca once. All the other trips abroad were always to the Canary Islands, when we went as a team.

That's me, of course, looking like any kid, going down to the sea, waiting for the little waves to come in and touch my toes. Dressed in a tracksuit because it was an overcast day. As I say, that's what it looks like. The picture was taken by Bennell. Maybe that's what he saw. Or that's what he wanted other people to see. I think I was twelve, maybe thirteen.

I knew what was going to happen in Santa Ponsa. I always knew because it always happened. I still get the flashbacks. They make me feel physically sick: the feeling of him ejaculating inside me; the taste of him ejaculating in my mouth. I don't know how you ever make those sense memories go away. Maybe you never do.

The trip to Santa Ponsa, I can vaguely remember Bennell asking my parents about me going away with him for a week. It would have seemed like a treat. Mum and Dad couldn't have afforded to take us all to Majorca. Paul was going to come, too. And what must have made it seem completely innocent: Bennell's girlfriend, Clare, was going to be there as well. It wasn't football. Just a family holiday. In fact he told people, while we were there, that Paul and I were his children. His sons. And that Clare was our mum.

He made Paul and me wear identical tracksuits and trainers all the time. Or, on sunnier days, the same football shorts and shirts. Before we went, he'd taken us to a barber in Chapel-en-le-Frith, near where he lived, and got us to have identical haircuts. You can see in the picture how it's been left long at the back. That was the look he liked. That was the feel he liked when he grabbed the back of your head. So there we were, in an apartment up off the back of the beach. Me and Paul, like twins. Like dolls he'd dressed up. And his girlfriend, Clare: we were the full set if anyone asked.

Just like at Dove Holes, even though Clare was there, Bennell used to come in and do what he did with Paul and me. She was in the next room. The apartment had a lounge with two beds in it where we slept. The two of them had a bedroom off at the back. It's difficult to understand, really. But it's what he was like.

Some nights, I would be able to hear him and Clare having sex in the next room but then, ten or fifteen minutes later, he'd come through to the lounge. In the dark, no words. I'd sense somebody there. He'd be kneeling by the bed – mine was the nearest to their bedroom – and he'd be wanting to have a go with me. He'd put his hand under the covers and start touching me; take my hand and put it down there to start masturbating him.

When he was finished, he'd just stand up and walk off back to his room. And then, the next morning, like always, it was as if nothing had happened. We were just away on a week's holiday, weren't we? He'd switch and so we'd switch, too: we were having a laugh, all happy together. Let's get up, have breakfast and go out for the day. We'd go tenpin bowling, go on drives in the car.

We spent hours on the beach: he loved lying in the sun. He used that tanning oil – you know, like the Hawaiian stuff – that smelt really strong. It's still a trigger for some of my worst memories, like the smells of talcum powder and his aftershave back at his house. He'd want to rub the oil onto us while we sunbathed. All over us. And we'd have to rub it onto his back.

In a way, Paul and I were really close: the two of us spent a lot of time together. There was a bond between us because of what we both experienced, even if we didn't understand it like that at the time. By the time of that holiday, the abuse had already been happening for a couple of years. It happened night after night but the next morning we'd behave like he did, like nothing had gone on. If Paul and I had talked about it, maybe it would have released it. But that seemed even scarier than Bennell. I'm sure Paul was the same as I was: just shut it down, try to make sure it couldn't hurt me. And get on with playing happy families instead.

I wonder about the girlfriend, too. Clare. What must have been going on with her? Maybe, in her own way, she was blocking things out like us boys were. Definitely, while we were in Santa Ponsa, there was one time when she came out of the bedroom and saw Bennell abusing me. But what did she see? I mean: if she'd actually taken in what was going on, she'd have said something or done something, wouldn't she? Or, at least, she'd have got out?

It was as if Clare had looked but hadn't seen. She'd refused to see. Out of fear? He was a scary man: cold silences, hot flashes of temper. He was physically strong. There was always an undercurrent of violence in Bennell: swinging nunchucks in the front room at Holmleigh or picking fights on football touchlines. Did he ever threaten her? More likely, it was denial. It couldn't be happening, could it? Maybe she was protecting herself. She'd pretend that what was plain in front of her couldn't actually be going on. I sometimes wonder where Clare is, what she thinks about it all now. I wonder if she feels as if she was one of Bennell's victims, too, in a way.

So, in that picture, I've walked down from the apartment to the sea. That trip to Santa Ponsa was the only time I can ever remember me and Paul having a row. I remember the morning so clearly. We were arguing about something and Bennell had walked in. Clare wasn't there. For no reason – Bennell didn't know what the argument was about – he dragged me to one side. And he grabbed me. Punched me, once, twice, three times, really hard on my arm. I had massive bruises there afterwards. He shouted at me to stop it and I got upset, burst into tears. He'd never been violent towards me before. *Why have you done that? I haven't done anything wrong.* He ignored me. Pushed his tongue against his teeth in a weird way, eyes just looking straight through me.

I walked out of the apartment and wandered round the complex for ages on my own. I just wanted to go home. I ended up on the beach and Bennell must have been there. To take the photo. And I suppose it's a nice image, isn't it? A boy by the sea. If you didn't know what had happened, you'd think I was happy, smiling even. But that wasn't what was going on. I can still remember I was crying right at that moment. But he's taken the picture and that's what he's seen: he's not seen the tears; he's not seen the bruises on my arm. He hasn't noticed or cared how it felt being me that afternoon. Of course he hasn't. All that would be the last thing on a psychopath's mind.

I was with him all the time. In many ways, when it came to being part of relationships as a teenager, I simply knew no different. Bennell's power over me was what I was used to and, in a weird way, I suppose I grew to feel safe being controlled by him. That was part of his power: I'd put my life in his hands, hadn't I? Whatever the situation, he was in charge. It was a kind of reassurance. A reassurance that came with not having to think, with being dominated and forced into complete submission. *Follow me.* Remembering the trip to Santa Ponsa makes me think of the price I had to pay for that.

In all sorts of ways, my experience with Bennell has poisoned every relationship I've ever had. Since then, I've always craved attention, even when it was of the worst kind. I've always felt like I'm meant to be the victim. I've always felt I needed to prove myself to women, to prove to myself that I'm like any 'normal' bloke. And, maybe worst of all, I've always been addicted to the kind of drama for the sake of it that was what life with Bennell was all about. I've been addicted to insecurity even when security – physical, emotional and psychological – is what I've needed most.

With Bennell, you never knew where you stood. You never knew what was going to be next, what mood he'd be in, whether something violent or scary was just round the corner. It was like life was lived in a state of hysteria: you were always on the edge. He did that on purpose. There was always something weird or dramatic going on. But, with Bennell, that was normal. It was how everyday life around him always was.

I got hooked on it, I suppose. Or became convinced that it was just how things were. I was in his world now and insecurity and being off balance all the time were a defining part of that. For sure, I've undermined my own relationships ever since by craving a sense of uncertainty. Danger, even. Instead of being comfortable with respect, with honesty, with love – the things I actually need in my life like anyone else – I've forever been drawn to uncertainty and drama for the sake of it, the insecurity that Bennell was all about. *What the fuck'll happen next?*

A while after that trip to Santa Ponsa, Paul stopped coming to stay at Dove Holes, stopped coming away with Bennell except when we were going off to tournaments together. I don't really know what happened. I know for sure Paul didn't tell his mum and dad because he kept playing for the team. And his parents never said anything to mine. If he'd told them anything at all, they wouldn't have let him anywhere near Railway Juniors or Crewe, would they? And our parents were friends. They'd have warned me off, too. More likely, Paul just said he didn't want to go to Dove Holes any more. That all he wanted to do was play football or that he wanted to spend more time at home doing schoolwork. One day I'll sit down with Paul, I hope, and find out how he got away.

All through our time as a team, boys would come and go: it's only in the years since that I've wondered what might have happened to them. A lad would suddenly just not be around: had he been dumped because he wasn't a good enough player? Had Bennell got rid of a boy because he'd tried it on with him and had been knocked back? Or had the boy been abused but been able to escape getting dragged in any further? At the time, I had no idea. And still don't really. Lots of the boys involved back then I don't even remember. At the time, I probably didn't even give them a second thought. I was too focused on myself, maybe: on where I was going to get to in football and what I was having to go through to achieve it. I understand now, though. The lads who somehow got out or got driven out? Those lads were the lucky ones.

16.

By the time we were thirteen and playing at under-fourteen, Railway Juniors had moved on from the West Derby League and we'd become a Crewe Alexandra team. At the end of that season, I signed schoolboy forms with Crewe. That made it official: I was affiliated to Crewe and wouldn't be moving anywhere else for a couple of years at least. I think every single boy in our team signed forms at the same time. It was quite a big deal. We started playing games against other pro clubs at a ground at Keele University. We even played games sometimes on the main pitch at Gresty Road. We'd go and play at other clubs, too. I remember playing against Manchester United at their training ground, The Cliff.

The club knew they were onto something special with us as a group. Even the first-team manager got involved. That picture was taken at

Lilleshall, I think, the Football Association's national training centre. We went over there for the day – it wasn't all that far from Crewe – and Dario Gradi was there too. He's the guy with the dark hair, doing the talking. Even Bennell's paying attention. Days like that made us feel like we were real footballers, I suppose.

We played at different tournaments and even went over to France one time. Thinking back, I can see now that there was something other than football going on at those tournaments. I was with Bennell all the time so I saw who he mixed with. There was definitely a little clique of them he was friendly with who I know now were other sex abusers. All the teams stayed in caravans up at the Canary Cup in Norwich and I remember that group of coaches hanging around together outside, as if they were holding some kind of meeting.

Bennell used to take me to Blackpool for the day sometimes. There was a shop in town where he'd buy magic tricks. He seemed to know the man who owned the shop very well. Definitely he was a regular customer. Other times, he'd take us there as a team to play against Blackpool. They were pretty regular games, against the team run by Frank Roper, the same guy who had the sports shop down in Cheetham Hill. Roper died in 2005 but players like Paul Stewart have spoken up since about being abused by him. Bennell and Roper were really good mates.

There were lots of other teams at those tournaments, of course, lots of other matches we played, and there were definitely other coaches who didn't like our team and wouldn't have anything to do with Bennell. I can still remember Bennell having arguments with them: you could feel there was tension at quite a few of our games. At the time, I just assumed it was jealousy because we had such a good team. In hindsight, though, perhaps it wasn't about that at all.

I was with Bennell so much of the time and it was at around that age that I started to feel as if I was set apart somehow from the rest of the team. Teenage boys at thirteen or fourteen start grouping together, don't they: loud ones, quieter ones, even one or two bullies? It was the first time I can remember any of my teammates saying anything about me and Bennell: *You're his favourite, aren't you? What goes on with the two of you, anyway?* I don't really think it was anything other than a bit of teasing but it upset me a lot at the time. Made me feel cut off from the rest of the team.

I don't think the boys my age meant any real harm, to be honest. Quite a few of them had been abused by Bennell themselves, of course, and even some of those boys started teasing me. Maybe they did it to protect themselves somehow. But what they said picked up on things they heard from other people, I'm sure. Things that got mentioned when we were around the club or playing in Crewe. Bennell was an important character around Gresty Road. The club was famous for developing young players and he was the man who found many of those boys in the first place. Him coaching us and how he behaved around us – lads staying at his house and us going away on trips with him – weren't hidden away from view. He was in and out of the offices all the time, always with a boy or two in tow.

Bennell used to take me to training and to Gresty Road all the time. I might as well have been on a lead. Looking at it from the outside, it must have seemed odd, mustn't it? People would have seen this boy trailing around behind his coach, afternoons and at weekends. I started getting talked about. I can remember getting stick from some of the senior players: it seems incredible to me now so I don't need to name names. Those players must have known something was going on, though. But they'd never dare say anything to Bennell's face or even in his earshot. I'd guess they were scared of him and scared of the power he had at Crewe. For the boys he coached he was the man who could make stars of us. For the club, he was the one who could find stars and make the club a fortune in the process. Developing and selling players had always been how Crewe were able to survive.

So nobody would ever have questioned Bennell. Even if they knew anything, everybody was either too scared or had too much to lose. But I didn't know that then. All I knew was how uncomfortable his reputation could make me feel. If I was left on my own, waiting for him – in the dressing room or in the physio's room – I'd hear some of the older players sniggering. They'd tease me. They'd say it straight out, laughing among themselves: *Oh, you're Barry's bum boy, aren't you? Bet he does such-and-such to you, doesn't he? Does he touch you up the arse?* They weren't threatening me and it didn't seem as if they took it all seriously. They knew but did they understand at all? Did they ever stop to think about what their words really meant? *You're Barry's pet, his little favourite, aren't you?* I think they just thought it was funny: to them, Bennell was what people used to call a dirty old man, but laughing and joking in the dressing room, they were never going to really think about the reality of what Bennell had done to me, were they? I'd never say a word back. What Bennell was up to was common knowledge around the club even if nobody wanted to think too much about the details. That's probably why younger players – my own age group – started saying things to me, too.

People at Crewe knew what was going on: players, staff, whoever. Even the coaches and players of teams we played against knew: we used to hear them calling us the 'bum boy' team, in the dressing room next door or out on the pitch. How did our parents not know? I mean, thinking about it now, that seems hard to understand. But, speaking for my own family, I can see how Bennell groomed them just as much as he groomed me. All they'd seen for the last three or four years was what seemed to be a fantastic thing in my life: a dream coming true. I never said a word. I'm sure other players didn't either. You only had to be abused once, probably, for that to tie you up in the secret for good. It's why it's only now that so many of Bennell's players have found the courage to speak out.

I don't know for sure what Bennell would have said to our parents but I know he always made sure he spent time with them, talking about how well we were doing and what great futures we had ahead of us. They could see for themselves what good players we were and what a good coach Bennell was. They trusted him. Parents were in awe of him in the same way us boys were.

I would guess that, any time there was an argument or another coach said anything, Bennell would have been able to reassure our mums and dads. He would have told them that other people and other teams were simply jealous of how successful we were. He was in control because he understood that, by this stage, people around the team were only hearing and seeing what they wanted to hear and see. Bennell could fool anyone now.

By the time I signed those schoolboy forms at Crewe at the end of the season, I was already broken. Lost, I was just submitting to whatever it was had to happen next. In many ways, I'd had enough of football. I'd had enough of everything. I was tired all the time. I was miserable all week, knowing what was going to happen at the weekend. But I just kept going. Kept playing football. Going away on trips. Kept staying at Dove Holes and, later, at the house he moved to in Crewe. I kept being raped and abused; by now it had happened to me hundreds of times.

It got worse, too: not violent exactly but forceful, harsher. He'd push my head down hard while he was raping me, pull at my hair. I can remember him tying my wrists up to the bedposts with football socks. Depending on his mood, I got really scared sometimes of what he would do. But I'd learned how to put on a mask. I was blank. My parents, teachers, friends: none of them knew what was going on inside me. I simply said and did what I thought was expected of me.

Usually when boys reached fourteen, Bennell would start to push them away, making room for younger boys to take their places. That didn't happen with me. Bennell still wanted me to be with him, even though he was getting younger lads, ten- and eleven-year-olds, to start coming to stay. He'd moved to this terraced house in Crewe that was so small I often ended up sleeping on the sofa downstairs. I've felt so guilty since. Maybe I felt guilt even then. Or shame, anyway.

I knew what was going to happen to those boys, what Bennell was going to do to them. I was in the house when he did it. But it never crossed my mind once to say anything: to the boys themselves, to their parents or to anyone else. Of course I was scared of Bennell but it went even deeper than that. It was as if I was under some kind of spell. In order to deal with what was happening to me – to deal with everything that had already happened to me – I'd just sort of shut down emotionally. Gone dead. To not feel the bad things, I'd learned not to feel anything at all. Emotions didn't matter. All that mattered was football and getting to where I was supposed to, fulfilling the dream.

I didn't speak to anyone. Who would I have told, anyway? Thirty and forty years ago, nobody talked about this stuff. 'Dirty old men' were guys who got sniggered about. Like in the dressing room with those older players at Crewe. And a boy like me, *Barry's bum boy*, would be made fun of without any understanding of what might really be happening to me. Rape, oral sex, wanking off: nobody wanted to get to grips with any of that, with what 'dirty old men' actually did. It made it easier for me not to talk about anything. Nobody wanted to hear. I don't remember, back then, anybody in school or anywhere else talking about paedophiles or sexual abuse or even using those words. People would joke and tease about it but really discussing it, out in the open, just wasn't done. That meant, in my case, shame never seemed to be something to share. The whole idea made people uncomfortable. That's what their laughter was covering up.

I saw Bennell start with younger boys and I know now that saying nothing meant I missed the chance to help those lads avoid what I'd gone through. In some cases, probably, I maybe even missed the chance to save lives. But I was locked up in Bennell's world: it makes me feel sick to my stomach even now. This was how completely he had me under that spell: I felt guilty about those younger boys but, in a weird way, I was jealous as well. I'd been so special to start with. That's how he'd pulled me in. And now here they were, new boys, ready to start taking my place. What would happen to me?

17.

I think about how many days – and nights – I spent in Bennell's company: it's strange how little ever got said between us. How much of it unfolded in silence. He'd tell me stories about himself. About his experiences in football, making out he was some kind of gangster, mixing with villains and being involved in robberies. He'd tell me jokes sometimes, trying to make me laugh. And then there were the times when he told me he loved me and how special I was to him. But, really, it was only ever about him.

In all our time together, he never once asked how I was feeling or what I thought about anything. When I spoke, it would only ever be to give him the response he expected from me. The only things about me that mattered to him, I suppose, were what he wanted from me and how I made him feel. How I might be feeling was of no interest to him at all.

All that time I was around Bennell, you might wonder why nobody stopped and asked what was going on. It would only ever have taken one moment, after all, for someone to suspect something was wrong. And make it stop. Mum and Dad? The rest of my family? What about school? I missed enough days and took enough holidays during term times that if it had been then like it is now, thirty years later, I imagine they'd have had social services down to find out what was going on. It was a different era and a different culture, I suppose. So many things got hidden away. When it comes down to it, anyway, nobody was to blame but Bennell. And the people who did know what he was doing and, for whatever reason, decided to do nothing about it.

The guilt still hangs there, though. For other people, maybe, but most of all for me: why did I let it happen and keep letting it happen? To me and to others? You know, Bennell carried on with me long after he finished with most boys. He was still abusing me when I was sixteen and seventeen. Old enough, you'd think, for me to know better. When most boys my age were thinking about getting drunk and sleeping with girls – some of them maybe even falling in love – I was still trapped in Bennell's twisted idea of childhood. He liked boys young – young to look at and young enough to control – so he did what he could to keep me that way.

I can say to myself now: *You shouldn't feel guilt. You were a victim. It's all down to Bennell.* I can say the same to other people who've been abused, and I mean it. But that doesn't make the sense of guilt go away. You carry it around with you: it's an emotion that's buried a lot deeper than logic can get to; a lot deeper even than the physical fact of what happens to your body when you're abused. Sense memories – smells, places, words – can spark you off. I'll flash back to him pulling at my hair, pushing himself into me, forcing my head down onto his cock. But it's in the emotions that linger – the shame and confusion and psychological hurt – where real trauma sits, eating away at your sense of yourself, sucking you back into a past you can never really shake off.

I've struggled with that sense of guilt for thirty years now. Rational or not, I feel guilty about letting Bennell happen to me. About letting him happen to other boys. And, closest to home, about letting him happen to my own sister. The picture at the start of this chapter, I can't remember where it was taken but it shocks me, how I look. You'd say it was a grumpy teenager, not wanting a photo taken. But I know that isn't the real story at all.

I'd already been abused and raped countless times before Bennell got to Lynda. How much did I know? And what should I have done? What could I have done? I can't tell Lynda's story. It's for her to tell or not to tell, now she's a grown woman with children and a family to care for. Her own life to live. I respect completely whatever she says or does now about the past. I love her and I always will. All I can honestly talk about is the effect Bennell's relationship with Lynda had on me.

Dove Holes was always a bit of a mess. Bennell didn't pay any attention to cleaning or looking after the place. When I first started going there, I met an older boy who used to come and clean for Bennell. I think he had been a footballer but hadn't made the grade. At some point, he stopped coming to clean. And my older sister, Lynda, started coming to the cottage to clean for him instead.

Lynda and Louise often came along in the car when my parents dropped me off at Dove Holes but I don't remember how the arrangement started. Early on, I can remember me, Bennell and Lynda sitting on his sofa together watching TV but I never saw anything going on between them back then. Whether it was innocent at first or things were hidden from me, I don't know. I probably wouldn't have wanted to know.

I think about all that now. I was confused about myself at the time in so many ways. Too confused to be thinking about Bennell and Lynda together. At thirteen or fourteen, I was starting to think about my sexuality. That sounds grown-up. It wasn't that I had the psychological tools to be rational about it, of course, but I'd wonder: *Am I gay, maybe? This bloke's been fucking me and I've not stopped him, have I? He talks about loving me. What do I do about that?*

It's only thirty years ago but, in the wider world, and especially in football, homosexuality wasn't accepted the way it is by most people today. Think about it: this was the mid-eighties; AIDS was happening and the papers were calling it the 'Gay Plague', weren't they? Homosexuality was scary and people still thought it was 'wrong'. AIDS made that worse. The idea of me being gay unsettled me. So did the idea of that being what people would assume if they knew about me and Bennell. Really, though? The confusion lay in not understanding anything about what the fuck I was or what the fuck had been happening to me.

I didn't know what Bennell was either. I didn't really think of him as being gay: he'd had that girlfriend, Clare. And I wasn't a man. I was a boy. That was something different in my imagination somehow. Even though I knew it wasn't 'normal'. And it didn't cross my mind to think about HIV, even though he never wore a condom when he raped me. Bennell being around Lynda: I was with him then, wasn't I? It was me he was after. So it never occurred to me that he might go after her, too. It just meant that, while Lynda was in the room at least, he'd leave me alone.

Anyway: it's quite a long way from Cheadle to Dove Holes. A forty-minute drive. I forget whether Lynda came up to clean at the weekend when Bennell and I were out or if she had a key and my parents drove her to Holmleigh during the week. I was probably thirteen when the arrangement started, with my mind buried in what was happening to me. I didn't pay any heed, I suppose, to what was happening to Lynda.

The first I really knew was when I was fourteen and we were away at Butlin's in Pwllheli, the whole team, for a weekend training. I remember that trip really well. I was getting quite a bit of stick off the other boys about being Bennell's favourite. It had moved into being bullying, really: one of the boys hit me a couple of times that weekend. By that age, I was already falling apart inside. I didn't feel good about myself at all. So what if they didn't like me? I didn't like me either. And I didn't hit back. The lads just thought it was funny.

We were all coming out from the chalets and Bennell grabbed me and took me into a gap between two of the buildings, out of sight of everyone else. He told me that he and Lynda were more than just friends. No details, but it was clear what he was telling me. *You better not say anything to anyone. Or I'll kill you. This has to be a secret.* He had a look on his face: you didn't know what he might do, there was that much anger, that much violence in him. I didn't say a word to him. I didn't say a word to anyone else, either.

In fact, it wasn't a secret for very long. Lynda would have been fifteen, going on sixteen. I wasn't there when the conversation happened so I don't know how it was explained to my mum and dad, that Bennell and Lynda were in a relationship. That this wasn't just a cleaning job and a friendship. All I do remember clearly is how much upset it caused.

I know my parents weren't happy about him being with their daughter but, in the same way as he'd groomed me they were under his spell, too. Bennell was a huge part of their lives. And it seemed like the best part: me making progress and becoming a player. I heard them having a go at Lynda about it but I don't think they ever challenged Bennell. Even though their daughter was so young and he was a man in his thirties.

I still can't really focus on how much I knew or didn't know. Maybe I was so scared of Bennell that I shut away any feelings I had in the early days of their relationship. Or perhaps, in the same way other people just didn't see what Bennell was doing to me, I didn't see what he was doing to Lynda. I never asked anyone for help and neither did she. I feel like I let her down, though, for sure.

Once it became public knowledge that Lynda and Bennell were together, I remember trying to tell my sister she should break off with him. But I didn't ever tell her what had happened – what was happening – to me: the one thing that might have made a difference, perhaps. Their relationship was already a long way down the line by then anyway. Lynda was seventeen. And there was nothing left to talk about, really, when she fell pregnant the following year.

When Bennell moved to Crewe, Lynda kept cleaning for him and started staying at his house regularly. By then, I wasn't staying over every weekend. I was fifteen, going on sixteen, the age at which Bennell would always start losing interest. I might have been special to him for a while but that didn't stop me getting too old. It was around then that I remember seeing for myself, for the first time, that Bennell and Lynda were together. That they were a couple.

Lynda finished with school. She got a job for a while. Eventually she moved into the house in Crewe with Bennell. Her mind was made up, for better or worse. Lynda's personality seemed to change, I think, in many of the same ways mine had under Bennell's influence. She sort of withdrew into herself. It was as if she wasn't ever quite with you, as if her mind was always elsewhere. Ask any parent, though: we assume that's just how teenagers are. That they all *go through a phase.*

By then, I'd signed apprentice forms at the football club and Bennell was still taking our team, even though he'd never kept coaching lads our age – sixteen- to eighteen-year-olds – before. He had both of us, brother and sister, where he wanted us, under control. When I look at that photo again, I can see it now, plain as day: Bennell had got himself deep into my soul.

18.

O ur schoolboy team at Crewe was as good as any around. That's us outside the old Leeds Road ground, ready to play Huddersfield, with me in the middle of the back row. We had a fantastic group of young players. I remember one night when we were fourteen or fifteen, we played Manchester United. 1988, maybe? 1989? That was the team that went on to become the Class of '92: Beckham, Scholes, Gary and Phil Neville, Nicky Butt, Chris Casper, Ben Thornley.

Those United boys went on to achieve great things together but that night they couldn't get near us and we beat them in front of everybody, Alex Ferguson included. Can you imagine how proud and excited that made us and our parents feel: Crewe lads taking a Manchester United team apart?

It wasn't long after that game the club announced who would be taken on as apprentices – YTS boys – when we turned sixteen. It was most of our team. Moving from schoolboy to YTS is one of those threshold moments for a young footballer: a big step on the path to becoming a professional player. So I was happy and excited, as you'd expect.

But I had an extra motivation: I assumed that it would be the end of things as far as Bennell coaching us was concerned. I was moving forward as a player but also I thought I'd be escaping Bennell at long last. He was still abusing me at that age even though it had become more sporadic, with him focusing on new groups of younger boys. I felt bad for those lads but I thought I'd be getting away from him now. The next two years I'd be coached by somebody else.

As I remember, it was Dario Gradi who called us all together and told us that Bennell was going to continue coaching us as apprentices, something he'd never done with a team before. The idea was that this was something that would make us happy, that we could look forward to. I remember looking around the room at Gresty Road. Some of the lads did look genuinely pleased and excited. There were others, though, who looked blank at first. As if they couldn't believe what they were hearing: in hindsight, I'd guess those were other boys who'd been abused by Bennell.

It was shattering. Even though I wasn't being raped as often as before, I knew this meant I would still be around Bennell every day for the next couple of years. I'd thought I was about to be set free. Instead, I'd be seeing him on the training ground, in the dressing room, at team meetings and at every game. In front of Gradi, I knew what to do by

119

now: I put on a false smile: *Great. That's great.* But I got home that night, went up to my bedroom – the little front bedroom where he'd abused me, off and on, for the last three years – and I just burst into tears.

Things had changed: Bennell had new boys he'd dress up in tracksuits and drag around with him everywhere, like he had me and Paul. Those lads would just have been starting to fall under the spell, being used and abused by a coach who was promising them the world. I think back to my own experiences. To what those boys experienced. I still carry the guilt: I didn't warn them. I didn't protect them. I shut my eyes to it: all of a piece with shutting down my feelings.

In many ways, nothing changed. Bennell could be brutal with young players. A bully. One of my best friends, when I was in my early teens, was a goalkeeper, Ash Stephenson. I know now that Bennell tried it on with Ash once when we were away for a weekend training in Blackpool. It didn't happen and Bennell resented that.

From then on, Bennell always bullied Ash in training. But Ash sort of escaped when he was fourteen: he went away to the national training school at Lilleshall for a couple of years before coming back to Crewe. As apprentices, Ash and I developed a really strong bond. We were proper pals even though that could never run to telling him about me and Bennell. We'd go clubbing, drinking beer and scouting for girls. When the other lads started giving me stick, Ash was one of the few who stuck up for me rather than going along with the crowd. I still value our friendship today.

Ash had an Asian complexion and there might have been some racism in there: Bennell hardly ever scouted non-white players. But anyway, whether he'd wanted to or not, Bennell wasn't able to abuse Ash. Maybe he even felt threatened by the two of us being friends. He knew by now that I'd never say anything to my family or to adults around the club about him. But, however scared I was of him, what might I be willing to say to my mate?

For whatever reason, Bennell was always unbelievably harsh with Ash. He'd run him, put him through endless drills, way beyond what might help Ash as a player. The intention was to break him, I'm sure. As a person, not as a footballer. I saw Ash being taken to the point of being physically sick, collapsing, traumatised and holding back tears. It was like watching somebody being tortured. It wasn't sexual but, for sure, Ash was physically abused.

That hard, domineering edge to Bennell's coaching didn't slacken off for a moment. And neither did his attitude to me on the training pitch. He kept after me, kept abusing me, even if it wasn't happening as often. If he'd left me alone completely, I suppose I might have represented a threat to him. So he kept me on a leash. Treated me like he'd always done. He'd rape me at his house in Crewe and, later, at the house he moved into in Alsager. And, in training, that meant the same psychology he'd used with me for the previous five years: isolating me, undermining my confidence, never responding positively to whatever I did in a session or however well I played in a game.

As we got older – we were in our mid-teens, becoming young men – the bullying I got went up a notch, too. We had one or two big characters in the team and others seemed to follow their lead. It wasn't homophobic. It was more personal, somehow. *Oh, bet Bennell's been banging you all these years.* It was about Bennell doing stuff to me, not saying that I was gay. Which, believe me, they would have said if they'd thought I was. They were bullying me but, at the same time, they knew full well how things worked with Bennell. And they knew what power he had. They might tease me but they'd never do it when he was about.

I knew some of those lads bullying me had also been abused, even though it wasn't until later that I realised how many. But, when I was getting stick, nobody intervened. Nobody said *That's out of order*, even though they'd been victims themselves. It was as if they were scared to break the circle. That was how they protected themselves: they kept Bennell's secret and chose to attack me instead. It was only Ash who'd say or do anything, and that would be to drag me away: *Come on, Andy. They're idiots. Don't think about it. You and me will go out.* He would have stood and fought those other lads if it came to it. But he'd never have said to me: *What's all that stuff they're saying really about?* He wouldn't have wanted to think about it any more than I did.

Thinking back to that bullying, it's a psychology that reminds me of the stuff you hear about going on inside weird religious cults. At the time, though, it stuck and it hurt: I was bullied for being abused by our coach. Not just by my age group, either. I got it off older first team players as well. They knew what was happening. They'd bully me but they wouldn't say anything about it to anyone else, inside or outside the club. And they definitely wouldn't ever say anything to Bennell. I sometimes wonder how they feel now.

How must I have seemed to those guys? Shy? Introverted? A bit of a strange one? I just put on a front most of the time. Tried to convince people I was confident enough to look after myself. When I was out on the pitch, I was a different lad: aggressive and assertive. Other players and coaches could see that and probably assumed I could handle whatever stick I got the rest of the time. The more fragile I felt inside, the harder the shell I had to put on to deal with the world.

So I just kept quiet and took the comments and the bullying that I was getting around the club. Inside, I was vulnerable, soft even. It probably wouldn't have taken much to break me in bits. But I'd learned how to hide all that – to wear that shell – and, besides, I was a very good player. The other lads knew that. I knew it, too, and I clung to it: it was all I had in the way of self-esteem. For the rest, Bennell still had total control over me and that was only reinforced by me being around him every day as a Crewe Alexandra apprentice. It was why I said nothing to him about Lynda, I'm sure, even though I didn't want her to be with him, now or ever.

She moved in with him but it was all wrong. He'd send her back to our house at weekends. My parents didn't know why he was doing it but they were upset anyway: I remember them saying to Bennell that he shouldn't treat her that way. I wish I'd said something or done something but, by then, I was too far in, too completely in his power. And Lynda was, too. He had us under a psychological lock and key.

Later on, when Bennell bought a house in Alsager, he and Lynda moved in there. That house in Alsager was where he abused me for the very last time. Until then, though, he carried on. Bennell and I would be in the lounge, just the two of us. He wouldn't say anything; he'd just pull his trousers down as if I should know what was expected of me. Which I did. *Go on, then. Do your stuff.*

He could have been discovered at any moment but I think that was part of how he got his kicks. He had a thing about dares, about pushing things to the limit of what he could get away with. It's horrible just thinking about it.

19.

I love that photograph. Seventeen years old, first-year YTS. There's nothing there but what you can see: an uncomplicated moment in a teenager's life. Probably it was Ash who took the photo but that's not why I've got a mile-wide smile on my face. Bennell had taken us to Puerto Rico, a resort on Gran Canaria. We'd been there before, staying in an apartment complex, training together as a team.

Bennell loved it there: it had always been a chance for him to get some sun and to abuse young players. This trip, though, turned into something completely different. For me, anyway. The photo was taken in one of the apartments, towards the end of our stay.

I'd just passed my driving test and a few of us chipped in and we hired a car for while we were in Puerto Rico. Crazy, really: just getting the hang of driving on the wrong side of the road. For the first time away on a trip, Bennell didn't have a go at me. I wasn't even in an apartment with him. Instead, it felt like just us lads together.

We were nearly adults, I suppose. Of course it wasn't as if Bennell not abusing me meant everything was okay. My head was all over the place, like it would be for years afterwards. Mashed. But something happened in Puerto Rico. I met a girl. A girl I really liked. It turned into the first romantic relationship I'd ever had in my life. That's what the smile in the photo's all about.

It was a classic holiday romance. Claudia was twenty-two. She was half-Danish, half-German and lived with her mum in Bredstedt, a little town north of Hamburg. Blond, very beautiful. She was a dental nurse, independent, drove her own car. We met in a bar one evening and things progressed pretty quickly. She asked me back to hers. It was amazing and would have been for any young lad my age.

For me it was amazing but weird at the same time, because of what I'd experienced over the previous five years. My head was full of questions about myself and my sexuality. Questions that ran back to a sense that the abuse had somehow been my fault; that I must have wanted it to happen. That I must have enjoyed it, even. Meeting Claudia was a trigger for discovering some very personal things: I wasn't attracted to men; I wasn't attracted to boys. But I was very attracted indeed to this girl I'd met now.

In hindsight, I know I tipped over in the opposite direction. Back then, homosexuality wasn't accepted without a second thought like it is today. Knowing I wasn't gay, I overcompensated with Claudia, just like I have in so many of the relationships I've had since. It was like a hunger: I had to be with a woman. For comfort, for reassurance, maybe even to prove something to myself. To show the world I was 'normal', whatever that was.

My relationships have always been too much about me and my past, never open enough or honest enough to last, always undermined by that hunger for female company, for sex and for what often felt like self-preservation. I became addicted to that drive, to feeling wanted, to feeling desired. Just desperate not to ever be alone with my past and my demons. I've escaped into relationships and then out of them, instead of learning how to build them and help them to grow.

In Puerto Rico that summer, though? I was completely taken with Claudia. I was completely taken with the situation, which was like some kind of *Inbetweeners* fantasy. She was a teenage boy's dream of an older woman. Claudia was pretty keen on me, too: as soon as I got back to England, she started writing to me. We'd talk on the phone. Every day. I can still remember her number! Then she decided she'd come over to visit.

Fantastic: she arrived at Manchester Airport and I picked her up in the little orange – orange! – Fiesta my parents had bought me when I passed my test. She came and stayed, met Mum and Dad. Claudia seemed so sensible, so polite. She was beautiful and she spoke such good English! My parents never gave the difference in our ages a second thought. We'd go for a drink at the local pub, watch music videos: *Nothing Compares 2U, Andrew!* We slept together in the little front bedroom at home.

When Claudia and I had sex those first few times, there was a shadow over us. Over me, anyway. I'd been abused by Bennell on that bed and I had to fight the memory of it: the feel and the smell of him. I was in bed with Claudia but, at the same time, he was there too. The desire in the moment kept getting mixed up with flashbacks and revulsion that had nothing to do with her. It wasn't right. Wasn't honest, somehow. I was having to pretend because I couldn't tell Claudia what had happened in this room in the past. But, whatever the feelings I was shutting away, I wanted to push myself. I had to. I wanted to be with a woman.

After that first visit, she came back again, every month, for two or three days at a time. It was intense. Claudia was older than me and I suppose was driving what was happening – she'd been the person who started the conversation in the bar in Puerto Rico, after all – but it felt to me like a release. Like a kind of freedom. And my instinct was just to dive in and keep going.

I was seventeen, beginning to look like a man. Inside, though, in many ways, I was still a little boy. Still the ten-year-old who Bennell had first abused. I'd dealt with it all by putting the mask on and just shutting down emotionally. I know some people who've had experiences like mine who are still locked up like that. You have your meltdowns – I know what those feel like: the giving in to it, the tears streaming down your face, hating everything about who and what you are – but, for the rest, it's as if you're frozen in time.

Part of the attraction with Claudia, I'm sure, was that it all felt very adult. Claudia, definitely, seemed very grown-up to me. It was the end of something – the start of something – and, even though I had no idea about where it was headed, it felt like rebellion. Against Bennell, against the life that he'd carved out for me, against the prison he'd locked me in. I'd got attention from a woman and now I craved that, more and more.

Bennell knew about Claudia. He'd take the mickey out of me, laughing. *Oh, you've got a girlfriend!* And I was still so close to it all that I would worry about how he'd react, what he'd think about me having a relationship with Claudia. I was with Claudia but, at the same time, I was somehow a step apart from what we were doing and what was happening between us. I couldn't shake that feeling loose, which maybe explains why I did what I did when Claudia invited me to visit her in Germany. She said she'd pay for the trip: she had a good full-time job; I was on about £30 a week as an apprentice. I said of course I'd come. And I told her just to get me a one-way ticket: Manchester to Hamburg. In the back of my mind, I think I had this mad idea. I wouldn't have said it out loud and maybe I wouldn't ever have done it. It was the kind of plan you make in a dream or in a fantasy. To escape everything: I could go off to Germany and just never come back.

I packed my bags, didn't tell anyone I was going: not my parents, not Bennell, not the football club. Claudia picked me up from the airport and took me home to Bredstedt. Her mum was a single parent and a lovely woman. She didn't speak much English and I only knew as much German as Claudia had taught me. But she was warm and welcoming, put food on the table in front of me straight away.

Bredstedt was a little village, surrounded by fields. A safe place to be, away from everything. Away from Bennell. And Claudia was really pleased I was there. Even so, comfortable as I felt, I was haunted, still on the edge of desperation. One day, Claudia went off to work and I borrowed her bike. I just rode and rode, twenty miles and more, no idea where I was going, down quiet lanes and along busy main roads.

What was going on in my head? I imagined Claudia would come home from the dental practice and I wouldn't be there and she'd be worried about me; she'd want to look after me, give me the attention I craved. She'd wrap me up, a boy away from home, and take care of me. I think back now and I can recognise that as pretty strange behaviour. Neurotic, really. Claudia was already giving me all the attention a person could possibly want or need.

Despite what I'd said, Claudia had bought me a return ticket. Had I really travelled to Germany with the idea that I was off to start a new life? I knew that would mean turning my back on the dream of being a footballer but, more and more, I'd been feeling as if I'd had enough. I'd had enough of Crewe, anyway. However much I loved the game, it was outweighed by still being around Bennell every day. Surely I'd be able to find a club to trial with in Germany if I still wanted to play? I knew Lynda was pregnant and that she and Bennell were going to get married. I didn't feel I could face any of that. I thought I'd made my mind up. I thought I was determined. In actual fact, I soon found out I was as fragile as I'd ever been.

Claudia had no idea about my history. Occasionally, all the trapped emotion would bubble up – a memory, an image, a moment would come into my head, out of nowhere – and I'd lose control. I'd be sobbing, just wanting to be held, but never able to tell her what was going on. I just told her I wasn't happy with Crewe, with life in England. When I didn't want to say more I could just blame the language barrier, even though Claudia spoke good English. She was completely supportive. *Stay as long as you like.* It didn't take long for my parents to track me down, though. They found Claudia's number.

Dad came on the phone. He told me that they'd been worried sick. *Why didn't you tell us where you were going?* I half-explained what was in my head: *I'm under pressure at Crewe. I'm not enjoying my football. I've had enough. This is what I want. I'm going to stay here in Germany.* Dad never used to shout at me and he didn't shout now but I could tell he was frantic. It must have seemed like I was just a moody teenager, off in a strop about something. Or in love for the first time. *This is your whole career, Andy. Your whole life. If you don't report back for training, it'll be over. Think what you're doing.*

I'd already missed three days' training. I suppose my parents must have got in touch with the club. Crewe would have been trying to find out what was happening. The next phone call was from Bennell. He didn't shout either but, where Dad had almost been pleading with me, he was threatening. *Get your arse back here. I'll cover for you with the club. But get back here. What the fuck do you think you're doing?* I could hear the anger in Bennell's voice and I just crumbled. Became a frightened, helpless-feeling little boy again. Packed my bag, told Claudia I had to go home and was on the next flight back to Manchester.

The relationship didn't end there. Claudia kept coming to Cheadle to visit. At one point, she even talked about getting an au pair job and moving to Manchester. Thinking back, it was a bit crazy. I was only seventeen. But, at the time, it felt good. Felt good that Claudia was giving me all this attention, making it clear how much she liked me.

I needed the sex: the physical contact and the reassurance about my sexual identity. But on an emotional level what I really wanted was for someone to put their arms round me and convince me everything was going to be all right. I wanted protection, like a child, with no questions asked. Which Claudia couldn't give me because I'd never told her what was wrong, deep down.

And even if Claudia had held me and told me everything was all right, what difference would it have made? Because everything wasn't all right. How could it ever be?

~

Once I got back to Crewe and to football, I slowly found myself getting hemmed in again. Cornered.

Mum and Dad were worried I was going to lose everything I'd been working towards. They weren't pushy even if I knew they were upset at the idea of me wasting my chance. At the same time, though, Bennell was soon chipping away at me. He made it plain: *Football should be all your focus. Don't waste your attention on girls.* It was as if I was being forced to choose between Claudia and a career. Our relationship eventually fizzled out. It hurt her, I know. Hurt me, too, but that meant just another emotion to bury away somewhere. I put on the mask and, like a good boy, did what was expected of me. Like always. I'd come too far to turn back now. I got on with becoming a player.

20.

The wedding. His wedding, my sister's wedding. Bennell and Lynda married in 1990 when she was eighteen and carrying their first child. It still doesn't feel like a scene from my life so much as a scene out of a film. A dark, creepy film. I'd like to forget it ever happened but I can feel tears pricking at the backs of my eyes right now. It's a physical reaction, as if I'm being slowly strangled by the memory of it. And at the same time, there's something unreal about how we were all dressed in our costumes and lined up like dolls, all in a row.

Did it really happen to me? To Lynda and to my family? I still remember those Sunday nights when Bennell would come round to our house to drop me off after a weekend in Dove Holes. I remember how Mum and Dad used to welcome him in. Cook him dinner and listen to his stories, him talking about what a good time we'd had and what a good footballer I was going to turn out to be. And then he'd come upstairs to say goodnight and abuse me under my parents' roof in that little front bedroom. The wedding was that whole disgusting, corrupt charade blown up super-size.

Bennell's best man was Paul's dad. He'd abused Paul for years but asked his dad to be his best man. I was an usher. My parents were there, of course, along with lots of other family: aunts, uncles, cousins. I can still see a picture of us all in my mind's eye. Bennell knew a lot of the rest of the family and he knew my younger sister, Louise, as well.

The service was at Norcliffe Chapel, the church in Styal. In the build-up, there wasn't the traditional sense of excitement at home, more a sense of resignation. My mum and dad weren't pleased that Bennell and Lynda were together but, come what may, they were going to support her. That was how they were: there for their children and, soon, for their grandchild. The wedding was something that had to be done. And that they had to pay for.

I can hardly remember anything about the day itself. I felt frozen, numbed to the bone. I felt like I was going to be physically sick. On the one hand, there's my family, the people I loved. On the other, people Bennell had asked to come: lads like Paul who he'd abused in the past, even some other boys who he was abusing now, dressed up in their best suits, their parents proudly looking on.

There were a number of his players, past and present, who were invited. Some of them he'd assaulted, but now he had them gathered round to watch him get married. I remember him grinning at me when he walked down the aisle to say his vows with my sister. How could anybody do that? Bennell had it all, all that he wanted; and here he was, getting away with it. Celebrating a wedding? For him, it was a celebration of his power over everyone there.

It was horrible. I couldn't wait for it to be over. And then we all had to go outside, to smile and shake hands and say congratulations. Inside, I didn't want to believe any of it was real. I don't know how Lynda felt that day, but I thought she looked beautiful. She seemed happy. I felt so angry, but guilty as well. I believed this was somehow all down to me; that I was the one who'd allowed this horror movie to happen.

All my memories, all the moments in my life, the things that he'd done to me, and to my family: suddenly, they were all here at once. In the same place, at the same time. All of it and all of us: people numbed by it like me; some shut up in silence; others more or less in denial; and those who genuinely didn't have the faintest idea what had gone on. There we all were, dressed up for the occasion, so it would look like this was our perfect day.

Bennell was there at the heart of it, knowing full well that at any moment someone might break the spell and say something, do something, to make it all blow up in his face. But that was part of the buzz for him: he knew nobody would. Nobody could. It would all carry on. That was his power. Not a flicker of doubt or fear. Completely at his ease. Hugging people, smiling and joking, without a care in the world.

At the time, I couldn't have put it all together in my head. Like I say, I felt numb. But I think about it now and it takes my breath away. What he'd done, and what an awful and twisted thing this was. I loved Lynda then and I love her now and it breaks my heart. It should never have happened.

I had teammates there for the wedding, some of whom had been abused by Bennell. We were still together, of course, as young players, and from a footballing point of view were doing really well. Over at the Milk Cup in Northern Ireland, in the FA Youth Cup at home, we were reaching finals and semi-finals.

I kept pushing myself to improve and to achieve as a footballer, but there was always something a bit robotic about me. Not as a footballer but in terms of how I conducted myself, how I behaved in training and around games. I was quiet, inward, followed every instruction to the letter. Like one of those little boys being marched around Butlin's. At ten years old, football had been my dream. Now, seven years later, it didn't feel like that any more. It was Bennell's dream or, at least, that's how it seemed. He could recruit me, groom me, abuse me, rape me and still turn me out as a first team player at the end of it. That was his perfect idea of how it should be.

I had some strength in me, though. A strength that came through, maybe, in unusual ways: courage and determination and a work ethic when you'd least expect those qualities to show themselves. I know, deep down, that I could have had a better career; that I never fulfilled my potential. But I also know that it would have been easy for me to have had no career at all; to have been broken in bits and to have run away from the game. But I kept going. To prove something, to myself and to Bennell: that I could still get there, however much he'd hurt me. The first step came at seventeen, when I found out I was going to be offered my first professional contract with Crewe.

It wasn't a big public announcement. Dario Gradi called us into the office one at a time. Bennell was there too. He had an interest: if any of us got sold by Crewe further down the line, he'd pick up his percentage of the transfer fee for having found and developed us in the first place. We were a strong group and six of us got offered professional deals including me. The rest of the boys were released.

There wasn't a lot of money at Crewe: all of us six were on the same wages, on the same two-year deals. But I'd made it to pro and there was the relief of knowing that I wouldn't be coached by Bennell any more. But it wasn't any kind of escape. He'd still be in my life. I was his brother-in-law. I'd be an uncle to his and Lynda's children. Bennell was part of my family now.

21.

There was one more trip to go on with Bennell, the summer before I started pre-season training as a pro, a year or so after he'd last abused me at the house in Alsager. That picture was taken in the States that June. It's him, isn't it? Every time I look at it, I can feel the anger rising in me. He loved the sunshine. And so that was perfect for him. He'd have had a lad put suntan oil on him and then he'd be lying there, where he could roll over to watch all those kids playing in the pool behind him. Bennell's idea of heaven.

It wasn't long after he and Lynda had got married. Bennell was coaching a summer camp in Florida. He asked me and a first team player, Craig Hignett, to go out to the States to help him. We flew into Orlando. Craig hired a car and we drove the couple of hours up the coast to Jacksonville, where Bennell was based.

I'd not felt comfortable with the idea but, like always with him, I'd done as I was told. I still didn't know how to say no. I just had to go. Craig, on the other hand, was a few years older than me and that made me feel safe, like I wasn't driving towards trouble again. So here we were: two lads, roof down, laughing and joking. Like a carpool karaoke: Craig's got a good voice and he sang the whole way.

This was 1992 and I was coming up to eighteen. As I remember, after the wedding, Bennell had suddenly shut his sports shop in Crewe and gone off to Florida with my sister. They'd stayed with a couple he knew and he'd opened a video shop there. He'd just sort of disappeared for a while but I guess he was setting up his summer camps, too. He came back to Crewe later in the year and we saw him back around the club. But then he headed off to Florida again for the summer, leaving Lynda at home in Alsager, on her own with their new baby.

Bennell must have been making quite a bit of money because these camps were attracting big numbers of boys and girls. It was a proper set-up: all the equipment and balls, little carriers full of Gatorade bottles beside every pitch. Kids everywhere. I remember it crossed my mind at the time that he wouldn't stop abusing young players just because he was in the States. I knew what he was like. He just had a hunger.

Craig and I stayed with a lovely family in the suburbs of Jacksonville; real soccer mom territory. Big house, set back from the road, and they really looked after us. It was a relief Bennell wasn't there under the same roof. He was staying with this family he knew and their children. We'd drive down to the sports complex every morning; Bennell would set up the drills and then get me and Craig to take over, coaching a certain number of children each.

In our free time, we met up with him and went to the fairgrounds and to the beach. One late afternoon, we were down by the sea: Bennell, a couple of younger boys, Craig and me. He hired two jet skis. He loved them: he'd go out on the water for an hour at a time, just like he used to in Santa Ponsa or Puerto Rico when I was younger. The idea that afternoon was that we'd take it in turns: one of the younger boys on the back with him, the other on the back of the other jet ski with me or Craig driving.

I'd taken my turn and walked back through the water to the sand. Craig was driving now and I turned round to watch the four of them. They were doing doughnuts, slaloming around: Bennell was trying to scare the boy on the back by doing tricks, splashing back over the wake, bouncing on waves.

They were a little way out, into deeper water, and Bennell and the young lad behind him came off their jet ski. He lifted the boy back on board and then was just starting to clamber up onto the thing himself, his trailing leg hanging out to the side. Craig drove towards them on his jet ski, laughing. He was looking to spray them but he overcooked the turn: as I watched, the two jet skis smashed together with Bennell's leg in the middle. You heard the crash. Craig and his passenger flew off into the water. And you could hear Bennell squealing from all the way back on the beach.

I just froze. I didn't move towards them. Nothing: a cold chill swept over me. Do you know what went through my mind? That maybe he'd drop. Him screaming, splashing around in the water. I remember the moment, clear as day. *I hope he fucking dies.* He didn't usually wear one but that afternoon he had a life jacket on. Which was probably what saved him.

Other people ran down towards the water. I just sat there. No emotion at all. They got him onto the sand and laid him out on a stretcher. It was only then that I moved over towards him. He was lying there, being given gas and air and all that. He had a compound fracture of the femur so the bone was actually sticking out through this big hole in his leg. They rushed him straight off to hospital.

Craig and I went to visit him over the next couple of days. He was in a mess: on painkillers, pins sticking out of his leg where they were holding the bone straight. He was helpless. Powerless for once.

It was the strangest feeling: I'd always come running, done anything he wanted me to do, but here he was, weak and miserable, and I felt nothing. I remember being aware that, for the first time, he couldn't scare me, couldn't do anything to me. *There you are. Helpless. And there's nothing you can do.* It didn't make me happy, though. Whatever agony he was in, I simply didn't care.

Bennell ended up being in hospital for quite a few weeks. He was in a bad way. You'd have thought the obvious thing would have been for me and Craig to head home. But Bennell had set up another camp and it was up to the two of us now to go and run it for him, 350 miles away in Atlanta, Georgia.

That was a proper road trip in Craig's hire car: we didn't have a clue where we were going or what we'd find when we got there. It was just the two of us now, though, and so I had this weird sense of freedom that came from knowing Bennell was stuck in a hospital bed back in

Jacksonville. We found our host families, set up the schedules and got on with it.

It was a brilliant time, really. Sun shining, lovely facilities, kids who really wanted to learn. I ended up coaching the girls and Craig looked after the boys. We were free to do as we pleased after the sessions finished each day. We found our way around, met a couple of girls. We didn't have Bennell in the background. We had the kind of good time young lads are supposed to have. And we were earning a few bucks as well.

Bennell had to stay in Florida but, after we finished in Atlanta, Craig and I flew home. I felt as if I'd finally come up for air after someone had been holding my head underwater for ages. Like a weight had lifted off me, for the time being at least. For a few months, with Bennell out of the way, I felt free and I took that mood into pre-season training back at Crewe, my first year as a professional player.

I joined up with the first team squad and we trained down at Keele University. It was a different world to youth football and, of course, Bennell wasn't involved: Dario Gradi was the manager and Kenny Swain was first team coach. All the time we were with Bennell as young players, he'd driven us really hard physically so my level of fitness was off the chart. All of us new pros were top in beep tests and the other fitness markers.

We were good technically, too, so possession drills came easy to us. We'd always played against older teams: training and playing alongside men now wasn't the shock to the system it can be to young players. Dario's coaching was quite repetitive but he was after a pure style of football: pass, pass, pass. Always wanting the ball.

Bennell was still in Florida, staying with the family that had put him up during the camp in Jacksonville. I seem to remember a couple of young lads from Crewe going out to stay with him. Then, later, I think Lynda went and stayed there as well. He was miles away from me and pre-season was great. The only strange thing I remember about that five or six weeks with Dario was getting flashbacks sometimes when he was talking to us as a group, all gathered round. It was like being a ten-year-old at Platt Lane all over again. I was fine when I was training and playing but when we stopped and stood in a circle to listen, those surges of anger came back to me. The feeling of powerlessness, of desperately wanting to lash out: I felt like rushing across and punching the coach, even though this was Dario Gradi not Barry Bennell.

That first season as a pro was good for me. Good for Crewe, too. We had a decent team: Craig Hignett, Neil Lennon, Ashley Ward, Tony Naylor. I was around the first team all season and made my debut away to Walsall in April, playing centre half alongside Steve Macauley. We lost 1–0 but I did all right and then, at the end of the season, I had a run of games as a sub, coming on every game with Dario using me mostly as a right back.

We played Walsall again in the play-off semi-final and beat them both games. Which meant that, at just eighteen, I was going to Wembley for the Third Division play-off final against York City. With Bennell out of the way, that season felt as if football became my dream again. Nothing to do with him. Mum and Dad were coming to every game like they always had and, without them making any fuss, I knew how proud they were. This was their dream they were living as well.

22.

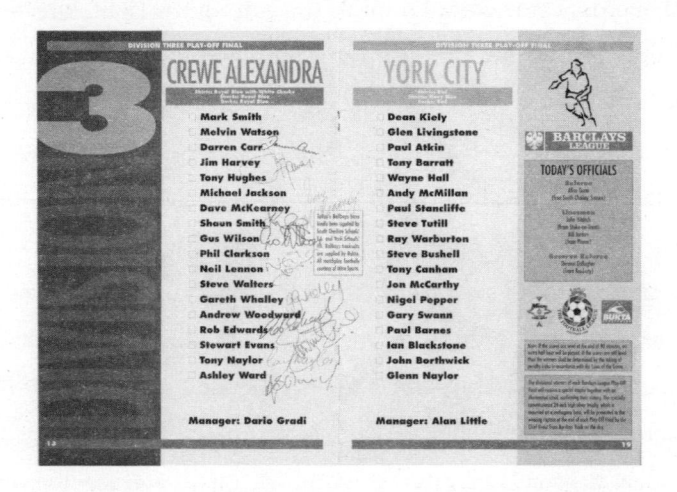

2 9 May 1993. A bit *Roy of the Rovers*, really: what every boy dreams of when he's got his heart set on becoming a player. Just eighteen years old and walking out into the sunshine at Wembley, fireworks popping off, music blaring and, at one end of the stadium, half the population of Crewe there, cheering us on under the old Twin Towers. It wasn't an FA Cup Final. I wasn't playing for England. There were only about 25,000 people in the lower tiers. But that didn't make it seem any less of an occasion to me.

I was buzzing. Most people will play their whole lives and never get to play there. And I'd made it less than a year after becoming a professional footballer. I'm not a great one for saving mementoes from my career but I treasure that Wembley programme: I made sure I got the team sheet signed by all of the boys. The Third Division Playoff Final: York City versus Crewe.

I could have been the hero, too. I was on the bench and came on with twenty minutes to go, to replace Rob Edwards, and I had my moment: a cross came over; I'd made the run up the right and the ball was heading towards me at the far post but I didn't shout for it. Instead, it glanced off Ashley Ward and went behind for a goal kick.

The game finished 0–0 after ninety minutes and went to extra time. York took the lead; we equalised from a penalty in the very last minute. That was as good as it got, though. We lost in the shoot-out and I didn't even get to take a pen. Even so, it had been some afternoon. For my mum and dad, for the Crewe fans, it must have seemed as if I'd just made a good start to a football career.

There was a little crowd of us that used to go out together to clubs and bars in Crewe and around Stockport during the season that ended at Wembley: me, Ash Stephenson, Neil Lennon, Mark Smith, Tony Naylor and Gareth Whalley. Being part of that group meant the bullying and snide comments about Bennell had stopped for the time being. When we went out, I'd have a drink, forget about everything and laugh – really laugh! – which was a rare thing for me.

Gareth was the same age as me; we'd been to the same secondary school and he lived round the corner from us in Cheadle. As a teen-ager, I spent as much time as I could with him. His parents used to have me round for dinner: it was like a safe house for me, away from home and away from Bennell. Even after I stopped staying at Bennell's, there was still tension at home. I'd stay round at Gaz's whenever I could.

My mum and dad got upset about me going there because they didn't understand why I'd want to be at another family's house all the time. I remember one big row with my mum. *Well, if you want to be there all the time, why don't you move in with them?* I'd been away from home so much as a boy, staying at Dove Holes and away on trips. That had finished but it was as if I still hadn't come back.

Of course Mum had no idea about what had been going on all these years; she had no idea that Bennell had abused me in that little bedroom at the front of our house. She couldn't have known that he'd ruined home and family for me just like he'd ruined everything else. And I didn't ever feel like I could explain. We just moved on, disconnected somehow, away for now in our own secret worlds.

I think people probably have an idea about young players on a night out: flash young lads with a bit of money to spend and a sense of entitlement. *Look at me. I'm a footballer.* I wasn't like that. I was just desperate to get attention from any girl or woman I met. With me, what might have looked like a big ego was actually a complete lack of self-esteem.

I met Andrea at Coco Savannah's nightclub in Stockport, a few weeks before the game at Wembley. I was out with Ash. She was working behind the bar. I was eighteen, Andrea was twenty-two. We went out for a drink. Like it always was when I met a new girl, I was over the top, wanting her to like me straight away: buying the drinks, paying her compliments, sending her flowers. Talking about being in love. I've always done it: jumped in too quickly and too far, as a way of getting attention. Andrea was a lovely down-to-earth girl, from a solid working-class family. They lived in Reddish, just on the edge of Stockport. Andrea was a really nice person. Probably just what I didn't need.

My experiences with Bennell left me with a completely distorted idea about how relationships worked. All the while he was abusing me, life was on the edge of a precipice: I never knew what was going to happen next; he was in control of my every waking minute and I'd lurched between fear and relief, one moment to the next, for the best part of six years. That became my model for how things were supposed to be between people.

I was hooked on the drama and uncertainty of an abusive relationship. It was all I knew. And then Andrea came along and it wasn't like that at all. She wasn't looking to unsettle me, scare me, mess around with my mind. She was gentle, steady, genuine. It might have been that, with Andrea, I could have learned a new way to be with someone. But I was miles off being ready for that.

Through no fault of Andrea's, our relationship – no drama, no danger – was probably doomed from the beginning. For one thing, even after we started going out, I would play up to any female attention. It was already starting to become an obsession: wanting the feeling of being with a woman just in order to blank out the memory of being with Bennell. It was what I wanted, to the point of desperation.

Every time I was with a woman, I wasn't with him. It sort of drove me. I'd get flashbacks to what he used to do to me; I still get them occasionally now. But I was fighting them: the next experience with a woman might always be the one to bury those memories a little bit deeper. I wanted to be touching a woman – knowing I was touching a woman – instead of touching Bennell.

So I met Andrea. She was at Wembley for the play-off final. And then everything happened so quickly. At the end of the summer, Andrea told me she was pregnant. Almost straight away, her mum and dad were telling us we had to get married. It was the respectable thing to do. I moved in with her parents. Then it was time to buy a house. And then came the wedding. All of it happened in less than a year.

I blew it, wasn't ready for any of it. I just did the next thing that someone said I ought to be doing. Bennell had spent six years turning me into a Yes boy, doing whatever he wanted me to do. I'd barely shaken him off and now circumstances – I'd never blame Andrea for any of this – were turning me into a Yes man. I didn't know how to stop and think. I didn't know how to ask myself – or anybody else – the important questions. All I knew was to shut down my feelings and plough on, doing as I was told.

I'll never forget the evening I told my parents I was going to be a dad. I don't know why but I made it all formal. Took them up to the little bedroom at home, made them sit down on the bed. *What's going on?* I explained that Andrea was pregnant. They were still dealing with Lynda's situation and now me. They were devastated: I'd just met Andrea, hadn't I? They hardly knew her. And now what would happen?

I moved in with Andrea and her parents almost overnight. They were lovely people, accepted me as part of the family straight away. They didn't judge me. But they did have a pretty clear idea about the right way to do things. As far as they were concerned, I'd got their daughter into trouble and they expected me to own up to my responsibilities. I'd had a year with Bennell out of the picture, him laid up in a bed on the other side of the Atlantic where he couldn't hurt me. I'd had a year pushing all that had happened to one side, I'd been fighting. I had that in me and football gave me something to fight for. Making it as a player was what it was all supposed to have been about, after all. And, on the outside at least, I was winning: playing for the first team, playing at Wembley, making Mum and Dad proud.

But then: how to explain? It's a feeling like you're hanging from a ledge, holding on by your fingertips. And you can do that: you're strong. You focus and you fight. Maybe at some point down the line you're going to be able to hoist yourself up and onto the ledge. But something changes and, suddenly, you know you're losing your grip. Strength deserts you. You know you're helpless again. You can feel yourself slipping away and you've got no idea how far it is you might have to fall.

I'd gone into the previous season, my first as a pro, feeling free. Bennell was still in a Florida hospital. I had a new manager and new teammates. It had felt like a new start. By the time the next season started, though, that sense of freedom had gone. Andrea was pregnant. I had to get a house for us. I had to get ready to marry. And all that felt like a pressure cooker coming to the boil in my head. I was going through the motions again, doing whatever I thought I was supposed to do next.

The fight went out of me and it showed in my football. I fell out of favour at Crewe and was in and out of the team: I hardly played that season. I can't blame Dario. A manager looks at his players and uses the ones he can depend on. He obviously didn't think he could depend on me. But, without the focus of football and given the pressured situation with my wife-to-be, I started to come apart. I didn't really understand what had happened but, all of a sudden, I could feel myself losing my way, on the pitch as well as off it.

23.

I can't begin to say how much I love my sons. How much they mean
to me. Now, grown up, when I think about who I am and what I
am, being their dad is pretty much the first and most important thing
that comes to me. My oldest, Jake, was born in March 1994. In the
weeks after we met, things had rolled along with Andrea. Through her,
I'd been introduced to a new circle of friends and acquaintances, people
who had nothing to do with my past or with football. And I enjoyed
that. When I found out that becoming a dad was going to be part of
it all, though, I panicked.

I was still a child myself in many ways; I'd been stunted by what
had gone on with Bennell. I wasn't grown-up enough to actually say:
I'm not ready for this. It's not what I want. But I wasn't grown-up
enough, either, to take a deep breath and make the best of the situation.

I just switched off from Andrea. Shutting down was the way I'd learned to deal with any difficult situation. It had become the only way to get myself through those years of abuse by Bennell. Life, somehow, didn't seem real. Probably, I was wishing it wasn't.

We bought a terraced house in Heaton Norris, just by Stockport. It was opposite Andrea's grandparents'. The house itself was pretty run-down but Andrea's dad was really good at building and DIY and he did a lot of work getting it into shape: a new bathroom, sorting out the lounge downstairs. He got it looking nice.

Our wedding that summer looked nice as well. But, when I look at that picture of the lads – Ash, Rob Jones behind him, Mark Smith, the young keeper, me and my best man, Neil Lennon – it seems obvious to me. I'm all done up in the gear but my face tells its own story. *Is this really happening to me?* On the outside, it looked perfect: first team player, in love, a new dad. Inside, though, it felt all wrong. Wrong for me and wrong for Andrea, too.

That feeling of unreality around the wedding day was tied up with where it was held, too. We were back at the same church where Lynda had married Bennell. The whole day echoed with my memories of two summers before. I don't know how or why I made the decisions I made. I had teammates from Crewe around me on the day. They were all I had in terms of friends, I suppose. I'd been cut off from any other mates during the six years with Bennell.

Neil Lennon was a good guy and a good friend but I was much closer to boys my own age: Ash Stephenson and Gareth Whalley. Why did I ask Neil to be my best man instead of one of them? Because it would look more impressive having a senior pro at my side? Because he'd be better at giving a best man's speech? He was very funny, to be fair, telling stories about our trips into training, mad nights out, my stag do in Blackpool.

And who in their right mind would hold their wedding reception at Manchester Airport? We booked one of their function rooms: the lot of us tipped up in the car park and then traipsed through the arrivals hall, wedding dresses, top hats, the lot. I stood up to make my speech and went through all the traditional thank-yous before losing the plot completely. Things just welled up in me: I started talking about my mum and dad, about the sacrifices they'd made to get me to where I was as a player

I didn't talk about Bennell, of course, but people there watching and listening must have been thinking: *What's Andy on about? And why has he just burst into tears?* My new wife's here, our four-month-old son's over there, my parents are sitting next to me and all the lads from Crewe are looking on. *How the fuck have I ended up stood here? What's happening to me now?* I wasn't coping: the pressure of trying to bottle everything up was starting to overwhelm me, to seep out as I lost control. No one said anything about me falling apart over my speech. People probably assumed I'd just got a bit emotional. And thankfully, at least Bennell wasn't there: he and Lynda were both in the States at the time. What happened later, though, was a very big deal and had a massive impact on me. Maybe that's why I can't be sure whether it happened before the wedding or after. It was right around the same time, anyway.

I got a phone call at the house in Heaton Norris. I forget whether it was Mum or Dad who rang. But I remember what got said. A young boy in Florida had come forward and made an allegation against

Bennell, a sexual allegation. He'd been arrested and was being held on remand.

It was as if all the air was suddenly sucked out of the room I was standing in. I could just hear my own breathing. I didn't know what to say. I didn't know what to feel, either. I just said: *Wow!* And then: *What about Lynda?* She was out there. So were their two children, my nephew and niece. What was going to happen to them?

A flurry of thoughts rushed through my mind. One: I know he's guilty and that means he won't be able to hurt anyone else now. Two: if I'd said or done something, maybe that boy wouldn't have come to harm. Maybe lots of other boys would have been safe, too. Then: *If they've got him over there, how long will it be before someone turns up on my doorstep, asking questions? Questions I don't want to answer?* Even then, straight away, I was thinking somebody's going to want to talk to me about all this. The idea of that terrified me.

I had to tell Andrea what had happened to Bennell but there was no way I could tell her what had happened to me. Instead, at weekends, I'd have a couple of drinks and then fall apart. Crying and crying. Of course Andrea couldn't understand what was going on. Why was I being like this? I was like a little boy, upset but without the words to explain why. It must have been difficult for her: she already had one young child on her hands, Jake. Now her new husband was needing to be looked after, too. *What's wrong with you, Andy?*

I should have been relieved he'd been caught. But, instead, it all boiled up: Lynda, the kids, what was going to happen to me now. There was nobody I felt I could talk to, nobody who'd wrap me up and tell me it would all be all right. The weeks after Bennell was arrested were the first time I started thinking I'd had enough of it all: him, football, my marriage, everything that was going on in my life. Scared of the past and, now, even more scared of the future. *Maybe it would be better if I just wasn't here.*

In a weird sort of way, Bennell getting caught felt like me being caught, too. The thought of going into Crewe every day was awful: whatever they said to the contrary, people there knew what had gone on, even if they didn't know the detail. They knew he was married to my sister and that they had two kids. Even if nobody said anything to my face, what would they be thinking to themselves and saying to each other? I was Bennell's boy, wasn't I? And now he was on remand in the States, accused of sexually assaulting a minor.

All the feelings and memories I desperately wanted to escape from began to take shape around the football club, the players and staff there and the place itself. If I wanted to get away from all that, it seemed to me, I had to get away from Crewe. From people who knew me and, some more than others, who knew something about what had happened to me.

Lynda and the children came back to England. She was convinced that the boy's allegations about Bennell weren't true. What were any of us supposed to think or do next? My parents did what they always did: supported her, looked after their grandchildren. They didn't make a fuss. I wonder, now, how much they talked to each other about all those years I'd spent being coached by Bennell, all the weekends and holidays I'd spent with him. If they talked about the times they'd spent with him, mesmerised by this bloke who'd turned me into a footballer and their daughter into a wife and a mother.

Nobody wanted to believe it was true. I know my parents asked questions. *Why would a boy say that if something hadn't happened?* But they were in denial, too. It didn't bear thinking about, maybe. After all, if Bennell was guilty, what would that mean for them and for the family they loved and cared so much about?

Difficult as it must have been for Mum and Dad, they did ask me: *Andy, did anything ever happen to you?* I just flat out denied it. *Nothing happened. Nothing at all.* Nothing more got said. I can remember the atmosphere in our little front room. I shut them down, didn't I? *Nothing happened. Nothing at all.* There was nowhere else for the conversation to go then, whether they thought I was telling the truth or not. Why didn't I say anything? With him safe behind bars, where he couldn't get to me? Because I still felt completely powerless when it came to Bennell. He had that control; he'd buried himself deep inside me, like a virus. I still had the overwhelming feeling that everything that had happened to me had been my own fault; that I'd somehow made it happen. To tell my parents would have been the same as telling the whole world. In my mind, it would have been confessing to something *I'd* done rather than revealing what he'd done to me. That would have meant shame I was sure I couldn't get past. What would people think of me? What kind of person would they imagine I was?

And I was still terrified of Bennell. What if he got out, got away with it in Florida somehow? What might he do to me when he came home if I'd betrayed him? There was the fear that he'd hurt me. More than that, there was the fear that he'd betray me in return. Tell everyone that I'd asked for whatever I'd got. Even with him in jail, I was scared, as well, of what breaking the secret might mean for me. If I said anything, everything I was and everything I seemed to be would fall apart. And what would I be left with then?

If I talked, the whole thing – my family, my football career, me as a son and now as a father and husband – would show up as a sham, as a lie. My lie. How could I admit to anyone what had really gone on: the real physical detail of the abuse and the rapes? How could I tell anyone I'd let him do those horrible things to me? Keeping my silence was breaking me into pieces, but I simply wasn't capable now of telling the truth.

24.

I know that look. He's got his head bowed. But I know there's not the least bit of regret or remorse in that expression. Self-pity, maybe, but otherwise it's just a sneer waiting to happen. *Who cares what anybody else thinks?* Bennell wrote to me from prison very early on after he was arrested. At that point, he wasn't asking for anything. It was almost like a love letter, talking about how close we were, about the special bond between us.

I don't know but, thinking back, I guess he must have been panicking. Not just about what had happened in Florida but also about what might happen back here. He must have known I would be at the centre of anything that was uncovered: how long he'd been at it with me, how far things had gone. He was trying to keep me close. Trying to make sure that, when it came to it, I'd be on his side.

Lynda went out to Florida and stayed with the couple they'd met and made friends with there. My parents went, too, more to be with her than to visit him. Even so, he was the father of their grandchildren and he hadn't been found guilty of anything yet. Lynda was sure he'd be found innocent.

She was every bit as much a victim as I'd been: Bennell, I'm sure, had the same power over her as he had over me.

It must have been an impossible situation for my parents. Even if they thought the worst, their first responsibility, as they saw it, was to Lynda and the children. There was a $20,000 bond needed posting for Bennell to be released on bail before his trial. Obviously they didn't have that kind of money. My mum got in touch with her father-in-law, George, and asked him to lend them the $20,000. *He's innocent. We need to get him out of prison.* George still had the fish shop and money left from when he'd won the pools, so he paid the bond and Bennell was released on bail on condition that he wasn't found anywhere near sports fields or children.

He lasted a week. Completely unbeknownst to Lynda, who didn't know where he was at the time, Bennell was found hanging around a kids' football pitch, watching and filming a game of under-elevens. He was re-arrested and put back on remand. The $20,000 was gone. A lot of money to lose in 1994. It was just another betrayal of my family. Another betrayal of trust.

All that counts for someone like him is his appetites. The consequences for other people don't matter at all. Bennell didn't give a fuck about anything else: me, Lynda, my parents and now my grandparents and the $20,000. All that mattered to him was his obsession, his hunger.

He couldn't leave young people alone. If he was headed over the edge, he didn't mind who he took with him. He didn't care whose life might be damaged along the way.

What must it have been like for Mum and Dad? Both of them working, my younger sister, Louise, a teenager getting ready for her GCSEs. I think they protected her as much as they could. They tried to keep her out of it, tried to get her to concentrate on her school-work. This wasn't stuff they talked about while they were eating their tea.

My parents told me bits about what was going on in Jacksonville but I was just trying to focus on keeping myself together. I was struggling to get in the Crewe first team, struggling to keep things steady with Andrea. She and I weren't arguing but I'd cut myself off, disappearing down a dark hole on my own. I tried to distance myself from what was happening in Florida. Pretended to myself that it wasn't my problem. I didn't have to get involved.

Truth was, of course, me not being involved wouldn't ever have been possible. Instead, what was happening in Florida kept dragging me in deeper and deeper.

Things were being arranged for Bennell's defence. They found news-paper cuttings that talked about what an amazing coach he was. People who knew him – players, parents, staff members at Crewe – sent char-acter references to back those up. I was asked if I would do the same: write a letter saying what a great bloke Bennell was and how much he'd done for me. How respectable and trustworthy he was. How safe I'd always felt in his company.

I felt torn in two. I couldn't get away from the feeling that, somehow, all this was my fault in the first place. Of course, Bennell had buried that sense of guilt deep inside me.

I knew there were other people who'd already agreed to write letters: Dario Gradi, Craig Hignett, Rob Jones. Other lads, too, who I knew had been abused by Bennell.

They'd all written something. The honest truth is I never even considered the possibility of saying no. He still had enough power over me that I knew straight away that I'd write one of these letters as well. There wasn't a part of me that had the will or the courage not to. I convinced myself that if I refused to do one, people would wonder why, after all the time I'd spent with him over the years. They'd ask questions I didn't want to answer. And, underneath all that, anyway, I was still the little boy who'd do anything Bennell told him to do.

Bennell wrote to me again as well. Talking about how special I'd always been to him, reminding me how much we'd been through together, telling me how important the letter might be. He'd say anything at all to get what he wanted.

And so I wrote exactly what Bennell wanted me to. Wrote it through tears:

Barry is one of the nicest, kindest, loving and caring people I have been fortunate to meet. I am so glad I have the pleasure of knowing him. If I was eleven again I would have no hesitation about staying at Barry's house. I have a son of my own and would entrust him in Barry's care completely and would have no qualms about letting him stay with Barry at any time.

Seeing the words on paper in front of me now makes me feel sick to my stomach. Guilty. Ashamed. The man had stolen my mind.

The case in Florida rumbled on towards Bennell appearing in court and I know how difficult a time that was for Lynda and my parents. I did my best, though, not to get drawn in, not to be a part of the drama that was swallowing up my family. It's only now, really, that I understand what was happening. I was retreating further into myself, becoming more and more cut off from my family, trying to keep the chaos inside my head under control.

I was disconnecting from the real world, from the rational behaviours and thought processes that help us all relate to other people and get on with our lives. Training at Crewe, being at home with Andrea: I was going through the motions. It was like this shell of me, putting on a face to my wife, to my teammates and to everyone else. Inside, my mind was racing constantly, like a car rolling downhill with no brakes and heading for a brick wall. Bennell, what he'd done to me and what I'd done to make that stuff happen: everything was spinning to the point where it felt like I was going to explode. More than anything, I had this overwhelming feeling of wanting to run and escape from it all.

In amongst it, I was a doting father and spent a lot of time with Jake. I used to pick him up from Andrea's mum on my way home from training. I liked doing all that stuff: feeding him, getting him down for his nap. The connection there felt instinctive, father and son. But as far as the marriage went, I couldn't connect with Andrea at all. It was nothing she did or had done: she was a new mum and finding that quite hard, especially as she'd gone back to work. We didn't have rows. I was too busy having my fights with myself, maybe. I looked at our life together and I just saw responsibilities I wanted to crawl away from. I was desperate for attention, for comfort and for understanding and I wasn't getting those things from Andrea. It was an impossible situation for her. She'd see me breaking down but I never sat and explained what was going on in my head. We never had the kind of conversation that might have brought me out of myself and given us the chance to make our relationship work.

I cheated on Andrea once or twice and, eventually, I met Rachel, my second wife. I was chasing the attention, the physical intimacy with women, that I'd become obsessed with even before Andrea and I got together. In hindsight, it's pretty simple what happened: I ran away. In spirit at first and then physically, too. Andrea didn't deserve it and I still feel guilty about having let her down. I'm thankful that she's been able to go on and have a good life and a happy marriage with someone else. And she brought up Jake, a son I adore and a young man we can both be very proud of.

At the time, though? Andrea was a lovely person but my demons meant our marriage never stood a chance. I kind of sleepwalked into it. I needed help and couldn't ask for it. Instead, I got to a point where my only option, as far as I could see it, was to go missing. To disappear. It was as if I was seeing my life through the wrong end of a telescope. No wonder nothing made sense.

In 1994, Bennell was found guilty in a court in Florida and was sentenced to four years in jail for having sexually abused the thirteen-year-old boy who'd spoken up about him. It didn't feel like something to celebrate. The court verdict was devastating for Lynda. It left her alone with two young children and it cast her marriage – her life with Bennell – in a whole new light. It was incredibly difficult for my parents, too. They knew they'd need to look out for their daughter and their grandchildren now. But where did this leave them in relation to Bennell, who'd been part of our family's life for the last ten years? It hit all of them hard: they must have realised they'd been living a lie.

Where did it leave me? I still had my secret, didn't I? No one had uncovered my lie. Him getting locked up felt like a relief. He was away and maybe he couldn't hurt me any more. For the time being at least. But him being behind bars didn't suddenly make what he'd done to me simply melt away. In jail, Bennell was out of sight. What I didn't realise then was that it would take the rest of my life to get him out of my mind.

As much as I felt like running away from my marriage, I felt I needed to run away from the football club, too. It wasn't working out for me at Gresty Road: the same self-absorption that cut me off from Rachel cut me off from what I needed to be doing as a player as well. In my mind, Bennell and the football club were one and the same. What I'd experienced: Crewe hadn't made it happen but, for the first time really, it dawned on me now that perhaps they'd let it happen. If I was going to really get away from him, I had to get away from there too.

25

I had my moments as a player. That's me being introduced to the dignitaries before the Third Division Playoff Final at Wembley in May 1995. Things can happen quickly in football, can't they? Bury had come in for me in the March of that year, just two months previously. By then, Crewe were happy to get rid. As I remember, the Bury manager, Mike Walsh, got in touch and asked me to come over and play in a trial game. For months, everything at Crewe had been a trigger for bad memories: the dressing rooms, Bennell's office in a Portakabin by the stadium, the club offices, the training ground. Everywhere I looked reminded me of Bennell and what had gone on. I didn't even have the release of a game on Saturday afternoon to look forward to. So I jumped at the offer.

A lad I'd grown up with, Michael Jackson, was already at Bury and he played in the game. He told me he loved his new club. I suppose it was a kind of pressure but it definitely felt like a chance to change things for myself. I was desperate to do well and I must have come through all right, playing right back. Mike Walsh pretty much signed me on the spot. The move meant a new team and a chance to make a fresh start.

Walking into a new dressing room can be a bit daunting but Michael Jackson was already there and another lad too, Tony Rigby, who I knew from Crewe. There was a good atmosphere around the club. I felt welcome. Away from football, I knew Bennell was in jail; Andrea and I had separated; I'd met Rachel. I was able to pretend to myself that I'd unpacked some weight off my shoulders.

I felt wanted, appreciated. I was getting some of the attention I craved: from a new partner and from a new football club. I'd been stumbling around in the dark and suddenly it was as if somebody had switched a light on. Everything seemed to look a bit different. I could pretend for a while I was free.

Football made sense again. I went straight into the first team at Gigg Lane. I had the chance to prove myself, to show what I could do in spite of Bennell, all over again.

Those first couple of months with Bury couldn't have gone much better for me. My first game, we beat Carlisle, who ended up winning Division 3 that season. Then we went unbeaten the next seven including play-off semi-finals home and away against Preston. A couple of months after signing, I was back at Wembley for another final and another afternoon in the sunshine.

Pity: it ended in another defeat. I started at right back. Their keeper had a blinder. The referee was terrible. And we lost two goals to long throws. You know how it goes. Chesterfield went up instead of us. But, for me, those nine games for a new club brought me back to life a little. At Crewe, I hadn't been playing. Suddenly I was in the thick of it. Whatever else was going on in my life at that point, if I got out on a football pitch I felt as if I knew where I was. I could get on with the fight. For those few months, at least, football was the one thing that took me out of myself.

Everybody was friendly enough at Bury. It was a great dressing room and there was plenty of banter and mickey-taking went on. But the lads talked about Crewe, talked about Bennell, and talked about it being the 'bum boys club'. Nobody was having a go at me about it. This wasn't bullying. And I wasn't being asked awkward questions. Michael and Tony had come from there, too, after all. But what shocked me was that what went on at Crewe seemed to be common knowledge. At Gresty Road, it felt as if a wall of silence had been built up around the club. By the club. As soon as I moved away I realised that even if people didn't know any details, Crewe boys had a reputation. The detail of what Bennell did, with me and others, might have been secret. But it seemed like plenty of people had an idea that he was a wrong 'un. And they assumed Crewe Alexandra let it go on.

Bury was a different world. Mike Walsh, the manager, was fantastic for me: friendly and supportive. He and his assistant, Stan Ternent, had a sort of good cop, bad cop thing going on. Stan had a temper and he would usually be the one to dig you out if you needed it. The two of them together were great.

The pre-season after we lost to Chesterfield, we went away on camp to the Isle of Man. Some mad stuff went on: I remember lads climbing through hotel windows after curfew to go down to the pub. Chris Lucketti – an absolute legend at Bury, by the way – actually snapped a drainpipe in half climbing down it one night. Phil Neville came with us, too, because his dad, Neville Neville, was Bury's commercial manager. Phil got some stick: *Manchester United and England player, you could go anywhere in the world for your summer holidays. So what are you doing coming to the Isle of Man with us lot?*

It was a very different culture: old-school, but it worked. There were some really good senior players: Phil Stant used to tell us stories all the time; not about football but about his time in the army. We had a great goalkeeper, Gary Kelly, who was crazy like goalies are supposed to be. Back then, players might have a couple of beers on the way back from games. Gary used to have a case of them waiting under his seat when we got on the bus home, which he'd get through all on his own.

There was a guy named Mark Carter – everybody called him 'Spike' – who just amazed me. I'd grown up at Crewe with this regimented sense of professionalism, the drills, the warm-ups. Bennell insisted on all that. Dario Gradi, too. But here was Mark Carter: going to away games, he'd meet the bus at the motorway services, where he'd be finishing up his full English breakfast. Then, at the ground, he'd not bother with a warm up. He'd sit in the corner, reading his *Racing Post*, put his boots on at ten to three, and then just wander out and play. He was Bury's top goalscorer the season I arrived at Gigg Lane.

I had no regrets at all about leaving Crewe. Leaving Andrea, though, wasn't so simple. It happened at right around the same time. Perhaps we weren't really meant for each other anyway but, for sure, us splitting up wasn't down to anything Andrea said or did. It was all on me:

internalising everything until I got to a point where I couldn't cope. Marriage, fatherhood, setting up house: it felt like I'd walked into a trap. Not a trap Andrea had set for me; just a trap laid by life.

I came home from training one day and announced I'd had enough. *It's over. I can't deal with this any more.* And that was it. No real explanation, nothing. I was gone. I'd already met Rachel, although we weren't in a relationship. But I ran off towards something new, to somewhere I felt like I could get the attention that would make me feel better about myself for a while.

I met Rachel in a club in Alderley Edge on a night out with teammates, the summer after Bury got to the play-off final. The start of the season didn't go well for me. I played a couple of games and I ended up in the reserves. I'd split with Andrea; Bennell was in prison but sending me letters; I knew the kind of pressure my parents were feeling, too. I jumped into the relationship with Rachel; probably I was clinging to it a bit. Rachel had been an air stewardess; a little bit older than me, beautiful, always dressed really well.

I was flattered by the attention, desperate for her to like me. That's how I always was around women and Rachel was no different. We got very involved very quickly. And then Rachel announced she was pregnant. She was really happy: wanted to stop work, wanted to start a family. I put on a face, acted delighted. Inside, though? It felt like history repeating itself. I said nothing but, straight away, I dreaded what might be lying ahead.

As much as I was struggling with what came next in my relationship with Rachel, I let Andrea down quite badly, I think. Things happened that I know, now I'm older and on a better footing with my life, I should never have let happen. We'd bought a new house together in Reddish but, once I moved out, she had to sell up and move somewhere smaller.

Jake was around two and we'd agreed that I'd have him with me at weekends. Much as I loved him, though, and much as I'd told myself I was going to be a good dad, there were times when I let other things come first. I always had an excuse ready but the truth was there were times when I wasn't there for him or for Andrea. She didn't really kick off about it but I can imagine what she was feeling. *What are you thinking? What are you doing? How can you let us down like this? This is your son.*

I'm glad things didn't carry on like that. Being with Jake at the weekends did become a regular part of my life, right through the next ten years or so. Thinking about how much he means to me now, I'm glad I did the right thing eventually. A bit crazy, really, though: taking your boy at the weekend, which is, of course, when a footballer is supposed to go to work. Often, Jake would end up sitting in the stand at an away game with Rachel. At that age, he must have wondered what was going on.

Rachel had a house in Urmston and I moved in with her, so Jake spent a lot of Saturdays and Sundays there as well. Andrea and I got divorced: she was incredibly patient and amicable through the whole thing. We sort of worked out what would happen between ourselves, signed the right papers and went our separate ways. Even so, it was another thing to add to the pot: a divorce being simple doesn't make it easy. And, at the same time, Rachel was pregnant and wanting to see our relationship move on. No wonder I was rubbish for Bury that year.

In no time that great start to life as a player at Gigg Lane began to feel like a distant memory. My football took a real dip and I couldn't get a game. Things had changed at the club, too. We made a poor start to the season – with me in the team – and then Mike Walsh got the sack. Even though he'd been with the club for five years, had taken them to three play-off finals, by the start of September the chairman had had enough and Mike was replaced by Stan Ternent.

As it turned out, it was probably the right decision. Bury struggled in the first half of the season but then went on a run and ended up getting promoted. I hardly played, though. It was a great season for the football club but definitely not a great few months for me. The pressure of knowing Rachel was going to have a baby drilled down into me. That feeling of being out of control, of having to force myself to keep it together on the surface while I was starting to crumble inside, wore me out. I was flat, physically and mentally. The energy and desire I needed to force my way back into the first team just wasn't there.

26.

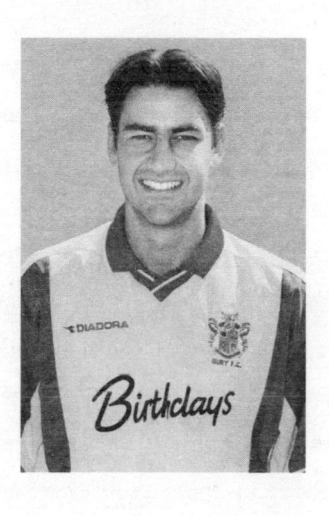

W hat a difference a year made. Look at that picture the club took of me the summer after I joined Bury in 1995: I seem happy, relieved, excited even. Ready for a new start. And then I think back to what happened to me over the course of the season. I played the first game of it. We got humped 4–1 away and that was my lot. I didn't play again for the first team that year. The weeks and months that followed just seemed to suck the life out of me. Really, I was still as much in Bennell's grip as I had been as a teenager. On top of that, I was getting more and more scared of where I was headed with Rachel, I was worn down, in a corner: emotions all over the place but me trying to keep a tight lid on. I was desperate to make sure nobody knew what was wrong. So instead of letting any of those emotions show, I shut down. The last ten years had taught me how to do that. I wanted to be blank, unreadable. Unreachable. Mum and Dad always came to my games but I wasn't playing. So I didn't even have to see them.

In my early twenties, I should have been taking control of my own life. It didn't feel like that at all: losing the plot as a professional footballer and crashing out of a marriage and into another intense relationship. It was as if I was just waiting for the next drama to unfold. I know better than anybody how I let people down. But I also understand how and why that happened.

Despite Bennell being locked up, he haunted me day in, day out. They say time's a great healer but I'm not sure that's true. In my case, it felt as if time passing made things worse: the deeper I tried to bury the memories – the longer I went without sharing my secret – the more power they had to undo me. That's how trauma works: it sits there, in the core of you. I was desperate to avoid telling it to anyone, but the story followed me anyway. Hunted me down.

It started with two detectives turning up at my parents' house in Cheadle. I wasn't there but they'd come to try to make contact with me. Now that Bennell was behind bars, found guilty of a crime in the States, they were starting to make enquiries about his activities in the UK. They were tracking down players who'd been coached by Bennell. Because of the Florida court case, they knew he was married to Lynda. She was living at my parents. The trail led them to me.

I'd just assumed, I suppose, that Bennell having been convicted in Jacksonville was the end of it. For now, anyway. When a detective rang me about him, it came as a complete surprise. A shock: everything inside me just sort of dropped. Although it was Bennell they wanted to talk to me about, it felt in that moment as if it was me they were after.

I arranged to meet the two detectives at Mum and Dad's. I was left alone with them. They explained that the authorities in the US had discovered what Bennell had done over there and now the police here were conducting a full investigation into what he might have done in the UK. They said it straight out: he married your sister; we know you had some kind of relationship with him. *You played for him for years, didn't you? What can you tell us?*

It was as if they knew I was holding back. Maybe someone had said something? I clammed up, told them nothing had ever happened to me. I didn't know who else they'd spoken to but I got a strong impression they were disappointed, surprised even. I think they'd expected me to be the person who'd crack, the person who'd be the first to say: *Yes. Bennell did stuff to me.* But instead I blanked them.

I was terrified. I just wanted all of this to go away. Bennell was locked up. Me and my family had enough on our plates. I knew how hard it was trying to keep things together in my head. I knew how often I'd wake up from nightmares, flashbacks to what he'd done to me out at Dove Holes. How would it help me if all this stuff was out in the open? What if I was the only person who said anything? If I was all on my own with this?

I didn't even know whether anybody would believe the story I had to tell. *I'd written that letter for him, hadn't I?* I knew there were other victims out there but I had no idea if any of them had admitted to anything. Here I was, sat in front of two policemen in my parents' front room. Everything felt as if it was closing in around me. Time ticked by. *No. Nothing happened.* It was like I could hardly draw breath. And on the detectives' faces: *We don't believe you.*

I was afraid for myself. That was part of it. Also, I thought saying anything about Bennell would be devastating for my family. They had enough to deal with. I'd never said a word about what Bennell had done to me and now here they were, the police in the house. I'm sure Mum and Dad were trying to work out for themselves what was true and what wasn't.

The one person I did finally say something to was Rachel. I explained the police had interviewed me and told her what it was about. I told her something had happened with me and Bennell but didn't go into any detail. *He messed about with me. Touched me. Nothing, really.* I'd never said that much to anyone before but, thinking back, I know I just told Rachel enough to end the conversation. Just enough to make sure I got some sympathy without having to tell her the whole truth.

The detectives went away and I thought that would be it. I'd told them nothing had happened so there was nowhere for them to go, was there? Things were quiet for a while but then they came back, wanting to speak to me again. Again, they were suggesting I might have something I wanted to tell them. And, again, I denied everything. Then, when they came back for the third time, they said that there were other people who'd told them things had gone on with Bennell.

They didn't say who those people were or what they'd said exactly. They just told me enough to put pressure on me: *We know you're holding stuff back. We want to know why.* That third time, I felt physically sick after they left. But still I locked everything up. Was it fear of Bennell? Fear of what all this said about me? I felt damned either way.

It was as if I was ready for my world to fall apart – and it was falling apart – before I'd give up my secret.

By now, it wasn't just me. The police had spoken to Mum and Dad; they had been there when they spoke to me. But we didn't talk about it together. Bennell wasn't around. They knew what had happened to Lynda but, as a family, we didn't sit down and try to work anything out. I didn't want to talk about Bennell and, actually, neither did my parents.

Every now and then, Mum or Dad would say something that made me think he had been on their minds: *Are you sure you're okay, Andy?* But this was all very painful for them, even without them knowing what had happened to me, and I think they wanted to box it off rather than dwell on it. *Let's not mention it.* How can you blame them? They just wanted to get on with their lives. It was only much later that I understood – and my parents understood – that ignoring trauma won't make it leave you alone.

I'd have nightmares, flashbacks during the day. I'd find myself thinking about Bennell and what he'd done to me. Suddenly a memory I'd buried would come into my mind, a snapshot of a moment: his voice, his smell, him touching me. The details: the rapes, what he'd made me do, my terrors about what he'd do to me next. There was the reality of what he'd done to Lynda and my guilt about that, too. I was exhausted from trying to push those thoughts and memories away and out of sight. Exhausted from keeping the mask in place for Rachel, for my family and, now, the police.

The detectives said I'd be anonymous but what did that mean? I was convinced I'd end up in court, having to face Bennell and that would be the end of me in the game. I convinced myself, too, that saying nothing was the only way I could keep my career going. But, of course, the effort of suppressing my emotions – keeping my secret – left me in no state to play football most of the time. When I did get a game, I was only ever turning out now for Bury's reserves.

27

The dream all along had been to be a footballer. To be part of a successful team. To win trophies. Goals and glory and the rest. That picture sums it up. The end of an amazing season. It was that dream that first drove me into the arms of Barry Bennell. Now, it felt like my only way of being able to get the better of the memory of him. The picture is of us winning. But it doesn't begin to tell the story of what I lost along the way to getting there.

You'd never have predicted the 96/97 season's happy ending for me from the way it started. Here I was, twenty-four years old, scuffing around in front of a couple of dozen people playing for Bury reserves in the Central League. Or sitting in the stands, watching the first team. I was a part of it, I suppose, in my Bury tracksuit, alongside other injured or out-of-favour players. But, really, it didn't feel like I was part of anything.

I'd get a game or be on the bench now and again. Most of the time, though, I was just going through the motions. The manager, Stan Ternent, had a job to do and Andy Woodward wasn't really in a fit state to help him do it. The gaffer didn't give me a hard time. He was focused on the next game. For weeks on end I just drifted around the place, like the ghost of Gigg Lane.

It got to a point where I'd exaggerate any little injury in order to make myself scarce. Truth was, though, I didn't want to be at home either. I just wanted to be left alone in the dark hole I'd clambered into. I'd phone up the club first thing in the morning and say I wasn't well. But I'd leave home at nine o'clock, telling Rachel I was off to training.

I'd drive over to Bury, park up somewhere quiet and sit there for three hours, staring into space, trying not to think. Pretending I didn't exist. I had this one thing on my mind that had become so enormous, so all-consuming, that the rest of my life seemed tiny and distant in comparison. It was as if I'd come adrift from the real world and the responsibilities that came with it: Rachel, football, family and everything else. Eventually, something had to give.

I don't remember exactly when it was that the dam broke: early 1997 sometime? The police were persistent: wouldn't go away, kept pushing and pushing. Not bullying exactly but they weren't taking no for an answer. These days, there'd have been witness support officers, counsellors and other people around the case. Back then, it was just those same two detectives, over and over again. *Andy, we know you've got something to tell us.*

What made me change my mind and admit to what had happened between me and Bennell? I'm still not sure, but I can remember us all sitting in my parents' lounge: me, Mum and Dad, Lynda and the children. I think Louise was there, too. The detectives knew what they were doing, piling on the pressure. You could feel it like a presence in the room. Hardly any air left to breathe.

It's probably the hardest thing I've ever had to do in my life. I still wonder now what made me able to say out loud what I had to say. I can see us all together, squeezed into the lounge. Maybe that's what did it. I looked across at my sister; what she'd been through sent a chill through me every time I thought about it. And Lynda's children, my nephew and niece: what would happen to them when Bennell came out? In that moment protecting them seemed much more important than protecting myself.

I'd had ten years and more burying my horrible secret out of sight, wrapping my life up in silence. To let all that go felt like standing on a cliff edge, shutting my eyes and taking a step forward. I wanted it all to stop. It wasn't bravery. It was more like giving up. I asked my family to leave the room.

I know it sounds like a considered decision but it felt more like something inside me just giving way, breaking. The two detectives sat opposite me in their suits. *Come on then, Andy.* They'd seen it in my face. They knew I'd cracked. *Yes. Something happened.* For the first time, I told another person that Bennell had abused me. Told somebody what he'd done to me. It was weird: as if I was listening to someone else talking. Was I really saying all this at last? My mouth was dry and I could feel sweat on the back of my neck, going cold against my shirt collar.

I told them he'd raped me, told them it had gone on for years on end, told them he'd scared me to death. I kept hearing my voice breaking. This was what I'd spent so long trying not to do: I could hear the words being squeezed out of me. *Yes. He buggered me. Yes. I had to suck him. Touch him. Do whatever he wanted me to do.* Really, though, I told them very little. The whole story would have taken much longer to get out of me. But they had their result. They'd got me to talk and that's what mattered to them. To this day, I still don't know which parts of my statement were used as charges against Bennell when the case came to court.

Eventually, one of them went into the kitchen and asked the rest of the family to come back into the lounge. I was sat there in tears. They explained that I'd given a statement. Mum and Dad looked like they'd just been told someone had died. We were frozen: nobody speaking, nobody touching. Those were awful moments even though, deep down, my parents must have been half-expecting what had happened. They knew about Lynda and Bennell and, if there was no story to be told, why had the police kept coming back to see me?

I think about it now: how lonely my parents must have felt. I know they were heartbroken. How do you carry on, how do you recover after you hear that news? My parents had always been so loving and protective towards my sisters and me. As far as they knew, it was just us. We were on our own. The only ones to have fallen victim to Bennell. They didn't have any idea how many other families were out there, being put through this same ordeal. I respect and admire Mum and Dad so much for carrying on, trying to deal with what they'd learned and looking after their family at the same time.

I told Rachel, too, afterwards. I spared her some of the details but I explained the police had been, that I'd given a statement. I explained what that statement had been about. For me, telling Rachel felt a bit like a release. A chance to be honest. I think in many ways the conversation was more difficult for her. You have to remember that, twenty years ago, the subject of abuse was much more hidden away. We hadn't had scandals like Jimmy Savile to bring things out into the public arena. It was difficult for Rachel to get her head round what had happened, both to me and to my family.

Maybe it was also difficult for her to reconcile the confident and successful young footballer she'd first met with the young lad who'd been put through the stuff I was telling her about now. Understandably, she'd always been unsettled by me disappearing off into moods; always wanted to know why I wasn't playing for the first team at Bury. Now she knew but it didn't make any of it easier to deal with. And even though I'd told her what I'd told the police, I hadn't fully opened up. I still had memories and emotions locked up inside me. Rachel must have felt like she was on the outside, looking in.

Telling her about what had happened with Bennell might have unlocked a door, but I still held back from being honest with Rachel about my feelings; I never had the kind of heart-to-heart with her that might have given us the chance to really understand one another.

It was a strange time. All that pressure from the police, all the visits and the questions. Then, finally, I tell them what had happened and it was: *Great. Thanks very much. We'll be in touch.* Except they never got in touch. They left me to get on with it. You know, back then, the police weren't in the business of offering support, putting anyone in touch with counsellors or anything like that. And that wasn't the kind of thing blokes were supposed to want anyway. I'd let this secret out and now I had to protect myself again, and in the only way I knew how.

Talking about Bennell to someone did have its positive effects. I felt as if I'd shifted a load off my shoulders, for a time. I'm not sure I was aware of just how connected my football was to how I was feeling about the rest of my life. Certainly, the worst of times off the pitch usually coincided with me struggling on it. At Bury, that had got to a point where I found myself exiled to the youth team for training sessions. After I gave the statement to the police, though, the lights came on again. And Stan Ternent, the manager, noticed.

Lots of professional footballers go through a whole career without ever getting their hands on a trophy. I had some great days at Bury and the picture at the start of this chapter is from one of them. I got back into the team in the spring of 1997. We'd gone up the previous season and now we were chasing promotion from Division Two to Division One, what they now call the Championship.

I played a dozen games on the spin, including a win against Crewe, but then got injured so, by the time we played Watford, second-last game of the season, I wasn't available. I still travelled, though: we won promotion after Dean Kiely saved a penalty and we drew 0–0. I'm in the tracksuit, right bang in the middle of the photo, beside myself with it all, like the rest of the lads. That was a good coach ride home.

The week after, we played Millwall at ours. Gigg Lane was rammed, everybody having a party even before we kicked off. Bury won 2–0 and that meant we won the league. I still wasn't fit so I watched from the stand but I got down on the pitch afterwards, picked up my medal and got my chance to show off the trophy to the crowd. It was brilliant but

I was in a bit of a daze. So much had happened so quickly and then, when I probably wasn't really expecting it, I was joining in the celebrations on one of the football club's greatest-ever days.

I've looked at grainy old video from that afternoon. I look almost as if I'm a kid who's won a raffle, like I can't quite believe it's me out there. There were a lot of old pros in that Bury team. I look like a little boy compared to most of them. It was a moment, all right: I suppose this was where I'd dreamed about being. Why couldn't it always be like this? Why couldn't it last?

28.

S tan Ternent was the kind of manager people refer to as 'old-school'. A 'man's man'. Actually, Stan was a lot more than that. He was devoted to his family; his wife and sons used to come to every game. His whole career, player and manager, was in the lower divisions, so he learned to battle and to work hard and to get on with it. Stan wanted that from his players as well. And he wasn't a bloke to cross: Stan's temper was famous. He probably still loses his rag now on a regular basis even though he's retired.

So, Stan was tough as old boots, probably not who you'd pick to be the first person in football you ever told about being sexually abused as a young player. I had to do it, though. I'd spoken to the police. I knew there'd be a court case when Bennell came back to the UK and that I'd have to be involved. I couldn't let the club find out about it just anyhow. It couldn't seem as if I'd been hiding something from them. I felt it was my responsibility to go and see Stan.

The manager's office at Gigg Lane is under the main stand, next door to the home dressing room. It was a little like having to go and see the headmaster. I knocked and asked if I could have a word. Stan got me in and I told him what had happened while I was a young lad at Crewe: not all the details but enough that he understood why I'd had to talk to the police. Enough, as well, for him to understand why I'd been so up and down since joining the club.

No surprise: Stan blew his top. Not with me. He was raging about a coach doing this to a kid and about how he could have got away with it for so long. He told me how much he respected me for coming and talking to him. *If you ever want to talk, Andy, the door's always open.* We agreed he'd tell the physio and talk to his assistant, Sam Ellis, who were the two other people who would most need to know.

Stan and I didn't have another conversation about it as far as I can remember. He didn't make any fuss. But he supported me in the best way possible. There are people in football, I'm sure, who would have listened to me, said all the right things and then got me out of the club as quick as they could. It's a pretty common and, I suppose, under-standable attitude if your job's hanging on winning games: a player with a problem is a player who's hard work, and you can do without that if you're battling to stay in the league.

Stan was the complete opposite: he didn't go easy but he took on board what I'd said and gave me the respect of dealing with me like he would any other player. For me, the fact that the manager knew what had happened to me made a huge difference for a while. Without him saying or doing anything, I had the reassurance of knowing that I had Stan on my side.

For over ten years, I'd kept this secret in football, afraid I'd be judged, ridiculed or worse. Now, for the first time, I had people around me who at least had an idea of what I'd been through. Stan and the staff couldn't have known what was going on inside my head every day, couldn't have known how I was struggling from week to week. But at least I felt I wasn't completely alone with it all.

The year after we won Division Two we managed to stay in the First Division. Great for a little club and great for me, too. If I was fit, I played. The First Division was tough and, around Christmas, it looked as if we'd get relegated. But we went on this amazing run and stayed up in the end. That run included winning 1–0 at Manchester City. After the game we got kept in the dressing room because the City supporters were rioting outside Maine Road. That was in February 1998. Things have changed a bit there since.

When I think about how long it was that I was abused, how intense that experience was, I'm proud I played as much football as I did. In a way, it pushed me on. When I was doing well as a player, I knew that part of it was fighting Bennell in my own mind. I was proving I could be a footballer in spite of everything he'd done to me. *You're not going to beat me, you bastard.* It wasn't great that he was in my head all the time but sometimes I was able to use that hatred to drive myself on. He'd stolen so much over so many years but I still had some fight left in me.

For the best part of eighteen months, I enjoyed playing football again. The club I was playing for definitely made a difference. Bury was a place with a real sense of community, a family club. I felt supported even though most people didn't have the faintest idea why that was so important to me. Bury in the late nineties was a great place to be. I felt part of something really good.

In the summer of 1998, Stan Ternent left to go to Burnley and Neil Warnock took over. Another manager with a reputation for being tough and aggressive. I've got to say right now, Neil was absolutely fantastic with me. I got on really well with him and his wife, Sharon. She was always really nice to me. When I asked Neil if he'd told her about what had happened to me, he said: *No. It's just you're her favourite, son.* I told him what I'd told Stan and he backed me up in exactly the same way. I know how upset he was by it, how angry and frustrated. *This is so wrong, Andy. So wrong on every level.* Neil asked me if there were other players involved. I told him that everything with the police was supposed to be anonymous so I didn't know for sure.

Neil pushed me on as a player. That first year with him as manager, even though we ended up getting relegated, I played more games than I had in any previous season. It was probably the best I played in my whole career. I know the manager rated me. One look at Neil Warnock's record will tell you what a good manager he's been. Twenty years on from his first season with Bury, he was still at it, managing Cardiff City in the Premier League.

Out on the pitch, focused on football, things were going as well as they'd ever done for me. That picture at the start of the chapter was taken at Griffin Park, I think. I'd just set Nicky Daws up for a goal, away to Brentford. I look at photos like that and remember how I could still get lost in the moment, swept along in the excitement of winning a game. Now, though, I realise there was a big disconnect between the surface of things – the ninety minutes of a football match – and what was happening inside me the rest of the time. The past wouldn't leave me alone. Perhaps the reason I paid it no heed at first was that my anxiety actually crept up on my body before it crept into my mind.

First, I started to get these weird tingling feelings, like pins and needles, up and down my arms. Then, bits of my life went missing. Everybody knows the feeling: time passing and you're not sure what's happened. You're driving and suddenly you realise you can't remember how you got from A to B. That was happening to me a lot. It was almost like waking up out of a dream: *Where have I been? What have I been doing?* It can happen when you're tired, when you're stressed. What I was experiencing, though, was something deeper-rooted. I know now that there's a name for it in psychology: dissociation. It's when a person disengages from their feelings, a defence mechanism. I didn't realise it then, but I was on the start of a downward spiral.

We were halfway through the 98/99 season. I didn't say anything to anybody. Neil was so positive about me as a player, I just channelled everything into training and games. I assumed these weird feelings would pass. The trouble was that, even though I had spoken to people, I hadn't really dealt with anything. Bennell was still there in my head, still had this psychological hold over me, and I couldn't do the work I needed to do to loosen his grip. Instead I suppose I simply tried to ignore it. We all did: after I told the police what had happened that first time, the whole family closed ranks on the subject. We never had a proper conversation about it between ourselves. It wasn't just me.

Lynda and my parents had their own reasons for not being able to process what had happened.

Our whole family was bound up with Bennell. I think about it now, where me talking to the police left us all: we were a decent, hard-working family who'd always tried to do things the right way. What were we supposed to do? What could we have done? It was in all of our natures to just try to get on with life. We shut it down, which meant burying all the hurt, the confusion and the rage. But burying something wasn't going to make it go away.

29.

I gave my statement to the police sometime in early 1997. They told us at the time that Bennell was going to be released and deported from the US and that they would be arresting him as soon as he got back to the UK. That was all. For a long time I heard nothing more. Then in September 1997 Bennell was arrested at Manchester Airport. He was in custody for the best part of a year until his case came to court.

In all that time, the police never came back to me for more information or to let me know what was happening. The first I heard was a letter saying I had to be ready to attend court for the first day of the trial. That I had to be ready to be cross-examined as a witness. This was early autumn in 1998. Right around the same time I started getting those strange pins and needles in my arms, those feelings of suddenly becoming aware of time having passed without me being conscious of it.

The prospect of going to court and coming face to face with Bennell after all this time was pretty horrifying. In hindsight, I shouldn't have been surprised that I had these weird physical symptoms. But the football was going so well and I was so focused on Bury that I didn't make the connection. I had to tell Neil Warnock about the court appearance, of course, because I thought I'd be missing training because of it. *Whatever you need, son. Just let me know.* I can remember the days beforehand, feeling the tension winding up in me. It had been hard enough saying what I'd said about Bennell to those two detectives in my parents' front room. The idea of having to stand up in court and say it all again was very scary indeed.

Before the trial, I'd had an idea he might plead guilty and there wouldn't be any need to hear from witnesses. From Bennell's point of view, pleading guilty would mean he spent less time in jail. I knew there were others besides me and that he'd already been convicted in the US. How could he deny anything? But the nearer it got to the trial date, the more it seemed as if he was going to go ahead and plead not guilty and that I would have to take the stand. Dread seeped into my bones.

Then, on the actual morning of the trial, a message came through: *You don't have to attend court, after all. Bennell's pleaded guilty to all charges.* There was no need for any witnesses to appear. He'd just be sentenced now. And that was it. He got sent down for nine years.

When Bennell was locked up the first time, in Florida, I'd tried to tell myself: *That's that. It's done.* I tried to distance myself from everything about him, the present as well as the past. I'd had no further contact with him while he was in prison. I don't know about Lynda or my mum and dad, whether they wrote or spoke to him. My parents still came to my games but cutting myself off from Bennell meant distancing myself from my own family, too. And the whole business with the trial left me cold.

I felt alone with it all: I still didn't know who else had spoken to the police or what they'd told them. Nothing was shared with me. Everything, they said, was to be kept completely anonymous. They couldn't even tell me who else had given evidence, which charges Bennell had faced. Whether what he'd done to me was why – or, at least, part of why – he'd been sent down.

After Bennell was convicted there was one more awful twist, though. My parents – the whole family – had always kept my Auntie Lynda's murder as a sort of secret. When we were kids, they'd never talked to us about what had happened even though I can remember going to visit Lynda's grave as a boy.

Mum eventually sat us down and told us what had happened to her older sister. But we didn't talk about it to anyone, not even to each other; so it just brought us kids into the circle of secrecy. It was only after Bennell's case finished that the whole truth of the thing came out. I can't be sure but I think it was the police who actually contacted my parents and put the pieces of the picture together.

Lynda's murderer had been sentenced to life back in the early 1970s, but he'd been released after serving twelve years. Unbeknownst to my parents, he'd moved to a house just a couple of miles away from us in Cheadle, had got married and worked as a painter and decorator.

But five years later, in 1989, he committed another murder, a local mum walking through the park under the Seven Arches viaduct nearby. He raped her as well, just like he had Lynda. He was arrested and, a few weeks later, he hanged himself while he was on remand at Strangeways.

The murderer's name was Ronald Bennell. Mum and Dad would have known the name after his conviction in 1971. And they must have seen the name in the local paper again in 1989. But they never made the connection between these two men with the same surname. I'm not surprised by that: they'd always avoided thinking or talking about my Auntie Lynda's murder. It was something awful to be buried, kept out of sight. Mum used to break down sometimes when we were kids: shaking and crying, Dad holding her tight. But it was only later I found out those tears were for her sister.

It's a coincidence that's almost beyond belief: that there should have been a link between Ronald and Barry. But now, all these years later, here were the police telling us that Ronald Bennell and Barry Bennell – one dead now and one behind bars – had been cousins.

I know how hard that was for my parents: finding out a truth that had been hidden – but hidden in plain sight – for over ten years. They were shattered by it. With Bennell in jail, Lynda had moved home. But even then this strange and awful connection was never discussed openly. They just pulled together, coping in the only way they knew how.

I never pressed them about the link between these two men. How they could have missed it. And I never told them, either, what I realised when I heard about these monsters being cousins and first saw a photo of Ronald Bennell. Because I knew his face straight away. The memory came back to me in the way a dream comes back to you: mysterious but crystal-clear.

I'd have been eleven or twelve at the time: Ronald Bennell would still have been in jail after he'd been convicted of my Auntie Lynda's murder. One evening, Bennell and I drove into Manchester. A housing estate over past the Trafford Centre, as I remember. He did it all the time: we'd get in the car and just drive. We'd stop somewhere and he'd visit people. He'd never explain who they were or why we'd gone to see them.

I've tried to work out the details since but I've never found the block we parked outside. It was an older couple we called in on. Were they Bennell's uncle and auntie? Ronald's mum and dad? I'm sure that they were relatives. At any event, we went up in the lift and I traipsed into this flat with him. I remember it was high up in the block, neat and tidy inside. I sat on the sofa while they chatted, ignoring me.

Hanging on the wall was a photo of a youngish man with dark hair. The lady we were visiting kept referring to him as Ronnie. I didn't know who Ronnie was or where he was. And it wasn't my place to ask. We left the flat.

We never went back there and I didn't give the evening a second thought until an afternoon nearly twenty years later. Like a sudden flash lighting up a dark corner, I made the connection. The face hung on that council flat wall was the same person as the one in the photo I was looking at now: Ronald Bennell.

Why did Bennell take me to that flat? I'm sure he knew what Ronald had done. He knew all about our family by then. I'd bet he put the pieces together before we did because I knew next to nothing about the Bennells. I never met any other members of his family. He told me once his dad used to abuse him, to beat him up. He told me he'd always hated him. He had a brother as well but I never met him either: him and Barry didn't get on. How well Bennell knew his cousin, Ronnie, he never said and I'll never know.

A fate, a destiny? What Bennell did to me; what he did to my sister; what his cousin did to my aunt. What all of it must have felt like – the horror – to my poor mum and dad. It sounds melodramatic to say it, but it's the cold truth. His family cursed my family. Our lives have been twisted, broken, haunted by the Bennells. And it's only our strength – and maybe our love for each other – that made it possible for us to live out those lives in spite of the pair of them, psychopaths both.

~

Because Bennell pleaded guilty, I never had my chance to face him in court and tell the truth about what he'd done to me. There was never a feeling of *That's it. I've stood up to him. And now he's inside because of it.* He was in jail, out of my life in a physical sense, but I wasn't sure where that left me. I knew that other people must have gone through what I'd been through, or something like it. Not only the abuse but the whole business with the police: the pressure, the admission, the giving a statement and then the wait for the trial. I felt this sort of bond with these other people. Only I didn't know who they were or where they were.

I remember hoping that one of the victims who'd spoken up would be Paul. I hoped Bennell had been found guilty because of me. I hoped the same for Paul because we'd been there together, right at the start, both of us just ten-year-old boys with our lives about to be ruined for ever. I didn't contact Paul at the time. And for years I never knew. He and I only connected on Facebook a while ago. *How are you? What are you up to?* But we never mentioned the trial, never mentioned Bennell.

It's dark, but it's a bond that will tie the two of us together for ever, isn't it? It's only recently I found out that Paul was in fact one of the lads who, like me, spoke to the police back in 1997. He was re-interviewed and gave further evidence before Bennell's most recent trial in 2018, something I chose not to do. By that time, I'd said my piece. I felt I was done with it and it was time others took their turn.

While the football was progressing at Bury and the Bennell case was finding its way into court, I became a father and a husband for the second time. I'm fond of that photo of the wedding. I look at images from my first marriage and I see a boy completely out of his depth. By the time Rachel and I got married, I'd been playing for Bury for four years and hadn't seen Bennell in five. As I'm sure Rachel could tell you, at twenty-five I still hadn't even begun to deal with the issues I'd been left with. But the photo from my wedding day at least makes me think the process of growing up had begun.

Troubled as I was, I'm looking like a young man, I think, rather than a frightened boy. Our first son, Joseph, had been born in October 1997. The wedding was the following summer in Urmston. I remember being really nervous on the day. My best man, Richard, even asked me: *Are you sure you want to go through with this?* The three of us – me, Rachel and Joe – went away on our honeymoon together afterwards. Just a little while before the Bennell case came to court.

Rachel and I were married for ten years. There were some ups and a lot of downs, to be honest. There were times I ran away from it all: I remember going to stay with my best man, Richard, and his partner, Zelda, at one point and them having to look after me, almost as if I was ill. Rachel and I were very different people and, at the time, I think I saw myself as some kind of victim in the marriage.

Rachel would get frustrated and angry with me. I'd be thinking: *Why are you being horrible to me? Why aren't you looking after me?* It's only with the benefit of hindsight that I've come to realise how difficult I must have been to live with, how demanding and self-centred I must have seemed. Back then, though, when our marriage wasn't working, I'd always blame Rachel. *Why can't you just be nice to me?*

I've got a much better idea now where the responsibility for our problems lay. A lot of it was with me, and the trauma that I carried around from day to day; the moods and the infidelities, which followed on from not handling the challenges I saw in front of me. One weekend I'd be out half the night, drinking, messing around with other girls. The next, I'd be sat at home, crying on my own in the dark in the front room. I was a mess most of the time. And so was our marriage because of it.

Rachel and I bought a house over in Bramhall a little while after we married. Wouldn't it have been great if that had meant me, her and Joseph making a fresh start together? Football going well for Dad, Mum enjoying bringing up the baby she'd wanted so much?

I had had a good season and a half with Bury, even though we were relegated in 98/99. I was playing and I knew Neil Warnock rated me. There was talk at the start of the following season about the manager moving on and he'd said to me that, if he did, the two players he'd want to take with him were me and the goalkeeper, Paddy Kenny.

I'd still been getting those weird tingling feelings in my hands and arms, though. And towards the end of 1999, those blew up into something much worse. Rachel had asked me to go up the road to Tesco for something and, while I was waiting at the till to pay, I had what I now know was my first full-blown panic attack. It's a horrible thing. All of a sudden I couldn't catch my breath. I was sweating, and my heart started racing, beating so hard it felt like it was going to burst out of my chest. I didn't know what was happening. Was I having a heart attack? I thought: *I'm going to die here.* I was sure of it. I dropped the shopping, jumped in the car and drove home as fast as I could. I stumbled in through the front door. *Rachel. Rachel. Call an ambulance.*

I was laid out on the sofa, my heart still pounding, trying to breathe, when the paramedics arrived. They bundled me into the ambulance and took me straight to A & E. They did all sorts of tests, checking my heart. At the end of it, they said: *It's okay. You've just had a panic attack. You can go home.*

~

Doctors know more about panic attacks now, twenty years on, what causes them and how to deal with them. Back then, it was just a case of them being happy I hadn't had a heart attack. *Just a panic attack. Nothing to worry about.* They just packed me off home to Bramhall. They didn't explain anything or give me any advice.

I'd been convinced I was going to die. *What do you mean, it's nothing to worry about?* I was trying to work out how this could have happened. I was young, fit. I was a professional footballer. I was sure there must be something physically wrong with me. I didn't make the connection with those milder symptoms, the pins and needles.

It never occurred to me that the attack might have had something to do with my mental state, the pressure I'd been under for so long, the fears and anxieties that were part of everyday life for me after Bennell. I just got home and went to bed, hoping desperately it wouldn't ever happen again. Anyone who's ever had a panic attack will tell you what a terrifying experience it can be.

I didn't tell anyone at the club about the attack. But it began happening on a regular basis, sometimes day after day: in training, at home, in the car. It would start with the tingling in my arms and then a fear would rush over me. *Something bad's going to happen.* There's a physical response to that fear. Your body trying to defend itself: blood rushes to your heart. And it pounds and pounds. I didn't know how to stop it. I didn't know when it would stop. The only thing I could imagine was that my heart was about to burst: *I'll be dead.*

It even started happening to me during games: Preston at home was the first. I had the tingling in my arms, the feeling of being disconnected from what was around me, the shortness of breath. I just fought it, focused on the football – or tried to – and eventually got through it. It was scary, though. I couldn't work out why this was happening to me, fit as a fiddle and playing well. It was only going to get worse.

The following Saturday, we were away to Gillingham. A routine game in the old Second Division. What had happened the previous weekend was in the back of my mind but, warming up and then kicking off, I felt okay. It hit me twenty-five minutes in. No warning, no tingling. Just a full-on attack flooding through me: I couldn't breathe; I could hear the blood pumping in my ears; felt like I was going to throw up. I went down on one knee, staring at the ground. This wasn't supposed to be happening to a footballer. I couldn't say, could I? I rolled over onto my side.

When the physio got to me, I told him my hamstring had gone. I left the pitch and got into the dressing room. I sat there on my own for what seemed like ages, trying to get my breath back. I didn't want to say anything to anyone. *A panic attack? What's a panic attack? Get a grip on yourself.* That's how it was back then. In football, the last thing you wanted to show was any kind of weakness. But, thinking about it on the coach ride home, I knew I had to do something. I couldn't carry on like this.

One afternoon after training the following week, I sat down with the physio and told him what had really gone on at the game. He knew a little about my past, about the abuse, and so there was already some trust there between us. He fetched the doctor and I explained what the attacks were like. That sometimes they passed in a minute or two, other times they seemed to go on for ever, lasting ten or fifteen minutes. I told them I was getting them almost daily. They could see I'd lost weight because I was having trouble keeping food down.

Panic attacks weren't what any of us would have described as a common football injury and neither the doc nor the physio were sure what to do. Back then, those guys would just fix players' bodies. They wouldn't expect to have to fix players' heads. But I was grateful that they realised they had to do something. The doc referred me to a psychiatrist and the PFA arranged for me to go the Priory in Hale. The psychiatrist diagnosed me as having panic disorder, a continual cycle of attacks, and gave me some medication that he said would deal with the symptoms.

The Priory was a big old house out in the suburbs, at the end of a long drive, and had a whole wing for residential treatment across all mental health issues: addiction, anxiety, whatever the problem was. I was certain I didn't want to be admitted, though. I wanted to fight this thing. *Just give me some medicine and I'll deal with it.*

The week before that Gillingham game, Neil Warnock had left Bury to join Sheffield United. They were in the First Division – the Championship – and they were the club he'd always supported. Andy Preece replaced him. The following week, Neil signed Paddy Kenny and asked about signing me. It must have been difficult for Andy but he was very understanding. We'd been teammates and now suddenly he was the boss. I was having my troubles and, of course, I wanted to join Neil at Bramall Lane.

Bury told Sheffield United that I was having problems. Neil came back saying that, as soon as I was back on the pitch, he wanted to sign me. In the back of my mind, I wasn't sure about the medication I was supposed to be taking. I was worried one of the side effects was that I could put on weight. But I kept training at Bury and kept going to the Priory as an outpatient for what they call CBT: cognitive behavioural therapy.

The psychiatrist who diagnosed me told me to remember that panic attacks weren't nice but that they would never kill me. Every time I'd had one previously, I'd been convinced I was going to die. Now he was telling me the opposite and that took some of the power away from them. The idea of the CBT sessions was they taught me techniques to recognise and combat the panic disorder I'd been diagnosed with, the shallow breathing and the racing heart. I learned ways to stop the symptoms before a full-blown attack took hold. Mental things like imagining a red Stop sign if I started to feel something bad was about to happen. Cupping and breathing steadily into my hands if my breath came short.

I became a little obsessed with it all, to be honest. I read everything I could find about panic disorder and ways of treating it. I wanted to understand exactly how and why the attacks happened. If I understood them, I thought I could control them. The CBT worked. For a while, anyway. I played my last game for Bury on Boxing Day 1999 and, by March 2000, I was back on the pitch, a Sheffield United player.

30.

D ad always seemed to have a camera ready. If I remember rightly, he took this photo while we were celebrating Christmas 1999, probably after I'd played for Bury against Burnley on Boxing Day. You can see there's real happiness in the room: Mum, Rachel, Joseph and me all round the dining room table at my parents' house. All the while things were going crazy in my life – the ups and downs with Rachel, my panic attacks, fretting over whether or not I'd be following Neil Warnock to Sheffield United – there'd still be moments of calm and content.

Those moments, when I think back to them, always make me wonder about what my life might have been if Bennell had never come into it. How different I might have been as a son, as a husband and as a father. As a footballer, too. It's bittersweet, looking at a picture like that one. I didn't deserve what Bennell did to me. Nobody deserves that. The people who were at Mum and Dad's house the afternoon that picture was taken didn't deserve it either.

I started taking the anti-anxiety medication in the New Year. It took about a month for it to get into my system and start working. I did a lot of work one-on-one with the Bury physio. It was almost like putting myself through private pre-season training. I needed to keep the weight off and I needed to get back to fitness, too. I missed a lot of football in January of that year. By early March, though, I was feeling pretty good. Not match-fit but getting there.

Neil Warnock asked about me playing in a game and they put one on, behind closed doors. I got through the ninety minutes and the Bury chairman and Neil talked. *He's ready. I want him at Bramall Lane.* Neil was as good as his word: he'd said he wanted me; he'd waited and, now, he'd come back for me. I couldn't have asked for anything more from a manager. He knew about my past and he knew about my struggles since, but he'd seen what I could do for him as a player. Neil believed in me.

Sheffield United were in the First Division. Neil had managed me when Bury were in that league before we got relegated and he'd watched me perform against top players like Dean Saunders, Niall Quinn and Paul Gascoigne. I still remember one goal-saving tackle on Gazza in a game against Boro, when he was running through on our keeper. Even the man himself applauded it! I've still got the ball he signed for me afterwards.

Neil knew I was good enough to play at that level. It was exciting, of course. I can remember Dad driving me across to Sheffield to sign a contract. He was looking forward to it even more than I was. He knew it was a great move, a move to a bigger club. But I think, deep down, he was just excited about me playing football again. He'd looked on while I was struggling and thought I'd never get back on the pitch again.

I joined Sheffield United on a three-and-a-half-year deal. Remembering that drive across the Pennines with Dad, I know it felt at the time almost like this might become my happy ending. But it wasn't going to be as easy or as simple as that. Almost as soon as I started training at United, I became aware that I wasn't right. My body wasn't right. Physically, pretty much from day one, I felt out of my depth.

It wasn't about ability. I could keep up with all the technical drills. I was as good as or better than the lads around me. Despite all the work I'd done with the physio at Bury, though, I'd started to put weight on. I'd always been the fittest in the group, all the way through from junior football, but I could tell I was short of that here.

I got on once, as a sub, soon after I joined but I felt sluggish in training, however hard I worked. Not just physically: mentally too. My mind wasn't sharp. I'm pretty sure, like the weight gain, it was a side effect of the medication. I wasn't living up to anybody's expectations and the rest of the season, if I was in the squad at all, I was only on the bench.

The plan was always that we'd move over to Sheffield. Neil had said we'd need to be closer to the club. For the first couple of months, though, Rachel and Joe stayed at our house in Bramhall and the club put me up in a local hotel. They'd come and visit but I had quite a lot of time on my own, too.

I was living at the Swallow Hotel. Nice room and everything, but any footballer who's done it will tell you it's quite a lonely experience when you're trying to settle at a new club. It wasn't a good situation for Rachel, either, having to cope with Joe on her own back in Bramhall. The three of us moved in the summer. I bought a house, a new-build, just outside Sheffield.

That should have been the start of something. Instead, it turned out to be the beginning of the end as far as football was concerned. In hindsight, I just didn't cope with the pressure. I was fighting to keep the panic attacks under control. I was still taking the medication but I stopped the CBT sessions once I moved to Sheffield. Things just piled up. I was suppressing anxiety and not dealing with what was causing it in the first place.

I'd had dark feelings in the past, about how pointless my life seemed, how much easier it would be if I could just make it stop. Those suicidal thoughts drifted back into my head now. I mean, every panic attack had me feeling like I was going to die anyway. *Am I going to have to fight this for the rest of my life?*

I needed to start talking to someone. That was what I was told, anyway, and the PFA put me in touch with a therapist in Stockport.

I know now that therapy isn't just about plunging straight in and dragging up stuff that's been buried. It takes time and patience. And trust. But this therapist immediately took aim with question after question, wanting to know every detail of what Bennell had done to me. Before the first session ended, I was a mess. In tears, overwhelmed, desperate.

I came out and looked across the road. There's a bridge that runs across that part of Stockport, over a little shallow stream. I went and stood on the bridge: the nearest I'd come to really being ready to end all this. *I just can't fucking have it any more.* I stood there, my legs shaking. I felt empty and there was this dizziness, like vertigo, taking over my body. I could feel myself going.

A couple of cars went by and beeped their horns at me. One pulled up at the far end, probably thinking to come back to me, to see what I was doing. But in that moment an image of Joe came into my head. My boy. *I mustn't let him down.* And I stepped back, back onto the bridge. Onto the road and back towards my car.

Compared to Bury, Sheffield United is a big club with big expectations. I was heading into my late twenties, on a good contract and with a team full of good players where I could have really made my name. It should have been perfect. I should have been all set up. But it just wasn't working. There was just too much else going on in my head.

It still breaks my heart thinking about it: what might have been. It still hurts me, too, the feeling that I let Neil Warnock down. I know – and he knows – it wasn't for lack of trying. I just couldn't get past the way I was feeling, body and mind. It was as if everything was fuzzy when it needed to be sharp. When I needed to find something extra, I was just empty inside. And Neil couldn't hang on any longer for me.

At the start of the following season, I found myself on the bench, playing for the reserves in midweek. I played one more first team game: we lost 1–0 to Lincoln in the League Cup. Next thing I knew, the manager had decided the best thing for me would be to go out on loan. That was September 2000. I never played for Sheffield United again.

31.

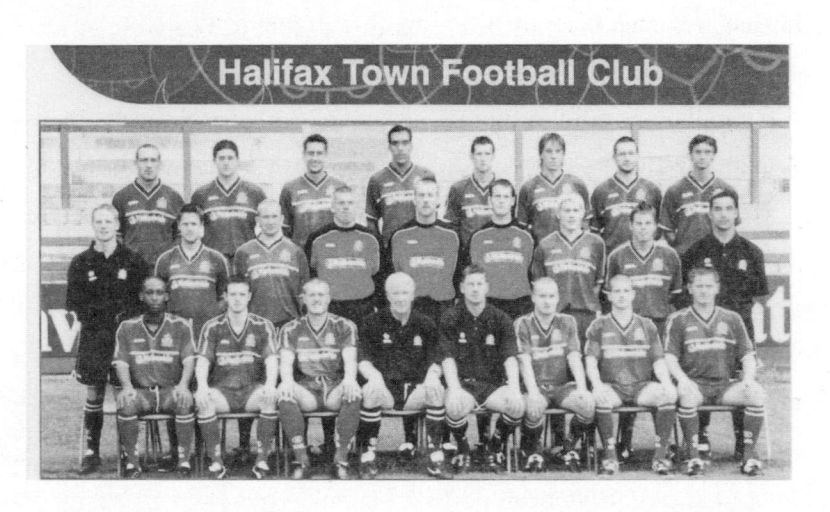

Halifax Town Football Club

That year, 2000, Tony Adams set up his Sporting Chance charity. It's an amazing organisation and the key to it is that it provides counselling and therapy while still respecting its clients as professional athletes. That's what makes it different. People are referred and have whatever treatment they have, but the point is they're able to go back to their clubs ready to join in training, ready to start playing again.

The treatment I had, though, didn't work like that. The medication I was on actually made it more difficult for me to function physically and mentally as a professional footballer. I was following a programme that was the same as would be set out for any other person in my situation dealing with trauma and panic attacks. At the time, nobody considered what I actually needed to get back to football and to take the opportunity I had at Sheffield United.

I wouldn't blame anyone for it. I didn't join the dots either. Sporting Chance was the first organisation to think about footballers and athletes in that way and, back then, I didn't even know it existed. Instead, my treatment actually worked against what I needed to do. I felt like I was sinking, like the point of my life – being a professional footballer – was slipping away.

Neil Warnock knew I was struggling and in the middle of September he got me into the office. *We need to get you some games, son. Get you properly fit.* Scunthorpe United, just up the road from Sheffield, were in Division Three – what's now League Two – and Brian Laws, the manager, had asked about taking me on loan. It was a step down but it would mean getting games and maybe, Neil thought, getting my head straight. *Just a month, son.* He thought it was what I needed and he was probably right.

I remember driving up to Scunthorpe for the first time. I was turning things over in my mind. I'd signed for a big club and now here I was, heading off to Division Three on loan. It felt like my career was going downhill. Downhill to nowhere.

As soon as I got to Scunthorpe, though, I was made to feel welcome. Brian Laws and his assistant, Russ Wilcox, were genuine people and pleased to have me there. I was wanted. Maybe this would be a fresh start after all, a release from the pressure that had been building up at United. Brian put me straight into the team, away to Southend, and I ended up playing twice a week all through October.

I seemed to get named man of the match pretty much every home game. Playing regularly was great but it didn't do me much good when it came to my Sheffield United career. Out of sight, out of mind: by the time I got back to Sheffield United in early 2001, Neil had decided I wasn't going to be part of his plans going forward. They'd sort something out with the rest of my contract and I was free to look for a new club.

By the end of the season, I had Brian Laws wanting me back to sign full-time for Scunthorpe. Then the manager of Halifax, Paul Bracewell, asked to meet me. Like Scunthorpe, Halifax were in Division Three. But Paul had big plans for the club and wanted me to come in as one of his senior players. He had a real reputation and he did a good job of selling me his ideas.

Although they were a couple of divisions down from Sheffield United, Halifax said they'd pay me something close to what I'd been earning at Bramall Lane. They offered me a three-year deal. And I signed. Rachel wanted to move back to near where her parents lived in Chorley, so we sold up in Sheffield and started looking for a house back over there.

It meant a longer drive for me but Halifax sorted out an apartment to use on the edge of town. At the start of the new season, it seemed like things were maybe getting straightened out. I'd be beginning all over again. Every club, every July, has the obligatory team photo taken. Puff your chest out, put on a big smile for the fans. Halifax was no different. The future looked bright that summer. The club and the town were excited. I was excited. Nobody could have guessed what was coming next.

Five games into the new season, 2001/2002, Paul Bracewell resigned as Halifax manager. We hadn't made a good start but he wasn't sacked. He just upped and offed. In hindsight, maybe I should have realised things weren't right. Pre-season felt a little bit amateurish. The squad was pretty small and pretty fragile, with a lot of very young players. Neil Redfearn, one of the players, took over as caretaker with Tony Parks helping him out. Then Alan Little was appointed manager in the middle of October and it all went downhill from there.

Alan did his best but it emerged that the club was in a mess financially. That put me under pressure because I'd been a big signing and I was the highest earner at Halifax. We were out training every day on this massive old council pitch, and you could just see heads going down everywhere. And it wasn't as if I was having a blinder every week. I was still feeling the effects of the medication, the lack of focus, being short on the fitness side. We didn't just lose games; we'd lose a whole run of them.

Every day seemed like a battle. That wasn't the club's fault, of course. I was having the panic attacks starting up again. Rachel and I had moved into a new house over in Chorley and then, in the spring, she found out she was pregnant. We went for the scan and they told us we were going to have twins.

I just wasn't sure if I had the fight left in me for all this. It was plain where all this was ending up: Halifax were going to be relegated. What should I be doing? *Try to find another club and get out? Or sit tight on my three-year contract and hope things would improve?* Sure enough, we lost 5–0 at Darlington in my last-but-one game for them and Halifax went out of the Football League.

What I hadn't realised was that every player's contract at Halifax included a clause about what would happen if the club went down into the Conference: a clause that gave them the right just to rip the contract up without paying any compensation whatsoever. After it happened to us, the Football League stepped in, I think, and those clauses became illegal from then on. But that didn't help me or the other lads Halifax wanted to get shot of as soon as we were relegated. A few of the players were re-signed on much less money. Most of us were just shown the door.

I'd lost my job and was wondering what would come next. I'd used the CBT techniques to keep the panic attacks under control but still felt anxious most of the time and exhausted with the effort of it.

The Priory thought I should try some talking therapy to deal with my underlying trauma. The PFA paid for a few appointments with another therapist, who had a very different approach to the first one. She spent time establishing trust between us. She engaged with me, didn't force things.

It was up to me what I wanted to talk about in a session – whether it was something from fifteen years ago or that happened yesterday. She was ready to work from there. I found it hard. Draining. But I told her more about my experiences with Bennell than I'd ever told anyone else, including the police.

Those first sessions of therapy didn't sort everything out, of course not. I didn't suddenly unload all the memories, get rid of my sense of shame or resolve any of the trauma. But they made me realise I was going to need to properly deal with what had happened to me. They were the start of a very long road.

I'd played thirty-odd games for Halifax. What happened at the end of the season was a real blow. I'd spent so long fighting to make a career in football. That had been the drive that had pushed me through the horrible stuff with Bennell. It had kept me going back for more, through relationships that weren't working, through injuries and through being diagnosed with panic disorder. Football, since I was a boy, had been the point of it all. A reason to keep moving forward. But now the game seemed to have kicked me in the teeth.

Rachel, Joe and I were moving house and about to have twins. It felt as if I'd run out of places to turn to. Places to run away to. I started thinking again about where to go next and about whether I actually wanted to stay in the fight. *If this is what life is going to add up to, haven't I had more than enough of it?*

I could feel anger boiling up inside me. Like wanting to be sick but not wanting to show it, swallowing bile down, swallowing poison. This anger I couldn't unload all came back to Bennell. If I didn't have football – if I wasn't a footballer – it seemed to me as if everything in my experience would have begun and ended with him. I'd been doing the fighting – fighting memories, fighting him – all this time but I'd been beaten, hadn't I? Even though Bennell was the one behind bars, it somehow seemed to me, right now, like he'd won.

Part 2

32.

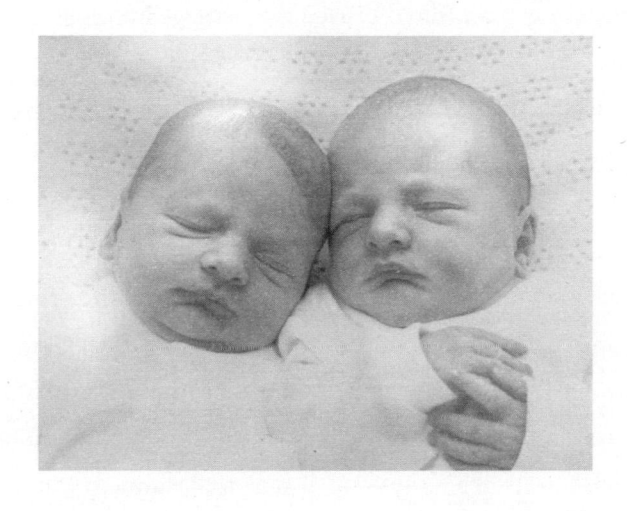

The twins, William and Luke, were due in October 2002. Even though things were so scrambled at the time, the picture makes everything simple. I love those boys: there they are, bundled up and together. It was a bit of a battle for them, a ventouse extraction. They look pretty tired out by it all. Rachel definitely was.

Me? I was worn down by everything. So much of my life has been about where the 'real' world and the world spinning round in my head have knocked against each other but not made any connection. On the outside, I was happy and excited about us having twins. That's what I tried to show Rachel, my parents, our friends. But inside, I couldn't live those emotions; happy and excited wasn't really what I was feeling.

Day to day, minute to minute even, it was just anxiety, fear and anger: the emotions that had me hooked back into the past, back to

Bennell. I know how hard it must have been for Rachel. She knew how much damage had been done to me. She was frustrated by it. She used to rage about the man who'd caused the damage but, sometimes, she'd rage about me, too. She wanted it put behind us: *Why can't you get hold of yourself? Why can't we just get on with our lives?*

Rachel and I had plenty of rows. And, because they were often about Bennell, it meant he became part of her life as well as mine.

She didn't even know the man, had never met him, yet he was having an impact now on her and her family. No wonder the sympathy and care she might have felt towards me would get overwhelmed by how she felt about Bennell. She couldn't shout at him. He wasn't there. So, instead, she'd shout at me. But it was the twisting-up of emotions that probably did more than anything else to undermine our marriage.

Whatever's happened to you, you still have to make your own decisions in life. I can't turn round and explain everything away by me having been a victim. I can't blame every wrong choice I've made on Bennell. But in my relationship with Rachel – in fact, in all my relationships – it's clear to me that a lot of my behaviour stemmed from him and from me not being able to get past the hold he'd had over me. It made me difficult to be with. Even more difficult to be married to.

I didn't connect with Rachel because I was still locked up in my own private, interior world, trying to manage the hurt and the confusion and hate that filled me up every day. Back then, I didn't see the pressure that was on Rachel. Back then, I was the one who was always suffering. It was just: *Poor Andy. What about me?* But I realise now how I made Rachel suffer: me being a victim made her a victim too.

On top of everything, that summer, I was out of a job. What was I going to do? Put feelers out? Try to find another club? I knew I had the ability to play in the Football League. I'm pretty sure Brian Laws would have taken me back at Scunthorpe. But, like I say, I was worn down. I still loved football but I couldn't any longer face the fight. And I knew I had to fight if I was going to play.

Physically, I was wrung out. Mentally, I was waving the white flag. *All right. You've beaten me, you bastard.* I started drinking. While I was playing football, I used to drink but I had discipline over it. I might have a few on a Saturday or Tuesday night but I made sure I never did in the days leading up to games. I was never one of those players – and there were plenty of them – who smelt of ale at the training ground every morning.

Now, though, I didn't have any reason to control it. Drink will only ever make you feel sorry for yourself. That's how it worked on me: I felt I wasn't getting the attention and the sympathy I needed. I met a girl at the gym in Halifax and, although it never became a proper relationship, I was chasing affection and female company, just like I had when I split up with Andrea.

To be truthful, that was something that had gone on all through my marriage to Rachel. I'd go out with teammates and I'd feel the need to be with a woman, to get comfort and reassurance and the boost to my ego. Those times didn't need to involve sex but they were still a betrayal and I felt guilty about them. Guilty and, probably, resentful towards Rachel as well, as if it was her fault I was off looking for the attention I couldn't get at home.

I think I was still tormented about my sexuality as well. When I was a teenager, I'd struggled with it a lot. Everything that had happened with Bennell: maybe I'd brought it on myself in some way. Maybe I'd enjoyed it. They're the feelings – shame, disgust, self-hatred – that haunt every rape victim, I think. Part of being addicted to female attention was a feeling that I had to prove to myself I wasn't gay. That I hadn't wanted to be raped by Bennell. It wasn't homophobia. What I was scared of was the idea that I might have been a willing partner in what he'd done to me.

I craved the reassurance of being attracted to women and of women being attracted to me. I remember being out with Rachel a couple of times and gay men trying to chat me up. I'd overreact – *No, no. That's not me. Please leave me alone!* – and she'd want to know why I got so defensive. It was probably the last thing in the world I could ever really explain.

Now, although I can't justify my behaviour, I can begin to explain and understand it. There was a shadow over everything that went on between Rachel and me: in the worst way possible, Bennell was a part of our marriage. No wonder it got ugly at times.

And, when I was drunk, my mind would turn to suicide, as a way of getting out from under it all. The alcohol would make me feel as if I maybe could do it this time. One evening in June, I went down into the garage, hooked a rubber hose up to the exhaust pipe of my car and fed it in through the driver's window. I sat there and started writing a note. But I couldn't bring myself to turn the key in the ignition. Not being a husband any more, not being a son any more: I could see past those. But I couldn't see past being a dad to Jake and Joe. And, now, the twins.

Once the fight to keep going in football left me, I felt like a failure. It was as if Bennell had taken the game away from me for ever. I started to wonder how Crewe had let it happen. I started to feel anger towards the club as well as towards him. People knew, didn't they? Why had nobody said or done anything? I wanted someone to blame: him, Crewe, even Andrea and Rachel. Even my mum and dad. Everyone had let me down. And now Halifax had turned me over, too.

I decided I was done with football and didn't look for another club over the summer. There was a little money still in the pot, even after the move over to Chorley. I thought about the possibility of going into teaching. Maybe my own experience would mean I had something to offer. Rachel and I talked about it: *You need to get yourself a proper job. Right now.*

I wasn't even thirty. People have an idea that anybody who's been a professional footballer will have earned more than they'll ever be able to spend by the time they pack it in. Let me tell you: playing in the lower leagues, it wasn't like that back then. In fact, it still isn't today. You stop playing and you can't just jog along. You've got to find a new way to pay the bills. You need to find yourself a second career.

I'd reached that moment. I had a family to support. The last thing I could do was spend what was left of our savings. That's why training as a teacher was never really an option. But helping other people in some way was right at the front of my mind. It always has been: I think I got that from Dad, the nicest man I've ever known. So, talking with Rachel, it didn't take long for me to start thinking about the emergency services.

I eventually narrowed things down to the prison service, the fire service and the police. I applied for all three and got interviews for all of them. I decided that working in prison wouldn't have been right for me: I wasn't sure about who, exactly, I'd be helping. But I went on to the next stage, what they call the assessment centre, for both the police and the fire brigade: written tests, group exercises, scenarios.

In the end, it seemed to me that the police was where I'd actually be able to make a difference. It'd be about chasing down the bad guys, protecting the good people. Because of what had happened to me, I think I was very strongly drawn to the idea of locking people up who'd done things that were wrong. I talked to my parents, to friends. People who knew me warned me against it as a career. They thought I was too soft, that I'd be in dangerous situations, seeing things I wouldn't be able to handle. They were probably right: I am soft, after all!

Definitely, being in the police force hardened me up in many ways. But being advised against joining maybe brought out the fight in me. I wanted to prove people wrong.

On the application form for the police, I mentioned that I'd suffered from panic attacks in the past. I said I'd got over them now, although that wasn't actually true. With police training starting up, with the twins being due and with our new house in Chorley almost ready, I started to feel anxiety building up in me. I wasn't taking any medication. I'd finished the CBT sessions. And therapy was just now and again. The PFA would fund sessions but only six at any one time: there was no continuity.

One afternoon, Rachel and I had been up at the new house. There's a shopping street in Chorley called Pall Mall, just near the football club. We were driving along when, suddenly, I had a full-on panic attack: heart pounding, no breath. *I'm going to die.* I hadn't had one for ages but here I was, the adrenalin spinning through me. I told Rachel I had to stop. I pulled over by the side of the road, got out of the car and started walking. I'd no idea where I was going. I just walked off up Pall Mall, trying to get my body back under control.

I knew panic attacks could come back any time. I'd probably read everything that had ever been written about them by then. But the last thing I wanted to do was to jeopardise starting a new career by talking about my problems now. I know a lot of players, once they finish, face a real crisis about what happens next. Look at the statistics: so many ex-footballers end up bankrupt or divorced or with addictions.

I suppose, by rights, I should have been one of those statistics but, wherever it comes from, there was still this fight in me. I think, deep down, it's always been Bennell I've been fighting. Autumn of 2002, I didn't hesitate. I made my mind up and joined the police. Maybe, inside, I was thinking: *Right. That's me. Now I'm going to spend my life chasing down and arresting bastards like you.*

33.

The photo was taken in early 2003. After police training, you have what's called attestation. Basically, it means being sworn in as a copper. Family and friends can come along. And take pictures, like Dad did. The ceremony took place at Lancashire Police HQ in Hutton. It's still a little weird looking at myself in that snap. Obviously because I'm in a uniform, not a football kit. But it's more than that. Even the expression on my face, it seems to me, is as if I'd actually changed as a person somehow. Which I suppose I had. I look grown-up, for a start. Joining the police meant stepping into a different world. The Force. But before I made the jump, there was one last football adventure to be had.

By the August before I started police training, I was convinced I was finished with football. But, out of the blue, I got a phone call from

Jimmy Quinn. Jimmy was a big, old-fashioned centre forward, a Northern Ireland international, who was working as a player-manager in non-league at a club nearby called Northwich Victoria. I'd never met him but he'd obviously done a bit of research and now he was asking if I fancied coming down. Next thing I knew, I was in the car driving over to Northwich to meet him.

I thought I was done as a player but here was Jimmy saying: *It's training two evenings a week and play on Saturday.* Even though they were semi-pro, the money was alright as well. I hadn't started with the police yet so I thought earning some extra cash would be a good idea. Rachel thought that, too. *It'll only be for a little while.* It was a strange feeling: I'd been dumped out of football but here I was, four months later, jumping back in. I agreed the money, began training and, at the start of the new season, I was straight in the team.

Jimmy knew nothing about my past. I was just a player to him and, to be honest, I found football at that level easy. Northwich were in the Conference, which is now the National League. Even so, I struggled to get my head round what was going on. It was almost as if I was watching it all happen to somebody else. I can remember sitting in dressing rooms, even running about in games, and I'd be thinking: *What's this all about? What am I doing here? I was supposed to be finished with all this.*

Northwich was a lovely little club and the lads were a nice bunch. I suppose things had come around in a circle and now it actually took pressure off me that nobody in the dressing room knew about my previous life. The only link to the past was a lad named Steve Garvey. We'd been together at Crewe, even signed as apprentices at Gresty Road on the same day. But neither of us mentioned Bennell. I think we were both happy being in a dressing room together again after so many years.

I explained to Jimmy Quinn that I'd be starting my police training in November. I was playing every game for Northwich and he said he had no problem with me being away. He'd find a way to work round it. I thought there'd be nothing to worry about. Police training was at a place called the Bruche in Warrington. It's closed down now but, back then, new police officers from all over Wales and the north of England would be there on courses: twelve weeks, residential Monday to Friday, home for the weekends.

At first, I'd slip away Tuesday and Thursday evenings to do a bit of training so I could play on the Saturday. Northwich was only a half-hour drive from Warrington. But I knew I had to tell the instructors sooner or later. I can still remember, a couple of weeks in, sitting in an office with an Inspector who wasn't having it at all: *If you carry on playing, you'll put your future with the police at risk. If you get injured while you're training, you'll never have a career in the force.*

It was a disappointment: I was quite enjoying my football and, definitely, the extra money came in handy. But Rachel and I talked about it: *This is your career now. You'll have to pack up playing.* I knew she was right and I knew what I had to do. I told Northwich I was going to have to retire. It seemed like the right decision. The only decision. At the time, I had no regrets. Those didn't come till later: once I'd passed training and become a PC, I asked around and other officers told me that what I'd been told was completely wrong. There were plenty of PCs who played sport part-time – and got paid for it

– as long as it was worked in around their shifts. You just had to let the police know what you were doing. If I'd not played those couple of months for Jimmy, I'd never have given football another thought, I suppose. As it was, though, I've felt let down since then about having to stop. Not that I'd have got anywhere playing for Northwich. The regret came with discovering that what the Inspector at Bruche told me hadn't been true.

When I started police training, William and Luke had just been born. We knew I would have to head off to Warrington every week but it must have been hard for Rachel. She was going to be left alone with three kids.

The training lasted three months. It was pretty tough. Long days for a bloke who was used to football training lasting just a couple of hours. A lot to learn, too. Playing football had been something that had always come naturally to me. I hadn't studied anything since leaving school and now I had to get my head round the law, police procedure and everything else that came with the job.

I had my doubts about whether this was going to be the right thing for me but I'd made my choice. I was going to battle through and there were things about the course that were really good for me. Discipline was important, even little things like making sure your boots were shiny and your uniform was spotless every morning. You didn't have to think about what to do next. You just did as you were told.

As well, it was a team environment. Twelve or thirteen of us in the intake, a bit like a group of footballers in a dressing room, all together in the classroom every day. We'd go off to the pub in the evening and get to know each other. I felt comfortable. More than that: it was different from the football environment room in one way. There were women on the training course, too.

Some bits of my life, some things I've done, I'd like to skip over, really. But what would be the point of telling my story if I did? By the time I started at Bruche, things between Rachel and me were at a low ebb. Because we'd just had the twins, it never crossed my mind at that point to leave, even though the marriage wasn't giving either of us what we wanted. But, for sure, I was only at home because I felt locked in to the situation, not because I wanted to be.

I'd come back to Chorley at the end of each week and, as often as not, Rachel would be angry with me, shouting at me: *You're away all the time. You've got another life going on. I'm stuck here doing everything on my own.* And I know now she was right. It must have been really hard for her but, at the time, all I could think of was how unfair this was on me. *I've come home and all you do is have a go at me.*

I should have been aware of how much Rachel had on her plate and responded to it but, instead, I just felt like I was being neglected. *What about me?*

So, when a woman in our intake at the training centre took a shine to me and paid attention to me, I grabbed at that. It was also another chance to prove to myself that being with women was what I wanted and needed despite all those years being abused and brainwashed by Bennell. Everything was always to do with the stuff that rushed round in my head, spiralling back to what had happened to me as a boy. I've come to realise now that those emotions couldn't ever result in a lasting relationship. They could only ever undermine one. By the end of the training course, what went on between me and the young policewoman had turned into an affair.

I did the attestation thing, had the photos taken and began life as a copper. That meant being out on my shifts as a PC for Lancashire Police. There wasn't even the routine of the training course bringing me home every weekend. I felt bad that I'd been cheating on Rachel but my craving for attention and the boost to my self-esteem overrode all that. Rachel didn't know I was having an affair but she could sense something had changed. That something wasn't right.

When she confronted me, I denied everything. How I behaved was wrong on every level and whichever way you look at it. I feel guilty about it to this day. As I've said, my past explains what happened, perhaps. But it can't ever justify it. Almost as soon as I walked into my new career, I walked out on my marriage.

It's only now I've come to understand why that cycle kept repeating itself. I'd throw myself into relationships because I couldn't ever face being on my own. But because I couldn't face my own company, that meant I could never stick things out in someone else's either. Escaping from Rachel – as I saw it then – was only ever really about me trying to escape from myself.

34.

When I started as a policeman I had my doubts. Mum and Dad had said they thought I was too soft to be a copper. I knew what they meant. I wondered if I'd actually be able to clap handcuffs on someone and arrest them. Would I end up feeling sorry for people and letting them go? But the new job worked like the old one had. As a player, once I was out on the pitch, I wasn't soft at all. I loved a tackle and the game brought out the fighter in me. It was where I could focus, whatever else was going on in my life. Once I was out on the street in uniform, it was the same. A lot of it was instinctive. I soon found out what it was going to be like. I was chucked in at the deep end.

My very first arrest was an assault, a domestic. I was with a more experienced officer and we arrested the guy but he had some sort of injury, so we had to take him to hospital instead of into custody. We were with him, waiting for a doctor, and he had no cuffs on. All of a sudden, he bolted, straight out the doors of the hospital.

Because I was pretty fit, I went chasing off after him. He hopped over a wall and ran off down the road. I managed to catch him eventually, get him down on the floor and get handcuffs on him. I just remember thinking *Thank God!* If my first arrest had been an escape I'd never have been able to live it down, would I? As it was, it taught me how this worked: I hadn't thought about it. I'd just got on with it, done what I needed to do. A police officer is there to protect the public. You're trained and, instinctively, you put yourself in harm's way if that's what's necessary.

That first arrest gave me a bit of an adrenalin rush. Not as exciting as football, but it was similar. It was a physical challenge and I suppose it was what you imagine policing to be: a cop chasing a robber. I soon found out how dangerous it could be, too, though. We got called out to a house where a guy had locked his family in a bedroom and was threatening violence. There were a few of us but me and another probationer were first in. Not thinking, wanting to be the heroes, I suppose. *Let's go and lock him up!* We ran upstairs, shouting: *Police! Police!*

The door was shut so I kicked it open. The guy was standing there with a claw hammer and he swung it down as I came through the doorway. Luckily, the hammer got caught on the door frame and stuck. The other probationer, who was a big lad, came through and wrestled with the guy, who was really kicking off. We got him out into the hallway and onto the floor and handcuffed. By then, more experienced officers had come up the stairs behind us and they dragged him off. It was only afterwards I realised what might have happened if the hammer hadn't got stuck. The guy had meant to do us serious harm.

Maybe I should have just kept my head down and tried to ignore everything that wasn't to do with the police. Sometimes, though, things come to you without you being out there looking. Back when I was playing I'd got to know a lad named Jim* a really talented young striker. The two of us hit it off. I was sure he'd go on to have a decent career.

As can happen in football, he never got his chance. In a reserve game, Jim was on the end of a terrible tackle. I was playing, too. I actually heard his leg snap. He was screaming in pain and everyone knew straight away it was serious. The tackle had broken both bones in Jim's lower leg. He had operation after operation but he never played again. He took his case to court and ended up being paid quite a bit in compensation. Not that any amount of money made up for having your career finished at twenty-one.

Jim and I used to go out now and again. He was a local lad from Bolton and we became pretty close. Close enough that he knew a little bit about what had happened to me at Crewe. I don't know how it came up but, one day, Jim told me he'd had a word with the solicitor who was handling his compensation claim. The solicitor told Jim that he was pretty sure I had a case against Crewe over my abuse, that they had been negligent. In his opinion, my career had been cut short because of the abuse I'd suffered as a child.

---

* Name has been changed.

I agreed to meet the solicitor and we went over some of what Bennell had done to me and I tried to explain the culture at the club and where Bennell fitted into that. I told him how everybody at Gresty Road seemed to know about Bennell's reputation even if they hadn't witnessed any abuse first-hand. It was painful, remembering how some of those Crewe first team players had referred to me as *Barry's bum boy*, without ever stopping to think what that really meant; how nobody at the club had ever challenged this bloke who'd abused dozens and dozens of young lads. My life had been ruined while I was on Crewe's books. It seemed to me they'd done nothing whatsoever to protect any of us.

Not long after, Jim's solicitor got back in touch and told me he thought I had a very strong case. He wanted to run it on my behalf. There was every chance, he thought, that I'd win. I had no money to pay for solicitors but they wanted to take it on: no win, no fee. They instructed a barrister and suddenly the whole thing was up and going.

It felt almost as if this had taken on a life of its own but it gave me a big decision to make. I was finding my way in a new career and a court case would mean bringing everything back up again, reliving the experiences I'd spent so much time trying to put behind me. Did I really want to go through the whole business of appearing in court and talking about Bennell? I remember the solicitor going over what we might stand to win if the case was successful. I had to explain: for me, it wasn't about that. It was about people taking responsibility for what had happened, admitting they'd let me and lots of other boys down.

It was a hard decision. I didn't want to undermine my police career, and I was worried going over it all might mess me up mentally again. But I also thought that speaking up was the right thing to do. I was back with Rachel by this time and she was right behind me with it. *Just do it. You need to do it.* I told the solicitor and the barrister I was ready to go ahead and started giving them information, putting them in touch with people.

Crewe had always had this reputation for bringing through young players and Bennell had been a big part of that. He was the star-maker and I believed, now, that people at Gresty Road had turned a blind eye to what he was up to. They didn't want to miss out on the talent he brought to them and didn't want to think too much about how he did it. I wanted the club to be accountable and, to be honest, I took things further than I'd ever have imagined I'd be able to.

It was the barrister who suggested I ought to try to get a statement from Bennell. He was already in prison. And he'd have known that my evidence had helped put him there, even though all statements had been made anonymous at his trial. The idea now was to get him to confirm that people at Crewe had known about what he was doing. I made a call through the police and found out that Bennell was at Wymott Prison, just a few miles from where we were living: a pretty big shock in itself.

The solicitor asked if I thought I could go and visit Bennell and get him to give us a statement for this civil case. We didn't need him to talk about what he'd done; this was talking about the club being aware that boys were staying at his house, spending time with him in situations they must have known weren't appropriate. We wanted him to confirm that the club had turned a blind eye to his behaviour, even if they hadn't necessarily known how far that behaviour had gone.

It was a huge thing the solicitor and barrister were asking me to do.

To be honest, I still get upset – upset with myself – that I agreed to visit Bennell. I went alone and, even before I got to Wymott, this feeling of dread came over me as I drove up that road in the picture at the start of this chapter. Nearly ten years since I'd seen him but I still wasn't ready to face Bennell, nothing like. But I was desperate for him to agree to give us the statement.

Suddenly, I was in front of him, in a big room with other visits going on around us. We were sat on plastic orange chairs across a table. He was smiling. He seemed pleased to see me, even though my evidence had convicted him and put him behind bars. He asked about the kids, about Lynda. He asked about me as if we were old friends meeting up for a pint. No remorse, nothing. Instead, he said: *I still love you, you know.* He was wearing prison-issue clothes and looked older but it was still him. And I was still a ten-year-old boy, sitting there in front of him. Like time hadn't passed. Like nothing had changed. *Oh, fuck. Why am I here?*

Before I'd had the chance to say anything, Bennell had taken control of the situation. It was as if he didn't care that he was in prison. Like we weren't in a prison at all: we were back at Dove Holes. And I'm sure he could see that weakness in me. He could see the fear: he could read me like a book. I had this mass of feelings – misery, vulnerability, shame – welling up inside. I was having to fight back tears, fight back the urge just to run out of the room. I had to ask him for the statement. *I had to.* Otherwise, why was I putting myself through this?

I explained what was going on with the case. That we needed a statement from him. *Surely, after everything that's happened, you can just help me with this?* He looked at me and said: *Yes. I'll do that. I'll do that for you.* And, just for a moment, it felt to me like him doing the statement might be a way for him to admit he'd done something wrong. Even though I knew he'd never say sorry, that he'd never feel as if he needed to. All that ever mattered to him was how he felt and getting what he wanted. How I felt didn't matter at all. It never had. Instead, he was getting a kick out of the fact that I was sat there in front of him again, needing something from him.

I told him that someone would get in touch about making the statement. I had the feeling he was expecting some kind of physical contact. A handshake, maybe. But I felt sick to my stomach. He said: *Take care of yourself. Give my love to everyone.* As if we'd just met up for a chat. And I got up, turned round and hurried away. He sat there, watching me leave. To this day, I still regret having gone in there to meet him at all. I'd said yes to the solicitor – I always said yes to people, didn't I? – without really taking in what the consequences might be.

I fell apart as soon as I was out of the room. I went to the toilet and vomited. I sat there in the cubicle, crying, staring at the wall. *What have I done?* I couldn't have known, really, how being there would make me feel. The visit had seemed like a logical thing and I'd wanted to do whatever I could. It was my case, after all. Now, though, in those moments after I left him, I knew. I knew what Bennell could still do to me. Driving away from the prison, I knew I still wasn't free.

35.

Lynda and my mum and dad had long since cut off all contact with Bennell. When I told them I'd been to Wymott Prison, they were shocked. Scared, I think, and disappointed. But that's just me supposing. We never talked it over. Lynda staring at me; Mum shaking her head a little. What was there to say? In our family we never asked why, did we? So many years of trying to wipe out the memory of him being a part of our lives and here I was, churning it all up again.

I went back on shifts as a policeman but, at night and on days off, I was overwhelmed with nightmares and flashbacks. Seeing him had undermined any progress I'd made completely. It was another thing I shouldn't have allowed to happen.

It must have been a bad time for Rachel. I was drinking, staying out all hours in Manchester. Trying to deaden my feelings. But I had the court case ahead of me. The chance to put Crewe on the spot. The chance to get financial compensation. And, if nothing else, seeing Bennell in prison had given me the chance to get him to agree to a statement. He'd promised he'd tell the truth about Crewe.

I was expecting to win my compensation claim. I was expecting the club to take some responsibility for what had happened. And I thought that me stepping forward might give other people the push to do the same. The whole thing had only come about because I knew Jim and, through him, the solicitor. I wouldn't ever have put in a claim on my own.

It meant a lot to me that the solicitor believed me when I told him my story, and that my barrister did too. Even the insurance company who covered the 'no win, no fee' element believed me. It meant a lot that, for the first time, people on the 'outside' recognised how wrong it was, what I'd been through. They believed me and they believed *in* me. I think they call what I felt *validation*. Without that, we'd never have ended up in court. Those professional people put a little fight back into me. The real shock – the real betrayal – came later, when it turned out that the statement Bennell produced wasn't the one we'd talked about at Wymott at all.

I never saw the actual document but I know what was in it. Bennell said he'd done what he'd done to me but that, in his opinion, neither Crewe Alexandra, nor Dario Gradi, nor anyone else at the club had known anything about it. The complete opposite of what he'd told me he'd write. Why? Did someone else go to Wymott after I'd been there? Had he talked to someone about what might follow if I won the case against the club? Or was it just him taking the chance to fuck me over one last time?

I know what I think happened but I won't ever be sure or be able to say what I believe. I just have to live with it now. I put myself through that whole experience at the prison to get kicked in the teeth. Telling me one thing and doing the opposite would have felt to him like he was in control. That's how his mind works. And, despite my evidence having put him in prison in the first place, now it felt to me too that he had taken back control.

Not long after I'd been to Wymott, I arrived to start my shift and there were two guys in plain clothes waiting to see me. *Andy Woodward?* They explained that they were from Professional Standards, the police department that looks into misconduct and complaints against serving officers. I had no idea why they'd want to speak to me and, to be honest, I panicked. *What the hell was going on here?*

The three of us went into a side room. They sat me down and said they'd been made aware that I'd visited an inmate at HM Prison Wymott. *You're a police officer. We need to speak to you about going into a prison. The interview's going to be on tape.* They knew nothing about the circumstances but they actually put me under caution. So I just told them everything: about Bennell, about Crewe, about my civil case. I had nothing to hide. They were the first police officers I'd disclosed any of this to since joining the force and they probably got a little more than they'd bargained for.

By the time I finished, they were in shock. I think they genuinely didn't know what to say. One of them muttered something about being sorry, as if I'd just told them someone had died. They assured me I had nothing to be worried about now. Everything was fine. In fact, I should talk to them again if I had any problems.

As they were leaving, the two officers from Professional Standards told me that, because they had a duty of care, they were going to put what I'd told them on record. They believed that, because of my circumstances, I shouldn't be involved in cases of a sexual nature or cases that had anything to do with children. I suppose I didn't pay that much attention at the time. I told them I'd joined the police without any caveats. Yes, they said, but this should be on your record and you should have support available to you through your career in the force.

I was taken by surprise that morning: I'd never planned to talk to the police about my background; I'd just wanted to get on with the job and put things behind me. But, straight after the interview, I had a sense of relief. It felt good that they knew. Maybe it would take pressure off me and keep me away from situations I might struggle with. Maybe the force would have my back from now on.

Eventually the case came to court. It was what they call a Criminal Injuries Compensation Authority case: me versus Crewe Alexandra FC. It took place in Manchester, in what felt like an empty room. There were no reporters or members of the public there. Mum and Dad had come along to support me. Rachel, too.

Crewe had two barristers: they properly went to work on me, trying to undermine my credibility. It's what barristers do, I suppose it's how an English courtroom works. They got stuck in to the psychologist who was called to explain what had happened to me, too. There was something very strange going on that afternoon: something didn't feel right.

Crewe had got statements from every member of staff saying nobody had known what was going on. They had Bennell's statement. And they made a big thing of the fact that, whatever the psychologist said about my mental state now, I'd put on my police application that I no longer suffered from panic attacks. The judge made his mind up and told me I should just concentrate on my career in the police. *Just go and get on with your life. Case dismissed.*

I'm still in touch with my solicitor and I know he's convinced justice wasn't done that day: he calls it the single biggest regret of a thirty-year career in the law. Outside the court, I watched Crewe's barristers high-fiving each other in front of me. I guess they'd known they were on a sticky wicket but they were made up because they'd somehow managed to get a result. It seemed as if, for them, it was all about their client avoiding having to admit liability and pay compensation.

For me, the money was by the by: it was never about that. It still isn't today. The case was about holding the football club to account, for my own sake and for the sake of other victims. The judge's verdict cut that down in an instant: basically, I felt like he was saying that I was a liar. Nobody from Crewe ever denied what had happened to me. But they were refusing to admit knowing about it. It still hurts me. Plenty has been made public since that shows how wrong a decision that was. I can't ever revisit the case. But other victims can.

My barrister wanted to take it further and go to the Review Panel. He was convinced the original decision was wrong: a case about Crewe had somehow been turned into a case about me. A case about my career having ended prematurely because of mental health issues was decided on whether I still had panic attacks after I'd retired as a player. It wouldn't have been possible for the judgment to miss the point more completely.

But I'd run out of steam. When the judge told me to go away and get on with being a police officer, it was like he was drawing a line under the thing. It felt as if he wasn't dismissing the case so much as he was dismissing me. I felt the system had closed ranks and I had nowhere left to turn.

The picture at the start of the chapter is in the woods up near Rivington, a village just outside Chorley. It's pretty: winding pathways, a waterfall and then wild, overgrown corners. That's where I went, a few weeks after the court case, to try to kill myself. I went back to work, like the judge had told me to. But everywhere I looked, I was convinced I'd been fucked over. Convinced I'd made such a mess of my life that it wasn't any longer worth living. I'd been betrayed by Bennell, let down by Crewe. Let down by my parents, even though they'd had no idea what was going on. And now I'd been let down by justice and the system.

I'd failed: I'd been a terrible husband to Andrea and now Rachel; an unreliable father to my sons, forever disappearing off into the night. I'd lost my battle to be a footballer. I'd lost any sense of self-esteem I'd ever had. *What was the point of me being around at all?*

I had a plan. I'd been on duty at the scene after a guy was discovered in Rivington Woods after taking his own life. He'd not climbed into a tree. He hadn't jumped. It was just a noose fastened to a branch. I would be able to do the same.

I drove out to the woods. I sat on a bench, evening closing in around me, and I drank. Drank a lot. I had rope in the boot. I stumbled around in the woods and found my spot, tied the rope to the branch. Did I want to be here any more? *No.* Did I want to finish with it now? *Yes.* I put my head through the noose. People describe these moments as a cry for help. But anyone who's been in the situation knows that isn't right. It actually comes down to chickening out. I was ready. I wanted to die. But did I have the nerve to actually do it? No. And it crushed me. I even failed in that.

However much I'd intended to take my life, I hadn't been able to go through with it. I was beaten by fear. Ask anyone who's stepped back from the brink like that, who's taken their head out of the noose like I did: you can't begin to explain the contempt and self-hatred that comes with not seeing it through. You can't do it but you still – desperately – want to.

Going on shift the following day, I was blank. I felt like a ghost. I'd told Rachel I wanted to kill myself but she hadn't believed me. Why should she? She probably thought I was just attention-seeking. At work, nobody would have had any idea what was going on inside my head. I still knew how to put the mask on; I'd had years of practising that. But I know what happened that night. And I know what didn't happen. I know how deep and dark that hole was I'd fallen into. I've probably been trying to climb out of it ever since.

36.

After that evening in Rivington Woods, shifts as a policeman felt strange, disassociated. I remember being first on scene at a suicide – a young guy had hanged himself off a scaffolding bar on a building site – and the thought crossed my mind: *How come you were able to do it and I wasn't?* I'd throw myself into dangerous situations without a moment's hesitation because, deep down, it felt like I didn't really have anything to lose.

Mostly, though, the guy who went out in uniform wasn't the same guy who'd put a rope round his neck in the woods. On shift, in a weird way, I wasn't me. Football had often worked in the same way. The focus and concentration excluded everything else, even the mess I was in. I took on as much overtime as I could. I volunteered for everything. Partly because things weren't great at home and it was a way to escape

Rachel and my responsibilities. But also because being at work gave me a chance to escape myself.

Despite everything, I did a decent job as a copper. Some of it really did appeal to me. On the beat, you're part of a team. You're relying on your partner and your partner's relying on you. There was competition between teams: who'd get the most arrests, the most detections, the best results.

My partner, Gavin, was like me: motivated and competitive. Anyone did a runner on us, I'd be off after them. I'd always chase them down. Instead of thinking like a police officer – about what I was going to do, according to the process – I had an ability to put myself in the mind of the criminal: as soon as we'd get a call to a job, I'd be thinking ahead. *If I was the criminal, what would I do? Where would I go? Where would I hide?*

I got a reputation for being in the right place at the right time. They used to call me a lucky so-and-so. I'd say nothing but I think there was more to it than luck. It was the same kind of thought process you develop as a footballer: not just reacting to what a centre forward does but, at the same time, trying to second-guess what he might do next. But being an officer on the beat is hard graft: long hours, especially on nights when you're fighting sleep. You've all the paperwork, the pressure to get everything exactly right: statements, files, court proceedings. It's stressful.

When I'd decided on a new career, I'd been strongly drawn to the idea of helping people, keeping people safe. I think I had a knack for communicating with members of the public: psychologists call it 'good empathy'. I'd been a policeman for about four years when a position for a Community Beat Manager came up. It's a job like the old-fashioned village bobby used to be, I suppose. You're based in one small community. You get to know the people who live there, kids through to OAPs, the role models as well as the wrong 'uns. You develop relationships and, using those relationships, you try to keep the community safe. You're embedded in the area you're responsible for. It's a position of trust: policing by consent. I applied for the job in March 2006 and I got it.

A few months later I received a Divisional Commander's Commendation for my work as a Community Beat Manager. I was nominated nationally for Community Police Officer of the Year that same year.

Even so, I had some low times around then. I felt like saying sorry all the time to the people closest to me. I felt like my life had poisoned their lives too. Life at home with Rachel was incredibly volatile. I'd leave or she would kick me out, for weeks or months at a time. I'd be off chasing attention or I'd come crawling back, lonely and unable to deal with my own company.

At one point I was living in an old static caravan, sat in the middle of a field, which I rented from a colleague at the station. I'd get drunk in there and really wonder: *Bloody hell. Has my life come to this?* But work kept dragging me through. In the new job – I was assigned to a village called Coppull, just outside Chorley – it at least started feeling as if I had somewhere I could belong. Somewhere where me being around made a positive difference.

The Community Beat Manager role meant being a point of contact for local people who had a problem. It meant meetings with other agencies, like the housing department and social services. I'd go into schools to talk to the kids and establish relationships with them. Coppull was a solid working-class area, a few housing estates and a couple of schools. It had been a mining village. Life was pretty tough for quite a lot of the people who lived there, which meant, from my point of view, there was a lot going on.

As soon as I started, I could see there was a problem with youths in the community who were just bored as much as anything else. They'd be round the old leisure centre, drinking, setting fires, smashing bottles. They had a little youth club but it was tiny and wasn't resourced. So, instead, they'd be by the leisure centre: a big field next door, dark, easy to disappear into. They call it 'antisocial behaviour', don't they?

I talked to the kids, tried to establish a little trust and respect. I asked them what they thought they needed. I had some ideas, even though I didn't have any budget, so I needed to liaise with the council and other organisations who actually made it all happen. Eventually, on that old pitch, we got a playground put in for the younger kids, a sort of garden walk area for the older people and a caged-in five-a-side pitch with floodlights, an artificial pitch and basketball hoops and everything. Youth crime in that area of Coppull went down by nearly 50 per cent. I went up there recently, just to have a little look around and remember. I took that photo and it gave me a good feeling. The facilities we put in are still being used today. I like to think I made a difference to the place.

For those teenagers, it was about having an alternative. I tried not to see them as troublemakers. Each of them had their own story and I knew as well as anyone what could happen if you got started on the wrong path in life. I used to spend quite a lot of time just sitting around talking to them, trying to explain how important the decisions you make can be.

I set up a little football tournament for the four local primary schools and put on a few training sessions on the big field by the leisure centre. It was for Year 5s and 6s. I got the local trophy shop to do me trophies and medals at mates' rates. It was great. I laugh now: they used to call me *PC Andy*, even the older ones in their early twenties. It made me feel like a character out of a kids' TV show.

It wasn't just the young people, either. I'd call in to shops and people's houses. They'd let me know if there were any problems and I'd try to find a way to fix things without the law being involved. I worked with the PCSOs, teaching them how to get the best out of the role. Those couple of years in Coppull were probably the best time I had in the police. That job just suited my skills and my personality, I think.

Maybe I should have stuck with it as a Community Beat Manager but other jobs were always coming up online. I'd been at Coppull for a while and thought maybe I'd done that now. I saw a post advertised working for a Target Team in my division. It was a burglary team, a sort of detective role, in plain clothes, where your whole responsibility was tracking down and catching people responsible for robberies and burglaries. You didn't do any other policing.

I liked the sound of it: going out and catching bad guys who were breaking into people's houses and stealing their stuff. I'd already seen for myself how devastating that kind of crime could be for victims: their homes had been invaded. It was a snap decision to apply, really. And, if I'm honest, part of the appeal was that I knew there'd be loads of overtime. I'd have an excuse to be out of the house when things were bad with Rachel. Or, if I wasn't living at home, I'd be earning the extra money to pay rent somewhere else. I applied, went through the process and – for better or for worse – I got started in the new job.

37.

I know it must look a bit like an old player showing off his medals but that commendation, for work on the Chorley Target Team, means a lot to me. You get handed a piece of paper like that and it says: *You're good at this. You made the right decision.* But, looking at it now, it's bittersweet. That was about as good as it got for me on the force. From 2009 onwards, it all went downhill.

At first, being on the Target Team was satisfying in many ways: you had to see cases right through to the end. With that came some pressure, good pressure. Once you opened a file, you had to make sure you closed it as well. I was based at the station in Chorley, not far from home. As I remember, there were five of us and a sergeant on the team.

At Coppull, I'd just been left to get on with it really, and, although I had a couple of PCSOs working with me, it got a bit lonely sometimes.

Coming from football meant coming from a team environment. Now, from case to case, you'd always partner up and I liked that. Being with someone on jobs helped stop stuff rattling around in my head like it did when I was on my own.

There was one part of the job that was weird for me from the off, though: TICs. It's not done so much now but, back then, if there was a prisoner on remand somewhere, charged with a burglary, and you suspected him of other offences, you could go to the prison and visit him. You'd talk to him about the other burglaries; offer him the chance to wipe the slate clean by agreeing to admit to those too. TIC: taking into consideration. If he agreed, you'd take him out for a drive, get him to point out other properties he'd burgled and describe how he'd done it so you could be sure you'd got the right guy. Then you'd check your own details and do a taped interview with him, matching everything up.

When it came to court, the guy might end up with a slightly longer sentence but, at the end of it, he'd be clear. Those other crimes would just lie on file but at least the victims knew that the person who'd robbed them had been found and dealt with. It worked. But I never did get used to going and taking blokes out of prison, even though I'd deliver them back an hour or two later. Just going to prison at all I found hard. HMP Wymott and seeing Bennell, losing the court case the way I had: I still hadn't really processed any of that.

The Target Team was all about chasing down bad guys. It was pretty straightforward: long hours but I felt like I knew what I was doing and why I was doing it. There was an unspoken thing in that line of policing, though: you wouldn't be doing it for long. The idea was that you'd be moved on to CID. I was probably a bit naive; I hadn't applied for the Team because I wanted to get fast-tracked to CID. But, once I understood how things worked, I didn't really stop to think. I just assumed: *Oh, yeah. CID. That'll be okay if it happens.*

~

So I ended up applying for the promotion because it was the natural progression. I think most police officers will tell you that, once you're on the force, you just move through as if you're on rails, even if you don't have any real kind of plan.

When you applied to join CID, you had to show that you had experience looking after complex cases, from detection through to conviction. That you knew how to handle the necessary paperwork, interviews, deadlines and the rest.

I wasn't exactly ambitious when it came to where I wanted to go with the police. But the next step was there in front of me and I filled in the form, let myself get pulled along even though, deep down, I knew I'd have been happier not climbing the ladder. But that's how careers work, I suppose: once you're in, it takes something pretty unusual to get you out. But, even if I had my doubts back then, I couldn't have had any idea how things were going to turn out later. Without even knowing, I'd already taken the fork in the road.

The CID exam was proper book work. I was one of the first intakes where Lancashire Police coordinated with the university in Preston and made qualifying for CID the equivalent of a Foundation Degree. There was a lot of law to be studied and the cases I worked on had to be written up to create a sort of portfolio. At the same time, Rachel and I decided to try to make a proper go of it together. We went away on holiday with the boys and Rachel fell pregnant with our fourth son, Izaak.

Rachel is an all-or-nothing sort of person. When she took our wedding vows, she meant every word: being married was for life and meant being faithful to your husband. She stuck to those vows, whereas I didn't.

I put on a mask for work, for studying and for the kids. But for my wife? I'd get drunk at weekends; I'd go off chasing female attention; I'd blame Rachel for my head being mashed, even though it wasn't her fault at all. I was scared about the responsibility of another baby and even suggested a termination. For Rachel, that was the worst possible thing to hear. She came from a Catholic family and it went against everything she felt and believed in.

Even though I was getting some counselling again, reverting to child mode was my default. *What about me?* It must have been unbearably difficult being around me at all, never mind being married to me. Only Rachel's perseverance kept our family together all those years.

Because of everything that was going on, that time seems a bit of a blur. I passed the exam and got put up from PC to DC: Detective Constable. I don't remember it seeming like such a big deal at the time though. Even that commendation for being a member of the region's most successful Target Team: I'm probably prouder of it now than I was when it was awarded. Back then, I always felt like I was just trying to get to the end of another day.

I joined CID thinking I'd be investigating complex crimes: robberies, serious assaults, murders, frauds. Instead, I soon found myself working on cases that had previously been investigated by PPU: the Public Protection Unit. For me, that was a disaster.

PPU, it was decided, were going to focus on domestic abuse. Other crimes such as rape and sexual assault were going to be handed over to CID. It meant working with some very vulnerable people: victims, witnesses and even the criminals themselves. We were responsible for investigating cases focused on child protection, child neglect and child abuse. Thinking back now, I can't really believe I got through some of the days.

I did CEOP work: Child Exploitation and Online Protection. Investigating child pornography cases, I'd often be viewing images and videos of child sex abuse, shut in a little booth for two and three hours at a time, in order to log and grade the material in terms of how serious it was. I was also conducting interviews with rape and abuse victims – children as well as adults – getting their statements before going and arresting the people responsible. I still can't believe that I was put in the way of those situations.

Details of what had happened to me in the past had been on my file for five or six years, ever since my encounter with Professional Standards after I visited Bennell in prison. They'd told me I'd be shielded from this kind of stuff. The information about me was there somewhere in the system but the dots never got joined up. They needed bodies to be doing this work and I ended up being one of those bodies. In the police, you never have the feeling you can pick and choose your jobs.

The force can be an unforgiving environment. Whatever gets thrown at you, you're supposed to be able to deal with it. And there wasn't ever any support offered apart from what might come naturally from a partner on a job.

That was true in relation to the CID role, too. Murder, rape, child abuse. Nobody ever asked: *Are you okay with this stuff? Do you need to talk to someone about what effect this might be having on you?* It was relentless, too: we'd have nine or ten different cases running at the same time. Imagine it: a child pornography trial, where I'd been the officer who'd logged the material. I'd be in court and have to go up to the judge's bench with a laptop to show them what I'd found. I'd be talking them through what we were watching while, in my head, I've got Bennell and my own experience whirling around. The abuser might well be sitting opposite us. I'd be looking at the images and knowing exactly what the victims had been through. I'd have my 'Teflon' face on – this was my job, wasn't it? – but inside I'd be in bits. And then, at the end of the trial, I'd just push on to the next job.

38.

Chorley police station: my years as a copper, I probably spent more time in that place than I did at home. After a while on CID, I was assigned for a spell with what they called Level Two Intelligence. In complicated cases, especially drugs cases, there'd be a need for officers to go out and gather intelligence on the ground, keep suspects under plain-clothes surveillance. I got put on those duties. I met my third wife in the office where Level Two Intelligence was based.

Catherine was a data analyst, really bright and really good at her job. She would put reports and numbers together to give a shape to investigations, working at the station but a civilian employee. We just hit it off. Catherine was twelve years younger than me and it felt like she offered me everything I struggled to find at home with Rachel. She knew I was married and, eventually, knew about the rest of my life, too. She gave me attention, affection, respect. We didn't argue. Catherine was a lovely girl, a beautiful soul.

I wasn't a good husband to Rachel. We were very different in so many important ways, not least that I wasn't faithful to the marriage. Meeting Catherine, though, wasn't just me craving female company, having another little fling. From the off, it felt much more important than that. We started seeing each other and, before long, Rachel and I agreed to separate and divorce. The divorce was a pretty painful time all round but I think it worked out in the end. Rachel kept the family home. She had four boys to bring up on her own now. I moved into a rented flat in Bolton with Catherine.

Those first couple of years together, I felt as if Catherine offered me a place of safety. We weren't going to have children. I'd had the snip after Izaak was born and, when we talked about the possibility of having the operation reversed, Catherine didn't want me to do it. She told me she was happy with things as they were. She didn't feel that maternal urge. It made a difference to me that she was a part of my life in work as well as outside it.

I'd often have the boys round at weekends and Catherine was fine with that. But it can't have been easy for Rachel. She had the four of them to look after on her own and then I'd turn up for a day or two and take our sons off like I was a treat for them, the good cop in a bad situation.

I was still seeing Jake, my son from my first marriage, too, even though I had no kind of relationship with Andrea. She and I hadn't spoken since we'd split up but Jake was older now, in his late teens, and he'd come across to Bolton to visit now and again. He used to spend quite a bit of time with my mum and dad. They went away on a few holidays together. Andrea's strong and she made a new life for herself but I'm very grateful that she never stopped me having a good relationship with our son.

So life moved on but, whatever I did, I couldn't shake off the past. In November 2011, Gary Speed – a wonderful footballer and a lovely man who was making a real success of managing the Welsh national team at the time – took his own life. Here is not the place to go into the detail of what happened to Gary or why it happened. But, early the following year, a reporter from the *Sunday Times* turned up on my parents' doorstep. They were actually looking for my sister, Lynda, wanting to discuss her relationship with Barry Bennell. First I knew was a phone call. My mum and dad wanted me to talk to this guy, wanted me to keep him away from Lynda, who was really upset and wanted nothing to do with it.

I met the guy at a hotel in Leyland. He didn't know anything about what had happened to me – all the victims in Bennell's court case had been anonymous – and I only spoke to him on the condition that I wasn't named in the article.

There was enough stuff on the internet linking Gary with Bennell for them to do their magazine feature anyway. What I gave them was background, really. I explained who Bennell was, how he operated and what he'd done to me and to other boys I knew. I wasn't in a position to say anything about Gary, of course: I didn't know the facts and it wasn't my place to make assumptions. But, if they were writing about Bennell, I thought it was important they knew what kind of bloke they were dealing with.

At the time, after I'd left the hotel, I just felt relieved, thinking that me talking meant the papers wouldn't bother Lynda or my family now. But, in the weeks that followed, I realised I'd pushed myself right out to the edge all over again.

It's one of the ways trauma works on you. It's buried and then, for whatever reason, it's brought to the surface again. Talking to that reporter unlocked it all: I started having flashbacks again, nightmares, panic attacks. I tried to bury it deeper, taking it all inside myself and hiding away my emotions from the people around me.

I know it was a frustrating time for Catherine: I wasn't the guy she knew. I was withdrawn, disconnected. It was as if I didn't want to be reached. I guess she thought I was hiding stuff from her. Actually, I was just desperately trying to hide stuff from myself. I started getting signed off work for a week at a time: I'd tell the doctor I was suffering from anxiety without ever going into the reasons why.

I spent those weeks off – and other times, too – drinking far more than I should have. If it wasn't alcoholism, it was something close. Real binge-drinking. And, with that, I developed the symptoms of bulimia, too. I'd eat and then vomit almost straight away. I'm not sure it was an eating disorder exactly: memories of Bennell and my feelings about myself used to make me feel sick. I'd eat and then vomiting felt like a way of getting rid of those thoughts. Like I was emptying myself of all this bad stuff.

Getting rid was what I wanted to do. Drinking and bulimia were definitely connected somehow. I'm sure that doing that interview was the trigger point for me losing the plot all over again. From then on, my career in the police, my relationship with Catherine and my grip on my own mental health all started to crumble away.

I loved Catherine. She gave me things in a relationship I'd never had before. She was supportive and understanding even though I was drinking too much and she couldn't really get inside my head and help with the issues I had. She didn't seem to get frustrated with me, never shouted at me, never pushed me to take responsibilities other than keeping myself together.

Catherine saw me through the divorce with Rachel and had been loving and welcoming when my sons were around. She knew first-hand about the demands of a career in the police. Her parents embraced me as part of their family. I felt safe with Catherine. We got married in June 2013.

It was a beautiful day, a beautiful occasion. The wedding was at a place called Haighton Manor, up near Preston. People who came said they had a great time. I did, too. I didn't feel under pressure. I felt as if this was a path in my life that I was actually choosing to take.

~

To this day, I only have good things to say about Catherine. She backed me up through some really difficult moments in my life. That same year, 2013, was very hard indeed at work. I found myself left with a complicated fraud case, expected to deal with it on my own. A guy in Chorley had been buying and selling cars off a forecourt and had done a runner. People who'd sold the cars hadn't had their money so they'd come back and taken the cars. But, at the same time, people who'd bought those cars in good faith were now out of pocket. There were dozens of victims involved. It wasn't a case just one officer should have been working on.

That year at work, the Stuart Hall case came in: the TV presenter who ended up in jail after being found guilty of indecent assaults on young teenage girls. It was on our patch. That inquiry became bigger than anyone had expected and a lot of officers got pulled into it, including me. I was there when Hall was arrested and I was part of some of the interviews with his victims. The Officer in Charge was a pal and I wanted to help out because of that.

Our whole team was under pressure but I felt that pressure more than most. Talking to Hall's victims naturally brought back lots of memories for me: I knew exactly how grooming worked and what it felt like to be a victim. I wanted to help but, at the same time, I felt trapped by it all.

My Inspector – a great guy, a friend – knew all about my background. But I don't think the mental health of serving officers is ever very high on the agenda in organisations like the police. Definitely it wasn't back then. At Inspector level and above, there's just this massive and constant pressure to get the job done. The cost in terms of the well-being of individual officers is the last thing on anyone's mind. The pressure to get results is overwhelming.

I can't really blame anyone but myself for the situation I allowed myself to get into. I had one or two superior officers who were very supportive and very understanding. But the demands made on the organisation – and the way the organisation functioned – meant I was always going to be headed for a fall sooner rather than later when it came to my career in the police.

39.

As part of any major criminal investigation, the Family Liaison Officer is quite an important role. The FLO is there to help with the investigation but also to support family members affected by what's happened.

It's about establishing trust and building relationships. On the one hand, you're getting those family members to produce statements and provide evidence. On the other, you're the way the police have of communicating with the family and keeping them up to date with whatever's going on with the case. FLOs are supposed to work in pairs and it's all quite strictly controlled: you document all the time you spend with the family and report back to superior officers.

While I was in CID, I did all the relevant training courses to become a FLO. My first experience of the job started with a murder on New

Year's Eve 2013 and ran into early 2014. I was fine with it, to be honest. I established a good relationship with the family and stayed in touch with them about the case for quite a while. I actually cared what happened to them. On the one hand, that meant I did a decent job. On the other hand, though, it meant I perhaps got more emotionally involved than was good for me.

My second FLO role was a case where a woman was charged with the murder of her disabled husband. It turned out the death was accidental, and she was released. I was assigned to support her as the investigation proceeded. She was an older woman and was completely traumatised by what had happened: first, she'd lost her husband; then, she'd been arrested for murder.

My partner on that case went off long-term sick and I was left to deal with the lady and her family on my own. I think I helped her through it all but, on top of the rest of my workload, I was struggling with the situation. My drinking and the bulimia episodes were now something else I was hiding, at home and at work.

My third job as an FLO was really difficult: again, maybe I just got too emotionally involved. A woman whose son was being investigated by social services allowed him to stay overnight with his six-month-old child. It should never have happened and she'd been ordered not to allow her son contact with the child. The son wasn't even supposed to be in the flat. The following morning, the baby was found dead and the son was arrested for murder.

I was assigned as FLO on the case. I got to know and understand the mum. She was devastated that she'd been a part of what had led to the baby's death. My partner and I could tell she was in a bad way and reported back that we thought she needed extra support. But you can never tell how close someone is to being pushed over the edge, can you? I know that better than anyone.

Two weeks later, the woman took her own life. It felt like we'd come up short from a professional point of view and from a personal perspective, her suicide left me in bits.

My head was cooked. The people I was supposed to be helping were vulnerable, in situations where they were facing more stress than they ever had in their lives. And the job was to empathise and support at a time when I needed more looking after than ever myself.

I was asked about how I was coping in the FLO role and, although I didn't go into detail, I let them know I wanted to move on to something else. A Level One Intelligence role came up. Completely different work and, although it was still Lancashire, a completely different environment. I put myself up for the job – I said I really needed to make the change – and got reassigned.

A lot of the job was around drugs: looking at the dealers coming into the town to sell and the addicts around the Chorley area who were their customers. There was less pressure on the role. Fewer cases I had to be responsible for.

I wasn't in great shape. I was living with a constant feeling of being disconnected. I had a couple of car accidents that were caused by me simply not paying attention: driving across a roundabout and hitting the car in front because I was thinking about everything except the road in front of me; reversing hard into a lamp post at Tesco one Sunday lunchtime after I'd popped out to get milk because the boys were coming over for lunch. But the Intelligence role still felt like the right move, like something I could handle. But then, December 2014, everything changed. Changed for the worse.

A CID job came in. A man had been seriously assaulted and it was touch and go for a while whether or not he'd survive. The sister of the guy who'd been attacked wasn't cooperating with the officers on the case, so it was decided to appoint a Family Liaison Officer.

The Inspector approached me one evening and explained the situation: *I need you to do me a favour. I want you to come along and meet this woman and be introduced as the FLO.* My first reaction was the right one: *No chance. I can't do that any more.* But I was a Yes man. I never turned a case down. And the Inspector knew I'd done a decent job as an FLO in the past: *Andy. Can you do your stuff and sort this one out?*

So I went with him to the house. He introduced me to the sister and to her parents. *This is Andy. He's going to be the FLO on the case and he'll try to fix any problems you've had with the investigation so far.* The family seemed reassured that the police were taking it seriously. I should have known better. I didn't question what was happening, didn't question not having a colleague to work alongside as you're supposed to. Going along with it ended up costing me my job.

Maybe it was bound to happen. I've always got too emotionally involved with what I was doing; I've always craved female attention. Although I was the FLO for the whole family, I spent most of my time liaising with the sister of the victim. That involved working to get her to cooperate with the investigation, reporting back to her on developments and, once her brother's condition started to improve, accompanying her on hospital visits to see him.

I can think of all sorts of reasons why what happened happened. What I can't think of, though, is an excuse. And I wouldn't want to run away from my responsibilities. However traumatised – however drunk – I might have been, I have to own up to my decisions. I saw part of my role as an FLO being to befriend the family, establish trust and empathy. But I crossed a line and, once I had, there was no going back.

The sister and I spent a lot of time together. She had my number as her point of contact with the investigation. Messages went back and forth between us. Those messages became more intimate. I told her about my background, about having been abused by Barry Bennell. There was the whole *You're married. I'm married. We're just friends, aren't we?* conversation. And then, one night, when we'd both already drunk too much, she messaged me and we ended up sleeping together.

I feel sick to my stomach just writing that down. *What the fuck had I done?* I knew it went against everything a copper was supposed to stand for. More than that, I'd completely betrayed Catherine, someone who'd only ever wanted to do her best by me. I'd married her convinced that, this time, things would be different.

I'd betrayed someone I was supposed to be looking out for. I'd betrayed my wife and my family. I'd betrayed any chance I had of getting my head straight after all these years. I went to see my GP. Told him nothing about what had gone on but said I needed time away. I was depressed, anxious, confused: I insisted he should sign me off work for a few weeks.

I said to the sister: *That was wrong. It shouldn't have happened.* I didn't say anything at all to Catherine but she knew something had shifted in me and in our marriage. I went off to stay at a caravan my parents had on Anglesey, the caravan in the picture. I told myself it would be time to think, to be on my own, and to work out what I should do. The truth is it was exactly the kind of situation I'd never been able to cope with: being alone. I went to pieces. I drank. And I responded to messages from the sister.

She came over to see me. *Just for the day. We can go for a walk on the beach.* She ended up staying the night. We had sex again, with the rain drizzling down, in a caravan stuck in the middle of nowhere. Shame, guilt, self-destruction? I'd hit a new kind of low.

One way of dealing with a problem is to pretend it doesn't exist. Another is to run away from it as fast as you can. In the weeks that followed that night in Anglesey, I tried both. I swore to myself and to the woman I'd been involved with that it would never happen again. And it didn't. But I tried to behave, I suppose, as if it hadn't happened at all. I didn't admit what I'd done to anybody.

I tried to maintain friendly relations with the woman but keep her at arm's length. I'd ask how she was doing. I'd respond if she messaged me. But I couldn't shake the memory off. In fact, I couldn't shake her off. I'd get messages from her suggesting we meet up for a coffee or go out for a walk.

Deep down I must have known that, as far as my career and my marriage were concerned, it wasn't up to me now. The woman I'd had sex with was now in a position to put paid to both. I felt trapped. The chance to wriggle out, it seemed like, just came right out of the blue. I don't remember how I got in touch with Zelda or how she got in touch with me. That's Facebook, right? I hadn't seen her for the best part of twenty years. Zelda had been my best man's partner when I married Rachel back in 1998. She and Richard were divorced now, and here she was, saying: *Why don't you come round? It'd be good to catch up.*

A chance to talk to someone different, a chance to forget about the crisis I was in the middle of. When Zelda answered the door, it was like a storm blew through me. She looked fantastic and was genuinely pleased to see me after all this time.

But there was something else, too. Seeing Zelda brought back memories, particularly of those days she and Richard had taken me into their home when things were bad with Rachel. Those days they'd looked after me, supported me. Right now, too, she represented a place of refuge. This might be what I was looking for: somewhere safe to hide.

40.

During those years I was abused by Bennell, I never knew where I stood from one moment to the next. That was part of his game. One minute he'd tell me I was special, that he loved me, that I wasn't like any other boy he'd known. The next, he'd be swinging nunchucks at my head or firing off an airgun in my direction. I never knew where we were or where we'd be going next.

Everything felt frightening, unstable and irrational. And I'd got used to life being like that; I'd come to expect it. And now, as an adult, something in me still seemed to crave that uncertainty, as if I wanted to be surprised by life all the time. I never felt as if I was in control. Instead, I'd cast myself as the victim and let people and situations control me. So big things happened. And often happened quickly.

I fell for Zelda, almost overnight. I went home and told Catherine:

It isn't working and I've met someone else. I moved out. No time to think or reflect; no time to question what I was doing; no time to consider whether it was true. Or to consider Catherine's feelings. Instead, I was gone and leaving her to pick up the pieces.

That photo at the start of the chapter is of me and Zelda, something she posted online. I hadn't given a thought for a while to the woman I'd had sex with when I'd been posted as her FLO. I'd tried to forget how unsettling some of her messages had been and how what we'd done threatened to pick my life and career apart at the seams.

I got an email from her. She hadn't known that I'd left Catherine. Now, the message was pretty simple. The email read: *Just look at what happens now.* I turned up for work that week and I was arrested. She'd walked into a police station the day before and had accused me of rape. I can only guess that she knew what that meant, to me of all people. She knew I'd been a victim, raped and abused. Now she was saying that was what I'd done to her, that I was a rapist and abuser in my turn.

It was the strangest feeling, sat in a cell on my own. The nature of the accusation was like somebody sticking a knife into me. I felt winded by the spite of it. But, at the same time, there was this weird sense of relief. I knew I hadn't raped her. And I knew I had the evidence in texts and messages to prove that. She'd been another secret I'd tried to keep out of sight but having it hauled out into the open now was a sort of release. I think I realised straight away that my time as a copper was over. I hadn't raped anybody but I'd crossed a line that I knew should never be crossed.

I got a solicitor and was interviewed under caution. I told them everything. What had happened had happened and there was no reason now to do anything but tell the truth. For once, revealing a secret wasn't a choice I could avoid making. I told Zelda what had happened, about me having had this inappropriate relationship. I told her this woman had made an allegation against me and that I'd been suspended. But I couldn't actually bring myself to say the word, to actually say that what I was accused of was rape. In the end, things didn't work out for me and Zelda but I've got to say that without her I'd never have been able to get through the couple of years that followed my arrest.

Zelda believed what I'd told her. She believed me and she didn't judge me. I'd been suspended, though, and what had happened really began to sink in: it broke me, the idea of being accused of what I'd been accused of. I had no idea what was going to happen next in my life: without my job – I'd been a policeman for longer than I'd been a professional footballer – I was cut adrift. Whatever this woman was doing now and whatever the pressure I'd been under at the time, I knew this whole thing ended up back on me.

Then, out of nowhere, stuff started turning up on social media about me and about Bennell. Even about Gary Speed. It was like I was being goaded. I was coming apart: vomiting three or four times a day. I lost three and a half stone in weight over those weeks. The anxiety wasn't about the rape charge. I knew that I'd be cleared of that but, with no job and no purpose, things crowded in on me. *What was the point of all this? What kind of life was I living?*

Those few months were a slow torture. While I waited for things to play out, I was being taunted on Facebook and online but the police wouldn't do anything about it. I was crawling from one day to the next.

From time to time, I'd go and stay at my mum and dad's house.

Dad had been diagnosed with motor neurone disease. They knew he was dying. And, on top of that, they were both worried sick about everything that had happened. I'd hide away in the worst possible place, in the little bedroom upstairs where Bennell had abused me. Even then, Zelda would come and find me. I'd be shaking but she'd climb into the bed with me, hold me, get me up and out of the house. *I'm here. We'll get through this.* It made a big difference that I could be more open with Zelda about my past than I'd ever been with anybody.

The wait for the Crown Prosecution Service to decide on whether or not to charge me stretched on. I couldn't believe how long it was taking to resolve things. Something had to give and in early 2016 I broke: I took a load of tablets and was admitted to hospital, where I was referred to the crisis team on the Mental Health Unit. The conversation was about whether or not I needed to be sectioned. Around the same time, Zelda had contacted Sporting Chance. People may know about the charity's work in relation to addiction but maybe they don't know so much about Sporting Chance and mental health. Any sportsperson can contact them if they're in trouble and be connected up to counselling and therapy.

The CEO came to see me and recognised straight away that I was struggling. I was referred to a psychiatrist who diagnosed me as suffering from PTSD – Post-Traumatic Stress Disorder – among other things. Sporting Chance was a lifeline. I got referred to a therapist locally and was booked in for a proper run of sessions with him.

I maybe didn't realise it at the time, but that was a chink of light at the end of a long and very dark tunnel. I was in touch with Professional Standards, asking why things were taking so long: *This is making me ill.* I'd started therapy by the time the phone call finally came. As far as the rape charge was concerned, the CPS had looked at the file and decided an outcome: *No Further Action.*

Even though I'd known I was innocent, it was a relief to hear it officially and to know I wouldn't be facing criminal charges. That's what I assumed, anyway. But this woman wasn't letting it go; she appealed and the case had to be referred up to a more senior level at the CPS.

I couldn't understand what kind of obsession was driving her to keep haunting me with it all. It was August before a final decision was actually made. Again: *No Further Action.*

Rape is an appalling crime that can do enormous damage, psychologically, to a victim. I know that from my own experience. And, if a man or a woman goes into a police station and says that he or she has been raped, they have the right to be believed. The right to have their allegation investigated impartially and thoroughly.

I'd worked on rape investigations, though. I knew how long these things needed to take and what sort of evidence you'd be looking for. I still have no idea why I was left hanging on, unable to work, living day to day, for over a year. It damaged me. But it also drove me to a point where I had to do something about my life.

I was seeing a therapist and learning so much about myself. I realised I had to be honest about things if I was going to get past them.

It was the first time I really faced up to that neediness in me: to be given attention and sympathy, for women to find me attractive, to be reassured I wasn't what Barry Bennell had tried to turn me into. Sex was bundled up with all of that. And, over the years, I'd been willing to jeopardise everything just to feel those emotions.

Those months in limbo were horrible but once I started sessions with the therapist, I really began to start to process stuff. *How had I got here? How had I got myself in such a state?* I talked to the therapist but I started thinking about my life on my own, too, outside our sessions.

I started joining things together, trying to make sense of things I'd done and things that had been done to me. Seeing how bad experiences had been behind so many of my own bad decisions. As a Detective Constable, you follow a trail of evidence. You try to put what's happened onto a timeline. Now, I was doing that for my own life.

In therapy I'd had before, all the focus had been on uncovering what had happened to me when I was a boy. Now, I was also thinking about what had happened since. The therapist suggested I start to write things down. He even asked if I had someone I could talk to who might help with it. A sort of journal: a way to look at things laid out in front of me instead of it all rattling around in my head. It turned out to be the key to a door. On the other side of that door was the man I am now.

41.

I had time on my hands while I waited for the CPS decisions. I saw the sense in writing stuff down, just for myself, as a way of making sense of my life. I wanted to do it but I wanted some help. Where could I start? Maybe I could talk and someone else could write it down? James Bentley was a guy I'd met when I was playing at Bury, a big fan of the club, and I remembered him writing a column for the Bury programme.

I followed James on Facebook so I dug out his number and gave him a ring: *James? I don't know if you remember me but I need your advice on something.* He and I met and talked. I explained why I needed help. It meant telling James a little about my background: what had happened to me before I turned up at Gigg Lane and what had happened since. I didn't go into detail but I saw James's eyes widening: this wasn't an ordinary football story and I'm not sure he knew what to say.

James admitted he didn't really know how to advise me: *But I know a guy, a journalist. Danny might be able to help.* James thought maybe this was a story that other people would be interested in. I took down his mate's number and said I'd get in touch. I had no idea where it was going to lead to. Certainly I had no idea it would turn out to be one of the most important phone calls I'd ever make.

Danny Taylor is the chief football writer for the *Guardian* and the *Observer* newspapers. He's based up in Manchester, so fixing up to meet wasn't a problem. I started from scratch with Danny. I explained about my therapist suggesting some kind of journal and then started to tell him some of what I wanted to get down on paper.

Danny's a great guy but, of course, he's also an excellent journalist. I began talking about Bennell, about Crewe and about how widespread I thought child abuse might be in football and I think he realised straight away that this might be a big story. Danny asked if it would be okay to record some of our conversation. He thought that might be useful for him but also useful for me, as a way of starting to organise my thoughts.

I found myself talking quite openly to Danny: we connected and because, as we talked, he was trying to put things in some kind of order, our conversation felt a bit like extra therapy sessions.

While I'd been suspended, I'd been able to think about my time with Bennell. I'd thought about the clubs he'd worked at – like Manchester City and Crewe – but also about other clubs where he'd taken us as boys and where he'd obviously had mates: Norwich, Southampton, Blackpool, Celtic and others. To start with, I was thinking about myself and my own situation but now, talking to Danny, I became more and more aware that all this went way beyond just one person's experience. I knew that, just with Bennell alone, there were hundreds of guys out there who must have been victims when they were boys.

It was probably after we'd met the first couple of times that Danny first suggested it: *Would you consider doing something in the newspaper? You know, football's what I write about. This is a pretty amazing story.* It was definitely something to think about. I'd taken the civil action all those years ago against Crewe because I wanted people to know what the club had done and hadn't done about Barry Bennell. I'd wanted to help other people who'd been in my situation. I'd had conversations with one or two other lads I knew. But doing something publicly? Being a serving policeman had made that difficult. But I was about finished with being a copper now, because the business with the woman who I'd slept with, who'd accused me of raping her, meant I was being investigated for misconduct. Danny was intending that this would be anonymous, too, but he still thought telling the story could make a real difference.

I'd had over a year to think about things while I was hung out, waiting for the CPS to do what they needed to do. I'd had the most recent rounds of therapy and I'd been talking to Danny. I knew that I wanted out of the police force. I'd realised that whatever problems I had as regards my mental health, being a policeman was now making them worse not better.

I also knew that I would have to face my misconduct hearing at some point. I hadn't raped the family member of a victim but the relationship I'd had with her was inappropriate, compromising and definitely against regulations.

I spoke to the Police Federation guy who was going to be representing me at my hearing. I told him I'd decided to leave the force and that I didn't want to have to stand up in front of a disciplinary panel and go through everything again. Knowing myself better now meant knowing that being at the hearing would completely mess my head up.

My rep wrote to the Assistant Chief Constable. I saw the Medical Officer and he agreed I shouldn't attend the hearing. I'd already put my hands up to what had happened. I'd given them the details about my past. About my present state of mind. Whether I resigned or got the sack, the outcome would be the same: I'd be leaving the police. I'd accept whatever decision the hearing arrived at.

The Federation rep had said I shouldn't attend. The Medical Officer, my therapist and my own GP said the same. But the answer came back that they were going ahead with the hearing and that I had to be there. I talked to the rep and made my own decision. I just didn't turn up: they could do whatever they were going to do in my absence.

The woman was at the hearing. She was called to give evidence and I heard she stayed for the duration. It was her last chance to kick off, I suppose. But I didn't go. I'd crossed the line by having a sexual relationship with her , so I knew the outcome was inevitable: I was dismissed from the police force on the grounds of gross misconduct. I feel bitter about the circumstances around it all: the lack of support I had in the FLO role; the way I was dealt with while the case was investigated; the way the hearing was handled. But the decision to dismiss me? I can't question that. I know what I did was wrong.

Zelda was amazing for me all through that period. Once I'd been sacked, she and I talked about me getting a new job and where my life might go from here.

Zelda was also the person I could talk to about my conversations with Danny. I trusted him and he assured me nothing would go in the paper that I hadn't checked first. But even so, was I ready for my story being out in the public domain? What about my kids? My parents? People I knew? Would they put things together and realise that it was me? How might that make them feel? But I needed to do the story. For myself but also for all the other people who might be out there, living with a secret like I had for over thirty years. I knew how positive a thing it might be for other victims to read my story and realise they weren't the only ones to have suffered back then. The only ones to still be suffering now.

By now, Danny and I had spent a lot of time together. Eventually, I agreed to do the article with him, to let it be published. But there was a kicker. Danny wanted it to have maximum impact: *Andy. Would you be willing to be named in the paper? Have a photo done? If you waived your right to anonymity, this would be so much more powerful. It would reach so many more people.*

I'd always said to Danny that I didn't want this to come back on my parents or on Lynda. It wasn't fair to them to involve them. They had their own stories to tell or not tell and I wanted to do everything I could to protect them.

I was worried too about what the effect on me would be if I put my name out there, if what had been secret for so long was suddenly something everyone could read in a newspaper.

I also knew that there was another possibility: that I'd do the story, expose the truth about myself, and there'd be no reaction at all. Maybe people would resent the fact that I was uncovering something that they'd rather was kept hidden. I might put myself out there and end up left hanging, high and dry.

From the first time I talked to Danny, my motive had been simple. I'd locked myself up inside what had happened to me; I'd buried the trauma and it had poisoned my life. I knew now how important it was to open up. I knew now that was the only way to get past being a victim and to become a survivor.

Maybe the most damaging thing of all is that feeling of being alone with your past: guilt, shame, fear and anger gnawing away at you, day after day. Danny and I talked about it a lot. *It's not just you. You don't have to live alone with this now.* He wanted what I wanted: to somehow give other victims the courage to come forward.

It felt almost like a duty to do whatever I could – now I was in this situation – to help people who'd been through experiences like mine. There was a chance that being honest about the past could stop people like Bennell getting away with it in the future.

There was one other thing I had to consider. While I was still on active duty with the police, I'd learned that Bennell had been released from prison. He was being investigated on two other charges. I didn't know what those charges were or how the investigations were progressing but I knew that Bennell was out on the street. I'd had no contact from him and had no idea where he was, but the thought of him being out there angered me. He couldn't get at me now but he might get at somebody else.

Telling my story – and other people perhaps coming forward to tell theirs – might help put him back where he belonged. I knew he'd never stop. He was what he was and always would be. He'd never feel remorse. He was never going to change. I knew what I needed to do.

It felt like I was walking out on the high board, looking down at the water: once I jumped, there'd be no going back. I had to trust myself. Trust Danny. What I had to lose suddenly seemed a lot less significant than what we all had to gain. Maybe this could be me beating that bastard at last. I agreed to do it: I jumped. And then I waited for the splash.

42.

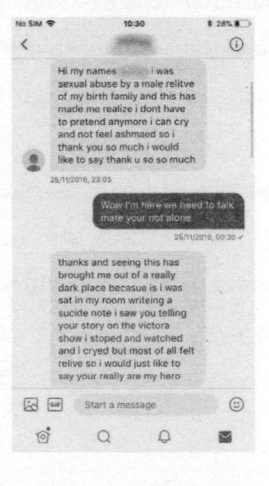

The whole process with Danny took something like two months. This was a big story for him and for football. I was more excited the nearer we got to it going in the paper. At the same time, though, I was dreading it.

There were conversations I needed to have. People I couldn't just spring this on. I spoke to Rachel: it was better she had the chance to talk to our boys in the way she wanted to. The hardest conversations were the ones with Mum and Dad. This was their story, too, wasn't it? They'd been there from the start, however much sometimes I'd tried to push them away. This man had been a part of their lives as well as the lives of their children. I wasn't judging them but I was afraid that other people might. I understood the pain and the guilt that they felt as parents but I'll never really know how they dealt with that grief and anger together, how they found the strength not to be destroyed by Bennell. They were still Mum and Dad. I know they were there for Lynda and their grandchildren. They'd been there for me, too: home was always the place I could run to when things were going wrong in my career and in my marriages. No judgements made: I loved them and I know how much they loved me.

Although I'd talked about my experiences to the police, to therapists and, now, to Danny Taylor, as a family we never had those conversations. What Bennell had done to us all and the effect on all our lives since: it wasn't a secret but it wasn't something we faced up to together either. Now I was planning to put it all out there in the public domain. How would that make them feel?

Dad was dying: there's only one way things go with motor neurone disease. But he wasn't gripped tight by the symptoms yet. He could still think straight, could still speak. When I sat down to talk to him and to my mum, it felt like all three of us were taking stock. *This is us, isn't it? Me telling the story, telling the truth about all of it. Are we all right with this now?* Their children had always been the most important people in their lives and now Dad was saying: *Go on, Andy. Do it.* Now and always, it gave me the strength that I needed. I knew I had my parents' support.

For Dad, I sometimes think me doing the story allowed him to settle up his account, too. Otherwise he'd have taken all that guilt – and the secret – with him to his grave. Mum was concerned about what the effect of the newspaper article might have on the family. Her memories would have gone back all the way to the publicity around her sister's murder. She remembered the guy from the *Sunday Times* turning up on the doorstep asking about Lynda and Bennell. I tried to reassure her. Beyond what was easily accessible fact, I wasn't going into any detail about the family. I was doing everything I could to keep them and Lynda out of the story. I promised that I'd try to protect them from any intrusion into their lives. To be honest, Mum was never going to say anything that didn't back my dad up. And he was sure: *Just go for it, Andy.*

The dream that had led me to Bennell had been football. And now I wanted to think about that: as well as having an effect on me, on my family and, perhaps, on other victims, Danny was sure this was going to be a very big deal for the game as well. I had such strong memories of how supportive both Stan Ternent and Neil Warnock had been at Bury and at Sheffield United, all those years ago. I still had their numbers and one evening, during the week before the story came out, I rang them both. When I was playing for them, I knew they both needed to get the most out of me as a player. Now, though, they had no vested interest in what I was doing. I was just a guy – an ex-player – asking for their thoughts and advice. Both of them were adamant: *Go on, Woody. Get it done, son. People need to know what's gone on.*

The story was being written up by a football writer. As well as being about me and about Bennell, it was a story about football. Danny was sure this was going to be a big deal for the game.

16 November 2016: I remember I saw the article online before I saw it in a copy of the paper. It was quite shocking to me, in a way, seeing my picture and my words: the truth of it laid out. I think Danny did a great job but, even so, my first reaction was: *Oh, fuck. What have I done?*

But that first day of publication was life-changing for me. Maybe for a few other people, too. Online, you can track how many people have read an article. There were a lot. Danny rang me early that morning: *Andy. I don't think you realise how big this is going to be.* He said the paper had already taken calls from other people. From other victims.

This may sound ridiculous but the most important thing in those moments was realising what was happening: *People believe me. They believe my story.* I remembered my court case against Crewe: the feeling of being doubted, trampled over, dismissed. Now it was different. I'd laid it all out: this is what happened to me. We're all the same, aren't we? Other people believing in us helps us to believe in ourselves.

The rest of that day and the couple of days after it were incredible. TV, radio, other papers wanting to get in touch. People finding me on social media, wanting to support me, some of them asking for help.

~

One call I remember clear as day was from Danny Taylor the afternoon the story broke. Steve Walters – who'd come up to Crewe from Plymouth all those years ago – had rung him at the paper. He needed to tell someone: *I was abused, too.* Danny said Steve was in tears on the phone, wanting to share his story. I was in tears on the phone to Danny when he told me. It was like a dam breaking. For all of us. It had started. I remembered the Christmas Steve and I spent together at Dove Holes; I knew he had been abused by Bennell. I hadn't seen him or spoken to him for over twenty years. When I left Crewe, I left everything behind, including friendships. But hearing that Steve had come forward meant everything to me. Knowing that one person had been helped by reading my story in the paper was all the justification I needed for agreeing to do the interview with Danny in the first place. Steve was the first person to come forward. As soon as he did, I knew he wouldn't be the last.

Hundreds of boys were abused by Bennell. I couldn't know what damage had been done to their lives but I hope that reading my story made a difference. Steve and others have said to me since that it was seeing my picture, reading my words, that gave them the courage to come forward themselves. *It was seeing you, Woody.*

People started getting in touch with me: victims asking for help and advice. It wasn't just lads from Crewe. Some of them were nothing to do with football at all but they'd all been abused. In a way, I was lucky I'd spent all that time in the police. I knew what to do and not do. I knew I couldn't start talking to anyone in detail about what had happened to them. That would have involved me in any potential criminal investigations. In fact, it could have undermined those investigations because of the rules of disclosure around criminal cases. In my time as a Detective Constable, I'd seen rape and abuse trials collapse because victims had had exactly those kinds of conversations.

Nobody was advising me on how to handle the calls I was getting, but I had that first-hand experience, so I directed people to the NSPCC and to the police.

As well as the calls from individuals, I was getting calls from the press and from broadcasters. I don't know, really, how I dealt with those next few days. I could pick up the phone to Danny, of course. But, other than that, I had nowhere to go for advice on how to deal with the attention that came with that first story in the *Guardian*. I didn't hear from the PFA or the FA at all until later on. And not surprisingly, I didn't hear from Crewe Alexandra, the club that should have been supporting me all along but had decided instead to pretend I didn't exist.

In amongst it all, I was contacted by the BBC about going on Victoria Derbyshire's show. I'd seen the programme and she struck me as someone who would understand my story and recognise why it was important. I thought that, if I did a show like that, I wouldn't be under so much pressure to do anything else. I knew that I had to keep going with this if getting the story out there was going to make a difference. I agreed to go on the show.

As a footballer, I never really suffered from pre-match nerves. I enjoyed the pressure that came with big games. Football focused me. This was different. I'd never known nerves like I felt the day before doing Victoria's show. I travelled down on the train. Zelda came with me. I remember her saying to me: *Are you all right, Andy? This is big, isn't it?* It wasn't so much the thought of going on TV; it was knowing my family would be watching. Friends, too. And people I'd known but not seen for years. I was scared of shocking them or hurting them, I suppose. At the same time, I knew there'd be people watching who needed to hear what I had to say.

I met Victoria and the show's editor, Louisa Compton, in a room at Broadcasting House. We spent half an hour, more, together, talking things through. I knew as soon as I met them that I'd made the right decision. They wanted to reassure me that they weren't just after headlines, that they'd deal with the story as sensitively as they could. Victoria kept saying: *Don't worry. Don't worry. I'll look after you out there.*

I told them stuff that I wouldn't be able to say on air: the circumstances around what had happened to me and the scale of the abuse that had been happening in football. That was probably still happening.

They went through all the questions they were thinking of asking me. They were lovely with me: sympathetic and sincere. I knew I wanted to do it. At the same time, I'd never been in a situation anything like this before. Almost before I had time to think, I was out on the studio floor. I could feel the heat of the lights on my face. But I was physically shaking: nerves, excitement, a chill in the studio air. I thought of my CBT and just tried to keep my breathing steady and my thoughts under control. Victoria started explaining who I was and what the story was about.

Somehow, I came across pretty calm and composed. It helped that Victoria stayed so focused, that she didn't just ask questions but really listened to my answers. I was churning inside but there is a strength in knowing why you're doing what you're doing. Part of it was saying: *There, Bennell, you bastard. There's the truth.* But, beyond that, it was the chance to say direct to other victims: *If something's happened to you and you need to talk, it's okay. You can. People will listen.*

No two people are alike and, for some, they have to bury their experience and move on. They can't let go. But to those who were struggling with what I'd struggled with – the pain, the guilt and the shame – this was my chance to say: *I've had the courage to come forward. You can too.*

Next thing I knew the interview was over and, I was back in the green room with Zelda. A little while later, Louisa came in: *Andy. I can't believe the response we've had.* She said they'd been inundated with messages and calls.

I had this overwhelming sense of relief: I'd done what I needed to do. What I'd probably been needing to do for the past thirty years. And people had listened. It was disorienting. As I was leaving the BBC that morning, people were in tears; complete strangers came up to me and hugged me.

Later, the show did a recap on the story and included some of the reaction from people who'd watched the interview. There was one person got in touch who they didn't want to put on air but they wanted me to know about. Louisa explained that someone had contacted the show to say they'd been a victim of sexual abuse. They'd been sitting in a dark room that morning, suicide note written and a bottle of pills next to the bed.

Louisa asked if I'd be okay with being in direct contact with this person. That screenshot is the message he sent me. I assumed it would be a guy about my age, probably connected in some way to football. It turned out, though, that this was a thirteen-year-old boy. He'd been in his bedroom, ready to take his own life, his parents sat unaware downstairs.

The lad had watched the interview and stopped himself. We spoke later on: I told him how glad I was that he'd not gone through with what he'd been planning to do. We talked about what he could do now: about speaking to a doctor, to his parents. To the NSPCC if that was what he needed. *You're not on your own, you know.*

When I think about my own life, that conversation is maybe the single best thing that's ever happened to me. To be able to have that impact on someone I didn't even know: me telling my story had stopped a young guy ending his. Pride's the wrong word but it's an emotion like that: I felt worthwhile, validated, as if I'd been able to do something that really mattered. A life had been saved: listening to me tell my truth made that young lad think again. He'd stepped back from the dark.

43.

I can't speak highly enough of people like Danny Taylor and Victoria Derbyshire. They were incredibly supportive and I still have relationships with them that are important to me. Back in 2016, they did their best to keep tracking the Bennell story. They saw that it needed to be widened out: it was a story about something very wrong at the heart of the national game.

Appearing on Victoria Derbyshire's show sort of opened the floodgates. In the days after, I got calls from every imaginable media outlet: TV, radio, press, online. It had seemed so daunting to me when Danny first suggested I waive my anonymity. But my response now – at first, anyway – was to say *Yes* to every request.

I had nobody advising me and I just trusted my own instincts: *I've started. If I really want to reach people and make a difference, I've just got to push on with this now.* If I stopped for breath, I was worried people in football – individuals and clubs – would start to try shutting me and the story down. So I kept talking. And people kept listening. People kept getting in touch: *I was abused, too.*

Zelda helped me through it all. She came along to every single interview I did: we'd talk before, talk afterwards. I knew she was in the room and on my side day after day.

I got through interview after interview. I was motivated. And, early on, I made the decision that I had to focus in just on my own experiences. Whatever I was asked, I stuck to that. It wasn't the time or the place to be blaming anybody, criticising what individuals and organisations had or hadn't done. That was for other people to do if they wanted to. The important thing was to simply get my story out there in the hope that it would reach the people it needed to. I knew I could do that – and keep doing it – now I'd found the courage to stand up and say out loud for the first time: *This is me. And this is what happened.*

Danny and the *Guardian* kept running with it: they interviewed Steve Walters and started asking questions about the clubs who'd worked with Bennell, like Manchester City and Crewe. Danny started challenging the Football Association, too.

Victoria's show invited me to go back down to London and appear with three other ex-players who'd come forward, who'd found the courage to talk publicly about their own experiences after seeing me on the BBC. I met Steve Walters, Chris Unsworth and Jason Dunford at the hotel the night before.

It was an emotional evening. All four of us had lived with a secret. We'd all felt some of the same things: fear, guilt, shame and anger. More than anything, we'd all felt as if we'd been alone with what had happened to us. Now, suddenly, we were in a room together, defences down, sharing what had been buried inside each of us for thirty years and more. I don't know what it was like for the other lads but listening to their memories brought a lot of my own back, vivid and raw.

We went along to the studio the following day. I don't think I realised just how big a deal seeing the lads had been for me. How on edge I was after the reaction I'd had from going on the show the first time. We went on air together and Victoria asked Chris and then Steve to talk about their experiences with Bennell. I was on the end of the row, listening.

The wave of emotion that rolled over me was like nothing else. Complicated, intense: the boys' stories were incredibly sad but they were telling a version of my story, too. Some of the detail was almost too hard to listen to. It hit me, physically. Because I already knew it too well. At one point Victoria asked: *Why had none of us talked to each other – or anyone else – at the time?* The question hung in the air. That was how the secret had worked on us: the silence Bennell had wrapped us all up in. How could we really explain?

I just wanted to hug these guys, to say I understood and that I was sorry. At the same time, though, I felt vindicated, proud: they were able to speak up now because I had. That's why they were here. I'd been able to keep it all together the first time I went on air with Victoria. Maybe how nervous I'd been had helped. I'd tried to breathe steadily, to concentrate on Victoria and her questions. I'd been able to keep my feelings under control for those fifteen minutes, at least.

Now, though, as I was listening to Chris and to Steve, emotion just overwhelmed me: I sat there and sobbed my way through half an hour of live telly. Me breaking down during the interview was honest in its own way. I'd broken down like that so many times over thirty-odd years, but on my own usually, at home or parked up in my car. Feeling pain wasn't something I had to be ashamed of any more. For me – and for Chris and Steve, too – it was time for that burden to be lifted: *What happened and what was done to you; it wasn't your fault.*

Seeing those other lads after so many years made me begin to realise the true scale of what Bennell had done to us all. I knew my own story and I knew how trying to deal with it had affected me. I understood the damage that had been done to my friendships, my family relation-ships and my marriages. My children, too. I had my history of addiction and illness and mental health problems that had followed me around since boyhood.

And now I realised that these guys – and dozens, maybe hundreds of others – had their own stories they'd struggled to come to terms with: not just what Bennell had done to them but all the grief and confusion since. And, like mine, their families and friends had been hurt by him as well. When you start to think about it, the impact Bennell had on all of us takes your breath away. How many lives had been twisted and scarred – ruined, even – by what he had done? Ripples on a dark, dark pool.

And now it was everywhere: this was becoming as big a story in football as anybody could remember. Uncovering Barry Bennell felt as if it would just be the start of it. You know: something's hidden away but then, as soon as you glimpse it once, you realise it's everywhere. Over those days and weeks, that's what seemed to be happening with child abuse in football. Something that had been out of sight for years was now out in the open. And nobody could ignore it any longer.

I guess I wasn't surprised when I got a call from the Football Association: *Hi Andy. Can you come and see us, please?* The subject had reached football's front door. Zelda and I went down to Wembley Stadium – the new Wembley now, not the old one I'd played at – and they were there to meet us: big plate of sandwiches, cups of tea, sympathy. Sue Ravenlaw, the FA's head of safeguarding, seemed a very genuine person and she was in tears.

I wanted to tell them what I was hoping all the publicity might achieve. I explained that, as far as I was concerned, what was past was past. The police and the courts had to take responsibility now. What mattered to me was the future and making sure that what had happened to me would never happen to anyone else. As far as I saw it now, me speaking had to be only the beginning.

I told Sue and the FA's communications guy, Danny Lynch, that I was keen to be involved in any way I could. I was sure I could help. I wanted to help. I met with the FA chairman, Greg Clarke. I didn't have to – *No pressure, Andy* – but he'd asked to meet me. Greg was very hospitable. He was shocked by my story, he said. He thought I'd been very brave to speak out.

By this time, a lot of people had already contacted the police – about Bennell and others – and the FA were in the process of setting up a helpline for victims. Greg promised they wouldn't shirk the responsibility for the issue. They'd do everything they could to find out what had gone on and make sure it never happened again. And, in the meantime, he was going to do everything he could to support me.

That day at Wembley made me feel optimistic. I was convinced the FA wanted what I wanted. I went out into the stadium car park, and told all the news outlets that were waiting to speak to me that the FA had been very supportive and that I believed we could make some progress from here.

At the time, that was really how I felt. They'd welcomed me in and said all the right things. Thinking back, though? Maybe all that was just a PR exercise on the FA's part. With all the publicity, they needed to be seen to be doing something, didn't they? Sue Ravenlaw has worked in the field of child protection for a long time. I'm sure she understands stories like mine and wants to change things for the better going forward. But the FA as an organisation? Greg Clarke? The inquiry they set up? I'm not sure. I can't help but feel that maybe they're so desperate sometimes to be *seen* to do the right thing that they don't ever get round to actually doing it.

44.

A lot of victims and a lot of members of the public found me on social media. I was overwhelmed, really. The support I got helped convince me that what I was doing was right. Reaching me online meant those other abuse victims, both inside and outside football, at least had a place to start. But poison turned up on those channels as well.

I was at home with Zelda. Evening time: we'd had some friends round. I was on my phone and, all of a sudden, my in-box pinged and up came a picture of Bennell. His name underneath it as the sender. My heart stopped. I knew he was out after serving his sentence. The message on Twitter read: *Hi Andy. Am feeling horny. Fancy popping round mine?* Then there was a video clip – like a cartoon – of Bennell sucking a lollipop.

I didn't know for sure where Bennell was. But I was sure he'd have seen all the publicity. That he'd have watched me on TV. Much later on I found out that, seeing those interviews, Bennell realised what would happen to him because of them. That he knew me talking was what started a process that ended with him back in prison. That evening, though, I had no idea what he'd be thinking or what he might be capable of doing. Even the possibility of it being him sending the message tipped me over the edge: I all but passed out. My heart was pounding and I was struggling for breath. Panic pushed back in on me.

We called the police and they came round, sat with me, trying to reassure me. At that stage they couldn't tell me it wasn't Bennell. They'd have to chase down the IP address before they could do that. They took a statement from me and then went off to investigate where the message had come from.

It didn't take them long to find out that it had been sent by someone in Crewe. They got back in touch and assured me it wasn't Bennell. They'd found the bloke: a dad, about my age. He said he was really sorry. It had just been a prank, meant as a joke. *A bit out of order*, he'd called it. The police asked me if I'd agree to a local resolution, without the need for criminal proceedings. The bloke would say sorry. I'd say: *Thanks for that.* Then we'd all walk away. Straight away, I said: *Certainly not.*

It seemed obvious to me that whoever had set up the account and sent the message must have had an idea how much harm and upset it would cause. It wasn't right to just let it slide away. This guy needed to take responsibility for what he did on the internet. Otherwise, the web becomes a place where it's too easy to hide. The police took it to the CPS and the guy was charged with trolling me under the Malicious Communications Act.

The whole thing played out over a year later. It was bizarre. It went to court and the guy pleaded not guilty, even though he'd already given a statement to the police saying he'd done it. In the meantime, the man's son, eighteen years old, turned up at the police station with a different story. He told them his dad had just been covering up. It was him who'd actually set up the account. So they'd both lied about it.

Eventually, they were both found guilty of perverting the course of justice and sent down for a year each. I never regretted taking it all the way through the courts; more hate messages and malicious posts should end up there. And there was something else: in the past, if the police had suggested sorting something like this out with a local resolution, I'd have agreed. I was forever doing what other people told me to. But things were different now. I'd put myself out there and this wasn't the time to be retreating back into the shadows.

I remember the day before the very first *Guardian* article came out, I had a talk with Danny Taylor. Right up to the last minute, he was making changes to what was going to end up in the paper. It was as if we had one shot at this and he wanted to make sure we got it right. There was one line in it that Danny still wasn't sure about: I'd told him I believed there were hundreds of victims out there. That Bennell, on his own, would have abused hundreds of boys.

Even though Danny knew me and knew the story better than anyone, he had his doubts about writing that. *Hundreds? Really?* He was worried that, if people thought I was exaggerating, that might undermine everything else in the article. I insisted, though, and given what's happened since I think we're both glad we kept that line in. It all moved on so quickly. Other journalists started doing their own investigations and interviews. Every day it seemed there was something new coming out. It didn't take long for it to become pretty obvious that *Hundreds* was the right number to have been talking about.

The FA, the police, the NSPCC were all getting calls and messages. Sporting Chance did, too. More people coming forward than anyone could have foreseen. Within a couple of weeks, the FA had appointed a QC, Clive Sheldon, to conduct an inquiry into historic child sex abuse in football. By the middle of December, the FA's helpline had taken 1,700 calls. There was a feeling that this was just the beginning. Greg Clarke called it the biggest crisis in the history of football.

The same day the FA announced their inquiry, they suspended Dario Gradi from all football activity. As it happens, I think that suspension was in connection with a story from his time at Chelsea and a scout named Eddie Heath who's dead now. But all the current conversation was about Barry Bennell. That meant a lot of people were asking questions as well about Crewe and Manchester City, the two clubs he'd worked for while I was growing up.

Manchester City were pretty quick to set up their own inquiry into what had happened when Bennell was employed by them. The idea was to find out what he'd done and who knew about it. Had the club done enough to protect boys in the system? Crewe said they were going to set up an inquiry, too. But they never have.

One man, though, has said his piece: Hamilton Smith was a director at Crewe back in the day. He'd told a Channel 4 programme in 1998 that he'd been worried about Bennell years before. He said he'd raised the matter with the board and with Dario Gradi but had been shut down, ignored. He'd even contacted the FA about it and they'd told him there was no case to answer. Basically he'd been told to shut up and go away.

Now, Hamilton Smith was being written about and talked to again. I read what he had to say in the papers and I watched him interviewed on TV. I could see and hear emotions swirling round inside him. Anger about what had been done to us boys. Frustration that the club had done nothing about it. Guilt that he hadn't done more himself when he might have. I'd felt all those things myself over the years. But from Crewe Alexandra? Not a word. Maybe nobody else at the club recognised what we'd been through. More likely, they decided the best thing to do was to hide themselves away, pretend nothing had happened and hope the fuss would die down.

I remember players at Crewe calling me Bennell's 'bum boy' and other teams calling us the 'paedo club'. And now Crewe were saying nobody had had any idea what their youth coach had been up to.

Maybe Crewe was that scared of what all this would mean for the club that people even convinced themselves they hadn't known anything. That's for them to say, I suppose. All the questions are there for them to answer. In the meantime, I know I'm still angry. There are plenty of others, too. We feel we were let down by the club back then and we're still being let down by them today.

One of the reasons Crewe gave for cancelling their inquiry was that the FA was doing one. They didn't need to, did they? The QC Clive Sheldon started taking evidence in 2017. I was invited in quite early on. We went through everything that had happened to me, all of it fact. No *I believe* or *I think*. Just the facts of what was done to me. I told him as much as I could remember. At the end, he just said: *Thanks very much. We'll be in touch with a statement for you to okay.* And I was out in the street to find my way to the station to get the train back into Manchester.

It came out a little later on that Sheldon and his team were being offered counselling to help them deal with hearing accounts like mine. I'm sure it was pretty difficult stuff to listen to and the FA had a duty of care: they'd employed Sheldon, after all. Still, I was pretty disappointed that the duty of care hadn't extended to the victims themselves.

None of us were offered counselling after going through it all for the inquiry's benefit. We were interviewed and then packed off home. Left to read Sheldon's findings when he got round to putting them down on paper. Compare that to Manchester City's internal inquiry, which offered every witness a counsellor in case they needed to talk about their experience afterwards.

It was over a year before the statement for me to check came through: less than a page, as it turned out, three paragraphs to summarise what I'd experienced over six years at Crewe. The whole experience with the inquiry left me feeling pretty bitter, to be honest. Worse, it left me doubting what the FA were really looking for their inquiry to achieve. Of course, safeguarding practices are better than they were. But I've been left feeling that the FA were going through the motions.

If my account – just one of many – could be skimmed down to a couple of paragraphs, how deep was this thing ever really going to go?

Even before the inquiry was completed, it was reported that it would find no evidence of a cover-up at the FA, no evidence of a paedophile ring having operated in football. So the FA was in the clear, but what about the rest of us? The witnesses and victims? Sheldon's report is now on hold pending fresh court cases and we're still left in limbo, aren't we?

Maybe it sounds like I'm being cynical. But I'm disappointed that the FA haven't involved me in any way: there's nothing I'd like to do more than go into clubs and talk to young players – and to coaches and parents – about what happened to me. I know my first-hand experience would be valuable in those situations.

In the weeks after the story broke, I felt a bit like I was being used, that there was a PR exercise going on and that getting me onside was only worthwhile because of that. Once the FA had ticked that box with me, there wasn't really any desire to build a relationship going forward.

I didn't hear from Greg Clarke for months. It came as a bit of a shock when he stood up in front of a parliamentary select committee and started talking about how he'd met with one of Bennell's victims, that he'd had to comfort a grown man who had been 'crying like a baby'. It was pretty obvious who he was talking about. And it seemed to me that he was just trying to get out from under the pressure of that committee. I'd been very emotional that first day I went to Wembley to meet the FA but there had been no tears. It had been a private meeting, too. Now he was making it public so he could make a show of how much he cared. Maybe it's because of the flak Greg Clarke took over that incident that the FA have steered clear of me since.

45.

B ennell's an old man now. Half his tongue gone after he had cancer. His voice all weird and squeaky. But even when I look at a photo like this one – I think it's about five years old – I can still see him how he was when I was a lad. A lad with a life he was taking over and destroying. He's hollowed out now, isn't he? Frail, skinny, losing his hair, his face all drawn. But it's as if I can't stop myself. He's this empty shell. But all my memories and my emotions fill him out again in my mind. They bring him back to life whether I like it or not. It's different now. He's locked away and, maybe, those memories are locked away with him and for good. Barry Bennell might as well be dead.

I don't know if him reading the papers or watching the telly had anything to do with it but, a couple of weeks after I went public about my story, Bennell was found unconscious in Knebworth Park, not far from where he was living in Milton Keynes. When the police first attended, it was in regard to what they write up in the report as *a safeguarding concern*. They reckoned he'd tried to top himself.

Back in 1998, he'd been sent down for nine years. That was the trial I'd given my statement for. He got done again in 2015 and sent down for another two years. But he was out and going by the name Richard Jones by the time he was discovered by the emergency services in November 2016.

I knew Bennell had been ill. The probation service got in touch with my mum at one point. The guy said he was Bennell's probation officer. He told Mum that Bennell had cancer and that, because he was ill and they didn't know how things would turn out, he'd asked to see his children again. *One last time.*

That was him all over: the melodrama, wanting everybody to feel sorry for him even though he'd never had a thought for the damage he'd done to other people. I know the man. How his victims felt never even crossed Bennell's mind. How he felt was all that mattered to him. My mum was upset and angry. She just hung up on the probation guy.

While he was ill, Bennell tried to contact some former players – lads he'd abused – asking them for help. Asking them for money. Over the years, I haven't used Facebook regularly. I'd be on it for a while, then just leave it alone for ages. After the *Guardian* story, though, I was looking at ways to keep spreading the word and I scrolled through my old friend requests. And there he was: Richard Barry. That was the name he used on his Facebook account, along with a photo. It had sat there for years, since 2009.

Why had he wanted to get in touch? To say hello, to threaten me, to ask me for help? I've got no idea. I'm glad I saw that friend request after I'd done the newspaper article and not before. After Bennell got out of prison around 2003 or 2004, he'd started posting all sorts of pictures and videos. Snaps of a new house, a car. Photos of his daughter, my niece. Videos of holidays he went on to Gran Canaria: the same place, Puerto Rico – the same apartment block – where he'd taken us as boys and abused us.

I look at those online images now because part of me wants to be reminded what a manipulative, nerveless bastard he was. But it's something else, too. Bennell was just out of jail back then, wasn't he? I look at that lifestyle of his and wonder: how did he ever afford all that? Where did the money to pay for it come from? Did he have someone who was helping him out? Those images – the holiday snaps, pictures of a new car – still bother me today.

When I heard what had happened to him in 2016 and that he'd been taken to hospital, I could see straight through him. Immediately, I knew exactly what he'd have done: he'd have pretended to be attempting suicide, trying to make himself seem like the victim now. He got taken to hospital in Stevenage but, a couple of days later, the police arrested and charged him on eight more counts of abuse. They saw through him too.

I knew how important it was for lads who were abused by Bennell to see him in court, charged and convicted. He was the guilty one and it being proved in public could help release some of the guilt you carry around as a victim. A conviction won't make the trauma of what happened go away but it can maybe make things clearer: you're being listened to; you're being believed; and you've survived.

I know there are still hundreds more charges lying on file against Bennell. He'll die in prison now anyway but I understand why the CPS are looking to charge him again. The possibility of fresh charges has delayed the publication of the Sheldon Inquiry, though, and that's frustrating for a lot of people, me included. But, at the same time, I know how important a trial could be for victims who've not yet had their day in court, their chance to say what happened to them and then see justice done.

Bennell was arrested in November 2016 and remanded in custody. He didn't go to court until over a year later but, by then, he was up for fifty-five offences relating to the abuse of twelve boys. A couple of those boys, now grown men, I'd sat with on Victoria Derbyshire's show: Steve Walters and Chris Unsworth.

~

Life rushed past at a hundred miles an hour after my story came out. I felt really strongly that I needed to find a way to make the immediate impact last if all the publicity wasn't going to be wasted. So much was being said about the past but I understood that it was the future that mattered now.

In December 2016, we set up an organisation called the Offside Trust. Steve Walters and Chris Unsworth were involved straight away. At the start I think the idea was just to support each other, to help other victims come forward and to look after them when they did. I remember the afternoon we had the press conference to announce us starting the organisation. It was in this big, oak-panelled room at the

Midland Hotel in Manchester. Zelda and I had got in touch with all the papers and the place was packed: journalists, photographers, TV crews. There was a real power in the room and a lot of emotion. Me and Steve sat sat up front with one or two others and talked about how we were 'brothers' now.

That was early December 2016. It felt as if we were really doing something positive. That we were going to be able to make a difference. We were 'brothers', tied together by shared experience and shared memories. But even that closeness couldn't mean all of us would always agree.

Even though I'd been right there at the very start of the Offside Trust, I wasn't able to stay involved for very long. Within a couple of months I was no longer a part of the Trust, no longer a director, no longer a part of what we'd set out to achieve together.

It hurt at the time. I'd wanted to enjoy that sense of family between us. I thought I'd find strength alongside guys who'd been through similar experiences and survived. But that didn't happen. Very soon, I was part of the Offside Trust's history. I wasn't going to be part of its future.

It felt as if every time I turned somewhere for support, the connection couldn't hold: I'd ended up now on the outside again, very much on my own. It wasn't great for me, to be honest, realising I no longer had a part to play with the Trust. I wonder sometimes if it's been good for them me not being involved.

That's past now, anyway, and I know the lads are still trying to find their way forward. I really do wish them all well for the future.

∼

Journalists get a lot of stick, especially when it comes to stories around football. But I have to say I'll always be grateful for the way I was treated by the media in the months after Danny and I did the story. I got the feeling that they really understood how serious the issue was and they were almost always respectful and sensitive when speaking to me. A lot of them did great work, as well, following up on Bennell and other abuse cases. Although they were the first, it wasn't just Danny Taylor and Victoria Derbyshire who believed in me. I got support and a fair hearing from just about every journalist I spoke to. They kept the story going and that helped keep me going, to be honest.

Every year, all the sports journalists get together for the SJA awards. In February 2017, I got invited to go along with Danny. And I was asked if I'd speak. Danny got Sports Writer of the Year and Scoop of the Year on the back of what we'd done together. The ceremony was held at the Park Plaza hotel down in Westminster: a huge room, tables laid out as far as you could see.

All those writers and broadcasters: it should have been scary, standing up in front of them. Well, it was scary. It had taken me a long time to get here, though. I'd given a statement to the police about Bennell in 1998. I'd talked to therapists. And I'd spoken to Danny, Victoria Derbyshire and to quite a few of the other people who were looking in my direction now.

So I was scared, but I knew why I was there and knew what I wanted to say. I didn't need a prepared speech or anything. For the first time in my life now, I feel as if I can trust myself to just speak from the heart. Trust myself to say the right thing. That evening, I thanked the media for their support, for believing the story and for not letting it disappear. I told them that all I wanted now was to do everything I could to make a difference in the future. The audience listened. You could have heard a pin drop. And then everybody in the room was suddenly on their feet and applauding.

It was an amazing feeling. I don't mean just the buzz of an audience of experienced journalists giving me that kind of reception. That was great, of course: I get goosebumps remembering it. But, deeper down, it made me realise I'd found something in myself.

For years, I'd been silent, desperate that what had happened to me remain a secret. Of course, that's what Bennell wanted. Not just from me but from all of us. And not just Bennell: other people and football clubs, too. But speaking up and putting my name to my story set me free. It had been all about silence for so many years. Now, all of a sudden, I'd found my voice. And I had something I wanted to say.

46.

It started with Jimmy Savile, didn't it? After that, and quite a few more high-profile sex abuse cases – including Stuart Hall's, a case I'd worked on as a police officer – the police recognised the need for a coordinated, national response to what had been going on. Not just with regard to people in the public eye but also historical cases involving institutions like schools, children's homes, churches and Scout groups.

Operation Hydrant, which was set up in 2014, made sure national statistics were available so there could be a national response, different forces around the country cooperating with one another, sharing information and working to an agreed agenda. Each force would still do its own investigations but Hydrant would be there to make sure there wasn't duplication or confusion or a waste of resources. And now, my story turned Hydrant's attention to football.

I know what happened to me. I know what happened to a lot of other boys at Crewe because I was there at the time. In the same house and, often, in the same bed. But I was still shocked when Hydrant's figures were rounded up. In March 2018, they published statistics relating to football, going back to November 2016 when my story first broke. In just over eighteen months, 2,800 cases of abuse were reported. eight hundred and fifty victims and 300 suspects were identified. Three hundred and forty football clubs were mentioned in statements, ranging from Premier League clubs through to amateur organisations all over the UK.

Court cases and convictions have followed. As well as Bennell himself, others like George Ormond, William Toner, Michael Coleman, Jim McCafferty, Robert Smith, James Torbett, Gerald King, Frank Cairney and Norman Shaw all got convicted and most of them are behind bars now. Another one, Kit Carson, drove his car into a tree and died on his way to the first day of his trial.

There would have been many more but men like Frank Roper and Eddie Heath have already died. More's the pity; they'll never face justice and the boys they abused may never find any kind of closure. Those men die and most of their secrets die with them. I don't think Hydrant is finished yet, though. There are still abusers – and their victims – waiting for court proceedings to begin.

It took a while after Bennell was arrested for him to come to court. The police investigation ran on and on. Every couple of months, Bennell would be back in court to be charged on further counts. He pleaded guilty to a few of the more minor offences and not guilty to all the serious ones, the assaults, rapes and attempted rapes. By the time the trial started in Liverpool on 8 January 2018, he was facing fifty-five charges.

Even though I had decided not to be a complainant this time round – I'd done my bit back in 1998 – the months leading up to Bennell's trial I found really difficult. Those Operation Hydrant figures tell you how big the story became. Because I'd started the ball rolling, people were forever asking me: *What are you going to do now?* Truth is, I was proud of what I'd done but I'm not sure I knew how to handle what came afterwards. I asked myself that same question: *What happens now?*

I felt as if it was down to me to be a spokesperson, even though I'd only just found the courage to speak up for myself, never mind for anyone else. I felt I ought to be someone for people to focus on even though, deep down, I knew how confused and uncertain I still was. I felt I should be organising plans for the future, even though I was just one man – one survivor – and wasn't really sure what lay ahead of me from one day to the next.

I don't think I'd have got through those months before and after my story broke without Zelda. She was the one person I could rely on to be next to me, ready to talk, ready to reassure, ready to go into battle for me if it came to that. She'd come back into my life when I was at a very low ebb and seen me through to the other side. I'd stayed under her roof and had the love of a family round me: Zelda had four children, who somehow managed to take all the fuss and the drama in their stride. Who put up with me even when I was struggling to put up with myself.

I'll always be grateful: I'm not sure I'd still be here if Zelda hadn't been there for me when it mattered most. We got married in July, in the village where we were living, Marton in Cheshire. It was a quiet one: the little parish church and then a reception at the pub restaurant a few minutes' walk from home. I'd been a footballer and had had two footballer's weddings. I'd been a policeman and had a policeman's wedding. And now? I was just trying to get on with life as a human being and the wedding was like that: no need for anything flash, no need for anybody to get rolling drunk. Just two people wanting to celebrate having found one another. Even so, it still reflected where I was at, I suppose: Victoria Derbyshire came along as a guest and Danny Taylor agreed to be my best man.

Life rolls on, for better or worse. Dad passed away the following month. It had been a long while coming and it breaks my heart now thinking about how he suffered towards the end: not able to move or to speak, pain in his joints all the time. Motor neurone disease is a cruel thing. He wasted away in front of us: a terrible experience for my mum, especially. Their love and their marriage had always been so strong. They'd gone through so much together. And now there was nothing she or anybody else could do. Mum cared for Dad right till the end.

It hit the whole family hard. We remembered Dad when he was young, full of life, doing anything he could to make us kids laugh, tucking us into bed with hugs all through our childhoods. He was at every game of football I ever played. I'll remember him as the man in that picture: in love with my mum, happy, a twinkle in his eye, looking for the next bit of fun to be had with us all. The one thing I'll always feel blessed by is that he and I had the chance to talk about what had happened to me with Bennell. After all, he and Mum were groomed every bit as much as me.

My parents weren't to blame for what happened in any way. Even so, I know how guilty Dad felt about it all. I hope those conversations lifted a little of that burden from him. My parents had always been so protective of us: maybe the softness and innocence of my childhood left me vulnerable later on. But I understood now, after all these years, what had happened and even why it had happened.

When I decided to go public and tell my story, Dad was right behind me. Even though he could see the upset and the hurt it might cause the family, he knew the only way forward was to get the truth out there. He knew, I think, that this was my chance. A chance to break the silence, to fight back by telling our secrets. When I told my story, I was telling it for him – and for my mum – as much as for myself. It meant everything to me that they were behind me doing what I had to do. Any courage I needed had come from them, after all.

I've lost track of how many meetings I was at during 2017. How many working groups and conferences I attended. How many organisations wanted me to help in some way: survivors' groups, charities, social enterprises and campaigns. Organisations focused on abuse, on child welfare, on recovering victims, on mental health. I kept saying yes to any requests I had from the media. I knew for sure that I had to keep the story rolling if things were really going to change. But I was frustrated there were so many false starts, the FA and the Offside Trust among them. One minute I'd feel as if something was about to happen, as if I could really see a way forward. And then things would go dead or head off in another direction altogether. It was all pretty dispiriting.

I was aware that, in some ways, nothing had changed. The FA had sent out letters to clubs reminding them about safeguarding. They'd set up the Sheldon Inquiry. Then, it was as if they sat back and waited for something – or, better still, nothing – to happen.

I remember being asked in one interview whether I thought children involved in football were any safer now than they had been a year previously. And I had to answer honestly: *No*. What I meant was that I couldn't see how anything, really, had changed. Everybody had agreed – said out loud – that what I and so many others had been through shouldn't happen to anyone else in future. But, apart from a lot of talking, I couldn't see what we'd actually achieved.

Perhaps I was naive to expect the whole culture around football – macho, secretive, controlling – to change overnight. I suppose I expected all sorts of new organisations and initiatives to suddenly be put in place. And I expected I'd be at the forefront of that, somehow. I wanted to be leading the charge.

But now, when I stop and think about it, I understand that's not how the world works, particularly when people and groups with their own ideas are being asked to work together. And when moving forward means admitting to mistakes you might have made in the past. I wasn't so patient. I wanted everything to happen tomorrow.

Bennell's court case started in January 2018 up in Liverpool. Even though I wasn't going to be called as a witness the trial loomed very large for me. Me having gone public had been the push some lads needed to go to the police with their own stories, after all.

Bennell facing all those charges felt like a very public justification of the decision I'd made back in 2016. A personal justification, too. Even after all these months, there were still doubts in my mind. It had been difficult for my parents since, and for my sisters, too. But they weren't going to talk about it: I'd done what I'd done and they respected that. Reading my words and seeing my face on TV wasn't easy for my own children either. Or for their mothers. But nobody ever said to me: *You shouldn't have done it, Andy.*

~

I was in court to see Bennell charged on the first day of the trial: 8 January 2018. Bennell was ill, apparently, so he appeared by video link to answer the charges. His face was there on the monitor the whole time and, to be honest, I spent a lot of the day just staring at him instead of watching what was going on around me in court.

He looked old. Beaten, really. He must have known this was the end for him. But I still recognised little tics and facial mannerisms, like shaking his head when he heard something he didn't like, his top lip curling in over his front teeth when he was annoyed. It was still him and that brought memories flooding back. At the same time, it made me aware of how much stronger I felt now. So I stared at him. I knew what he was thinking the whole time. But, that day, I felt like I could face him at last. Or, at least, I could watch him on a video screen without going to pieces.

Listening to him was strange. He had to identify himself as Barry Bennell, or Richard Jones as he now was. He had to enter a plea for every one of the charges against him: guilty for a few, not guilty to all the serious ones. He still looked like Bennell but, because of the throat cancer and having lost half his tongue, his voice sounded like somebody else's. I have to admit there was a little of glimmer of satisfaction: you could hear that he'd suffered while he was banged up. That this experience had cost him something. Cost him physically, anyway – a part of who he was.

I'm not sure if it was because he was ill but Bennell was never called and never cross-examined. The prosecution had interview material, witness statements, everything they needed. They had the bastard bang to rights. Bennell had no defence. If anybody had ever done things that were indefensible, it was him. His barrister didn't spend much time on evidence or cross-examination of witnesses either. Instead, it felt to me that her plan was to undermine the victims who'd accused him, to question the integrity of every lad who'd ever been raped or abused by Bennell. Every lad who'd finally found the courage to face him in court. It's not her fault: it's the system. Time and again this seems to be how it goes with victims of sexual abuse. But the system is wrong, and it's my belief that was happened in that courtroom was morally wrong.

I travelled to Liverpool to be in court for the sentencing. The jury weren't convinced by Bennell or his brief. He was found guilty on fifty counts of child sex abuse. The judge had demanded that Bennell appear in person.

I wanted to set eyes on him one last time, before he disappeared off to prison for the rest of his life. I wanted him to know I was there and that he was there because of me. I'd done what I'd done to try to make sure he faced justice. It meant I'd beaten him – that we'd all beaten him – at last. As it happened, it didn't turn out like that on the day.

The way the court was laid out, there was only room for a certain number of people to be sitting in direct sight of Bennell. It was right, of course, that the lads who this trial was about were on those benches. There were some people sitting on them, though, who had little or nothing to do with the court case, people who certainly had never been abused by Bennell. There wasn't room for me, anyway.

I'll not pretend it didn't upset me. And it left me with a feeling of unfinished business, too. The important thing, though, was that Bennell was found guilty and that more survivors were reassured they'd been believed.

The judge called Bennell 'the devil incarnate' and sent him down for thirty years. In fact, the sentences amounted to a lot more than that: if you totted up each charge, he got given hundreds of years. He will die in jail, anyway, where he belongs.

Thinking back to that day in court now, I remember a sense of relief: *That's him done. And that's me done, too.* Just over a year before, I'd told the world what Bennell had done to me and to hundreds of others. I'd pushed and pushed since to make sure our secrets weren't any longer hidden away. Bennell had finally got what he had coming. Why, though, had it taken so long?

The single most important thing for me, though, was knowing – in that moment – that his crimes were finished and had caught up with him at last. Barry Bennell wouldn't be able to abuse a child or steal a young person's life ever again. With that came a realisation for me personally, too. I'll never be able to set aside or hide from the emotions that come with remembering the things he did to me. But my feelings towards him? That shabby, frail old man? Nothing. Leaving court in Liverpool on 15 February 2018, I just felt numb.

47.

B y the time Barry Bennell started serving the first day of his thirty years I felt emptied out. It was like a kind of full stop, the end of a story, wasn't it? That's what I'd imagined it should be: *All done. Now I can get on with the rest of my life.* It's natural, I suppose, to think that you can do or say or think one thing that will resolve everything, box it away and tidy up the mess.

Since I'd first spoken to Danny Taylor, I'd imagined that moment of clarity must be just round the next corner: *I'll be fixed. I'll forget. It's all going to be okay.* Except that moment never came. At the start of 2018, I was still haunted by flashbacks and gripped by panic attacks. I still had spells of drinking too much and of thinking I'd be better off if I just wasn't here. Despite being back in therapy, I kept sabotaging my own relationships – including my marriage to Zelda.

I couldn't see a way through it all and didn't have an answer to the question I kept asking myself: *What happens now?* Since first telling my story, I suppose I'd been waiting for somebody else to make sense of things for me, to take me to one side and say: *This is what we're going to do together. This is how we're going to make things right.* It's only really now that I realise it was never going to happen.

There was no point in me dwelling on feeling I'd been let down, even though I felt, overwhelmingly, that I had been. That mindset, I know now, would have condemned me to being the victim of my circumstances for ever. At some point, I had to recognise that any kind of future was going to be down to me. What kind of relationship can you have with anyone else if you can't be honest – and comfortable – in the relationship you have with yourself?

Telling my story, all those other guys coming forward, Bennell being convicted: those didn't add up to the end of a story or even the beginning of one. They were just steps on a long road: working out just what had happened to me and why; working out a way to put a person who'd been broken back together again.

Talking gave me a chance. Long before I spoke to Danny Taylor and Victoria Derbyshire, I'd started the process. I'd never have got to the stage of talking publicly about my experiences without having already begun being able to put thoughts into words. Twenty years ago, I'd talked to the police. I'd talked to my managers at football clubs. I'd talked to my family and to partners and friends. I'd talked to therapists and counsellors.

Some of those conversations had moved me forward; others had actually held me back. But, by the time I decided to talk publicly, I was already convinced that talking was the right thing to do if I was going to move my life towards a better place . I wasn't trapped now by wanting people to like me or respect me. Now, I was just being honest about what had happened.

I didn't know who my words – my story – might find a way to. Those numbers from Operation Hydrant – and Bennell's conviction – told me, though, that plenty of people had been listening. They'd been able to take a little of whatever courage I'd found in myself and make it their own. That was something powerful for a person like me, someone desperate to find a sense of meaning and a sense of purpose.

As it turned out, the story didn't just reach an audience in the UK. I did interviews for outlets from all over the world. The sexual abuse of children by coaches and administrators, after all, isn't only happening here. In Brazil, football had found its own whistleblower. Alexandre Montrimas is an incredibly brave man: a goalkeeper whose twenty-year professional career was cut short when he spoke out, for the first time, about the abuse he'd suffered as a young player. For years, nobody wanted to listen to Alexandre. Too many people had too much to lose, perhaps. But now the scandal was out in the open. In Brazil, now, they'd heard and read about me and wanted to know more.

It was actually the President of the São Paulo players' federation, Rinaldo Martorelli, who invited me to come to Brazil. The union was driving the campaign for better safeguarding over there. They wanted to hear about my experience and about the situation here in the UK. Of course I said yes. I'm a football fan. Why wouldn't I want to go to Brazil?

But I was well aware of how little I knew about the specifics of what was happening in São Paulo and elsewhere in the country. That's fine, they said: *We just want you to come and tell us your story.* A reporter from Sky News, Sally Lockwood, agreed to come along. It was important to me that the trip to Brazil got coverage here at home at the same time. That 'football family' thing is a bit of a cliché but maybe it meant something when it came to the reason for me being there.

It was an amazing experience. On one level, it was incredibly exciting. I met Alexandre Montrimas at the Allianz Parque stadium and we watched a Palmeiras game together as well as filming an interview. They took me down to Vila Belmiro, where Santos have their stadium and where Pelé made his name. That's where the picture a couple of pages back was taken. Alexandre's on the left with Rinaldo Martorelli standing between us. I was driven around this huge city, São Paulo, trying to take in the difference between the wealthy parts of downtown and the poverty in the *favelas* they took me to visit. Those run-down neighbourhoods are where Brazilian clubs look in order to find the next star, the next Brazilian international, the next big-money export to Europe.

It was in those *favelas* that the truth of what I was seeing really sank in. Kids were playing on every scrap of waste ground: football was a game they loved but it was also, potentially, their only ticket out of the poverty they were growing up in. And it wasn't just them: parents and extended family would be counting on every promising young player to change their lives, whatever the cost. That might mean sending a boy to an academy hundreds or even thousands of miles away. It could mean putting all their trust in a coach, a scout, an agent

– whoever came along and said to them: *Your boy can become a professional footballer.*

I dreamed of becoming a player because I loved the game. In Brazil, the pressure is on a different scale altogether. Football is one way – maybe the only way – to escape a life of poverty for both the boy and his family. They'll do anything to make it happen. And that makes it all too easy for them to fall prey to the Brazilian equivalents of Barry Bennell. In comparison to the UK, safeguarding isn't well established for young players in Brazil. There isn't the funding available, for a start. Boys end up away from home, thrown unprotected into ramshackle club accommodation, friendless and – when the worst happens – helpless.

The scale of the problem in Brazil is mind-blowing. It's a terrible situation that the São Paulo players' union are determined to change. But what could I say about a situation that probably affected the lives of thousands of boys across Brazil? Had affected maybe hundreds of thousands over the years? Beyond stressing the need for safeguarding, there probably wasn't much for me to add to what the guys who'd invited me over already knew. Over the next couple of days, though, I got to understand why Mr Martorelli had asked me to come.

I went into a couple of clubs and talked to groups of young players. Speaking to those boys – together and one-on-one – I found the real reason for me being there. I was amazed how many of them knew who I was. The boys would listen to me on headphones – they had someone translating for me – and then I'd take questions, from them and from coaches and administrators in the audience. Maybe I couldn't affect the big problem but I was able to connect with some of those young players.

On the other side of the world – in a different time and in very different economic circumstances – I'd had the same dream these boys had now. They knew all about the hopes and the fears that I'd felt, like them, trying to realise that dream. I could see it in those boys' eyes. They were vulnerable, lonely and naive; even those – the majority, I'm sure – who had never been abused. But here was a guy in front of them who had been a professional player himself and was speaking from his own experience.

I spoke about what had happened to me. What had happened to me when I was their age and what had happened since. And I made one or two simple things as plain as I could. Being abused by grown-ups, grown-ups who should be looking after them, helping their dreams come true, was wrong. Totally wrong. And could damage a boy's life for ever. If it happened to them, they had to find someone to tell. If it happened to a friend or a teammate, they had to be willing to listen.

I was overwhelmed by being in Brazil, hearing about the game's problems there, trying to imagine these boys' experiences and the dangers they might face. It was humbling, too. I stood up to speak. I had pictures on-screen from my own childhood to show them. They had their headphones on, listening, concentrating. Eyes flickering from the pictures to me and then – it seemed to me – away to their own thoughts.

It was so quiet in that room. Incredible to think: on the other side of the world, a man they've never met, speaking a language none of those boys could understand, just telling a story, his own dark story. And there was still a connection could be made. The situation in Brazil is so difficult. There are so many clubs and so many boys and there's so little in place to protect them. The organisation the guys in São Paulo have set up – Stop Abuse In Sport – has a lot of work to do. They know they're just making a start.

I'm really glad I was able to be involved. That I met some of those young players and maybe made a difference, even if it was just one or two I was able to reach and help steer away from danger. What I realised while I was in Brazil was that the message is the same wherever you are. No child should suffer like I did. *If it happens to you, if it happens to a teammate, you have to break the silence: Speak out.* And every adult in the game has the duty then to listen.

In public, I can have a role to play, I hope. The safeguarding and child protection protocols that the FA and other organisations have put in place are a place to start, for sure. I believe, though, there are lessons to be learned from history and personal experience. To really move forward, systems and structures need to be backed up by a real understanding of how abuse happens. A personal understanding of the impact of abuse and what it does to the rest of a person's life.

More than anything, we need to recognise we'll never get to a place where we can say: *That's all right then. It's boxed away. We've dealt with that.* I'm passionate about playing a part in the future. I want to help in any way I can. Whether that's going to be alongside clubs, campaign groups or governing bodies isn't just up to me, I suppose. If I can help, I will.

I know that sharing my story and my experience can benefit others. That I can help break the grip of secrecy by telling the truth myself. There are fundamentals every young person deserves to have passed on to them: *You're not alone. It's not your fault. You don't have to be silent any more.*

There are tools now that can help young people – and survivors, too – take back some control of their lives. The subject of child sex abuse in sport stands alone as an issue that needs confronting. But it bridges in to something wider, too. There's been a really important conversation going on over the past few years about a national crisis in the area of mental health: loneliness, trauma, anxiety, depression, addiction, eating disorders, self-harm, suicide.

I've had to face most of those demons at some point or other over the past thirty years. I'm still coming to terms with some of them now. I'm lucky to have had help through the PFA, Sporting Chance and individual mental health professionals. Help that I couldn't have done without. Although I've lived my experiences and thought a lot about them, that doesn't give me the expertise to show other people how to handle their own problems. But if I can help anyone else find a way towards their own resolutions, then that's definitely worth doing.

I understand the importance of having a voice. The importance of being heard. For the last year or so, I've been working with a friend, Colin Radcliffe, on developing an app called DE-press-ON. The idea is to create a platform that people suffering with depression can turn to for information and guidance. The real key, though, will be for it to give people the chance to share experience and inspiration. It's new technology being used in a way it's not been before in connection with mental health. I'm just hoping that, once it launches, DE-press-ON can work for people in the way we imagine.

~

You could say that I've done a lot in the past couple of years that has taken me out of myself. Walking out to meet those boys in São Paulo or standing behind a lectern at a conference on safeguarding or sitting under the lights in a TV studio, I've often felt strong. I've felt as if I knew what I was doing there. It's having a sense of a purpose, I suppose. But when I come away from that, when it's just me and memories and thinking about what's going to happen to me tomorrow, I'm still fragile.

There's no switch to reach for. You can't just turn off the fear and the anxiety trauma condemns you to. You can't just step out of the dark. The shadow of Barry Bennell will haunt me for the rest of my life and every day now is another day I have to spend learning – or trying to learn – how to deal with the pain and confusion that he left behind.

48.

T hat picture was taken during my last year at primary school. I was ten. He was the boy Barry Bennell spotted playing for Stockport Boys. The book I'm looking at, naturally, was a book about football. The game was all I ever thought about. I'd already told Dad I was going to become a professional player. Then Barry Bennell came into my life and the life of my family, claiming he held the key to making a boy's dream come true.

Maybe he really believed he would help me make my way in the game. I doubt it, though. My dream, my feelings, my childhood were never what he was interested in. Psychopaths don't ever care about anyone else. Taking what he wanted, really, was the only thing that ever crossed his mind. And Bennell decided, on a dank afternoon in Didsbury, that he wanted me.

I trusted Bennell with my childhood. He made sure of that and made sure my family trusted him with it, too. Everything good that could ever happen to me in football was going to be because of him. And I did make it. I did become a professional footballer, something very few boys with big ambitions like I had ever manage to do. But that wasn't because of him. It happened in spite of him.

What really happened *because* of him was something else altogether: a life broken in pieces, a daily struggle with fear, guilt and self-doubt. Bennell used to tell me he loved me. Actually, he took me to the darkest places I've ever known. He forced me, just a boy, into a life I couldn't hope to understand. *Look at the picture.* A grown man, obsessed only with his own desires, took over that lad's mind.

Bennell's power was so strong that my mum and my dad and my sister – and hundreds of other boys and their families – were brainwashed by him, too. He manipulated our emotions, backed up public charm with hidden terrors. He did what he did. He raped and abused hundreds of young players. He raped and abused me hundreds of times. *Look at the picture:* how could that boy possibly have imagined what was going to happen to him? Happy, innocent. Shining eyes and a big smile. Prey.

I lived through six years of it with him: at Dove Holes, at Butlin's, in his car, in the little front bedroom at my family home. Whenever and wherever he wanted. Whatever he wanted. He ran me down a tunnel with no light at the end of it: I couldn't think, I couldn't speak, I couldn't breathe without him saying so. This was what I had to do and I did it, without daring to question. Without daring to try to escape. I'd nowhere to run to, anyway. Barry Bennell had soon swallowed up everything: a boy's whole world.

When I felt good, those moments out on grass, kicking a ball, were all down to him, weren't they? And all the bad stuff? The dark stuff? Well, that was my fault. He made sure I felt that it happening was somehow down to me. Bennell stopped eventually, like he always did, and moved on to the next young lad he could find. At that point, for him, I stopped existing. He wiped me away like he wiped cum away off a backside. Left me to get on with my life, a life on my own, cut off in secrecy and silence.

I couldn't tell, could I? Mum and Dad just saw a lad making his way as a professional footballer, going out with teammates, drinking ale and getting off with pretty girls. I'm sure they never questioned what they saw for an instant. Bennell had wrapped them up in his make-believe. He'd sucked all of us in, hadn't he? The deception, for him, was always part of the thrill.

But did nobody else see what was happening? Lads would turn up, train and play, and then disappear. Were they the ones who fought back? Or the ones with parents who doubted something in what they saw? Why did none of them ever say a word? Maybe he had a different kind of hold over those boys, after all.

And what about the club Bennell was at the centre of? Other coaches? Club staff? The manager? Did none of them know? Even though every team we played against, even some of Crewe's own first-teamers, made jokes about something that was apparently common knowledge. Of course they knew. I'm convinced of that. And the truth of it will out eventually. For now, I'm just stuck on the question: *Why didn't anybody stop him?*

When the abuse stopped, maybe you'd imagine all the rest of it stopped, too. The reality, though, is that once Bennell was in your head, he was there for ever. Like a stain that had spilt onto your soul. For thirty years and more, it was as if he was part of every single day. I've spent a lifetime, it feels like, being bounced around emotions that all run back to him.

Those twisted-up emotions – and me desperately trying to bury them – have damaged me and damaged every relationship I've ever had. Andrea, Rachel and Catherine could tell you how he's hurt them. Hurt our marriages and our children. This past year, things have fallen apart with Zelda, too. Four divorces now: shocking. Unforgivable, probably. The ripples have spread out, relentless, from the centre: me.

Everything Bennell did to me – everything the memory of him has done since – he did to my family, too. How must my mum and dad have felt when the truth finally crawled out from under the stone – my secrecy – that it was hidden beneath? My parents only ever wanted me to be happy and to be safe. Unknowingly, groomed and betrayed themselves, they delivered me into the hands of a man who made sure I never would be.

My sister Lynda, too: how could anybody do what he did to her? She has her own story to tell or not to tell. And I respect her choices, her way of dealing with what she went through. But I know she was tricked, hurt and undermined, just the same as me.

Even so. Lynda's made a life for herself in spite of him. She's a wonderful mother and daughter and I'll always be proud of her.

My mum and dad had to face the truth long after they could do anything to change what had happened. In their lounge at home, they listened as I gave in and told the police what they wanted to know. They saw me then: sobbing, wrung out, scrambled. And I know they blamed themselves. That's how it works with men like Bennell: for years, I blamed myself for what he'd done. But my parents didn't break. They stayed strong for each other. And strong for me, for Lynda and for their grandchildren.

So there was a strength there that somehow kept my family from being pushed over the edge Bennell had pushed them to. And that strength is in me, too. I played nearly 200 games as a professional footballer even though I was in bits for most of that time. I was a copper for even longer than I was a player and, despite the way it ended, I did things in uniform I'll always be proud of.

When I did that first piece in the *Guardian* with Danny Taylor, I talked about Bennell settling on the softer, more vulnerable boys. Me among them. And that was true. *Look at the picture*: I *was* soft. I was loved, maybe overprotected. Of course, behind the happy smile is a ten-year-old boy and all the vulnerability that comes with that. I had no fear. Why would I? I trusted and then I was betrayed.

But I'm here to tell the tale. However hurt I've been, however deep the shadow thrown by Bennell, however often I've wondered whether all this was worth the candle: like the rest of my family, I've kept fighting. Fighting him, fighting demons, fighting with myself. Soft and vulnerable, maybe. But Mum and Dad put something into me. A strength they always had themselves and that I think I share with them.

I sit with Mum now. She's not been well and I've been stopping at home since splitting up with Zelda. We talk about that strength and she stares down what we've all been fighting. *We're like that song, aren't we?* She says: *We get knocked down. But we get up again. You're never going to keep us down.* I can feel that strength in me. Now more than ever.

Over the last couple of years, it's been as if every day I've challenged myself to remember things more clearly. The more clearly I remember, the better I can understand. The better I understand, the greater my chance of putting the pieces of my life together again. I have to have that strength: to fight, of course, but also to get past guilt and get past fear and get past hating who I am. At least some of the blame and the threats and the self-loathing are locked up in jail now, with Bennell, where they belong. Little by little, I'm struggling to free myself. To open up to the world. To be true to myself so I can be honest with others. I suppose I'm learning to be me.

I'm lucky to have found a partner, Joanne, who knows where I've been because she understands abuse and what it leaves behind. I've been chasing reassurance, acceptance, empathy without judgement or conditions, all my adult life. I've always thought it was all waiting for me round another corner. With someone else. It's why I've run away so many times. Run into and then out of marriages so many times.

What I need now is to build a relationship for the first time in my life in which I don't end up in the default position: being the victim of my circumstances. I know that Joanne understands me and what I need from her. We've talked about why I need those things and she's shed tears with me over that. My instinct is that we'll find a balance between us, the honesty to give us a chance. Definitely, there'll be no secrets from now on.

I've spent a lot of time with Mum these past few months. A roof over my head but, more than that, a chance to be together without old doubts still driven in between us. We know where we are and we know where we've been. It gets difficult from time to time: this is all still raw, still painful. And Mum misses Dad even more than I do. For her, whatever came along, it was always the two of them would face it together.

The house is still full of memories for both of us. Still keeps its store of shadows left behind. But I admire her so much: her strength and her integrity. She's who she is all the way through to her bones. She shines a clear light. And that's been helping me to see myself, at last, for who I really am.

I've come back to where I started, literally: the streets and parks and places where I grew up, contented, before I ever met Bennell. Every day, I run into people from my childhood: kids I played football with, girls who made big eyes at me, their mums and dads and families, too. Now, though, they know what's happened to me. That doesn't make things awkward like you might imagine. It actually makes things simple. It's almost as if I can pick up with the past where I left off thirty-odd years ago. All those people have read the stories and seen the television interviews but they see someone else, too: Andy, the ten-year-old lad off the estate who loved his football and played for Stockport Boys.

There's still so much I have to work through in my mind. My guess is it's a process that will never really end. There are plenty of grim days: I'll be ambushed by a particular memory, a feeling, a place. A smell, even. Moments from those years I spent under the complete control of a man who believed he owned me are lying in wait for me all the time. I crash. It's like I'm falling again. Darkness – the terror, the humiliation – comes washing through me when I least expect it. But now I understand enough about myself to take hold. Like I'm tumbling down a mountainside but suddenly find a rock or a branch to grip tight on. Slowly I know how to pull myself back up onto firmer ground.

We all need to tell ourselves who we are: I was the boy who dreamed he'd be a footballer. Then I was the guy who really was a footballer. Then I was the policeman. I was a husband: too many times! I was a father. A brother and a son. But all those pictures I had of myself were always blurred, spoilt, in jagged fragments. I was never completely any of those people. I was never the person I should have been or could have been. And those around me suffered because of that, just as much as I did maybe.

Someone took me away. For a while, he took all of me, every thought and feeling. Every waking moment. And when he finished, he didn't give me back myself. He just left the pieces of me, broken, where they lay.

Like I say, for all that time I was convinced – he convinced me – I'd been the one to blame. And, don't get me wrong: I did things and said things and thought things only I can own. I can't hide from the responsibility for choices that I've made. But I'm slowly coming to terms now with why it's all unfolded in the way it has.

Every time I turn over another secret, something comes loose in me. A little more of my guilt and shame and regret drops away from my shoulders; I feel a little more free, even. Bennell did what he did. To me and to all the others. It lies with him and he's behind bars now for the rest of his life. He'll never be free.

I know, deep down, that Bennell won't ever face up to what he's done. Or feel remorse. To be honest, I don't think he really thinks he ever did anything wrong. He wasn't *trying* to be evil. He didn't think he was. Right and wrong would be ideas that had no meaning for him, anyway. So there was never a moment for him to wonder how I felt or about the damage that was being done to me.

He said it all the time: *You're different from all the others, Andy. You're special. I love you.* But his love wasn't anything any of us would recognise or understand in that word. He loved himself. And he loved others only in respect of how they made him feel. Nothing else mattered. He loved his desires and his appetites. For the rest: he didn't fucking care.

Over the past couple of years, I've maybe grown into another identity. I became the victim who survived, the one who found the courage to tell everyone what had happened to him. To tell everyone what had happened to lots of other boys as well. I'm grateful so many people listened. Just by listening, they've made me feel as if I've done the right thing at last. The calls, the messages, the social media posts. People I run into – old friends and complete strangers – in the street. Those connections make me feel as if I've done something worthwhile. There's a satisfaction in that: doing something necessary and important, no question. Those connections can make me feel happier being me.

That said, I understand enough to know that other people can't give me the self-esteem I need to live life how I want to now. That's got to get found and dug up – like a miner digging for coal – from somewhere inside myself. Opening up is a painful thing: that's why I locked my feelings and my secrets away for so many years. I was a helpless little boy, terrified of where I was but even more terrified of what lay behind the door Bennell had shut: the door that led to the rest of me. For thirty years, I was frozen. Couldn't face in here. Couldn't face out there.

All I could do was stumble through each day, crawl through the wreckage Bennell left behind.

I needed a key. And I found it when I realised what it was in me that had made the darkness fall; that had made things that shouldn't happen to anyone happen to me. What had locked me up was silence: my silence. And the silence of others. It didn't happen overnight but I can look back now and recognise what a little courage, a little honesty and a little patience granted me. I found a voice. A voice I could use to speak up for myself and, maybe, to speak for others. I've said out loud what it was Bennell did to me. And said out loud what it was that other people didn't do: he needed their silence to enable him, after all.

I don't know what comes now. I have to work. I have to pay the rent like anybody else. I have to build and rebuild relationships: with my family and friends, with my children, with their mums. With the people I let down because I couldn't face up to myself, my challenges and my responsibilities. I've started and I'll keep going. I'm strong enough and I've come far enough to know there's no turning back from here. I'm learning how to live.

It's a blessing: to have one thing you know, for sure, that you were put here to do. For me, that moment of grace came with breaking the silence that had shut me down. What I had to say needed saying, for sure. I feel I need to keep saying it.

We can put laws and structures and protocols in place. We have to. But there's something else that has to happen; otherwise the next Bennell will always find a way around our best intentions. That's what they always manage to do. To really make sure there are no more victims, every boy and every girl needs to hear the message: *You're not alone.*

You don't have to keep those secrets. You can speak. You must speak. And the rest of us must listen.

It's what I believe I have to do: telling my story is what's made it possible for me to start turning my past into a future. I want to share my experience and share the lessons that I've learned. I want to talk to parents, to children, to administrators, to other survivors.

Most of all, though? It's the one conversation I know I can't ever have. Breaks my heart, but it pushes me on. *Look at the picture, the one at the start of this chapter:* the happiest boy alive. Whenever I talk to anyone about my life, whenever I put it down on paper like I have done here, it's for him. I want to talk to him, now I know exactly what it is I need to tell him. I wish for what can't happen, but it's what inspires me every single day. *Look at the picture. Look at me. Andy. This is what I have to say.*

Acknowledgements

My mum, Jean, and my sisters.

Andrea, Rachel, Catherine, Zelda.

Gary Cliffe, Ash Stephenson, Steve Walters, Chris Unsworth, Mike Fallon, Kevin Carroll.

Daniel Taylor, Victoria Derbyshire, Louisa Compton.

Vicky Kloss (Manchester City), Neil Warnock, Stan Ternent, Gordon Sorfleet (Bury FC), John Powell (The Kenilworth), Colin Radcliffe (DE-press-ON), James Bentley.

Hannah Black, Fiona Rose, Emma Knight and the team at Coronet.

Joanne Foubister.

Tom Watt.

Grant Best.

I would also like to thank everyone who's supported and encouraged me since I first spoke publicly about my experiences. Without that support, writing this book and helping others to come forward wouldn't have been possible. I'm very grateful.

Where to Find Help

The following organisations offer help and support:

NSPCC
www.nspcc.org.uk
call 0808 800 5000

Childline
www.childline.org.uk
Childline offers free confidential advice,
call 0800 1111

Samaritans
www.samaritans.org
call 116 123

Photographic Acknowledgements

The author and publisher would like to thank the following for permission to reproduce photographs:

Kevin Carroll, Crewe Alexandra, Will Dickey, The Florida Times-Union, Bury FC, Halifax Town FC, Ann Cook, Shutterstock, Rex/Shutterstock Other photographs from private collections.

Every reasonable effort has been made to trace the copyright holders, but if there are any errors or omissions, Hodder & Stoughton will be pleased to insert the appropriate acknowledgement in any subsequent printings or editions.